TO THE KANKAKEE
LIBRARY

Ray K___ M.D.

920 - PARENTS
FOR MEDIA +
LECTURES

OR CALL
PRESENCE ST. MARY'S
E.R. @
815-937-2100

CALL

theTOTAL PARENT

the TOTAL PARENT

THE COMPLETE GUIDE TO
CHILDHOOD ILLNESS & INJURY
PARENTING • EDUCATION SUCCESS
TEACHING VALUES & CHARACTER

RON KURZEJKA, MD

The Total Parent
Copyright © 2010 Ron Kurzejka, MD
Published by Arbor Ridge Publishing
595 Industrial Drive
Bradley, Illinois 60915
(920) 727–3687

TheTotalParent.com

ISBN–13: 978-0-9819529-8-7 HC
Library of Congress Control Number: 2010906393

Cover Photo: Bill Jurevich, The Image Group, theimagegroup.com
Cover Design: Dunn and Associates
Interior Design: Desktop Miracles, Inc.

Publishers Cataloging in Publication Data
(Prepared by The Donohue Group, Inc.)

Kurzejka, Ron.
   The total parent : the complete guide to childhood illness & injury, parenting, education success, teaching values & character / Ron Kurzejka.
      p. : ill. ; cm.
   Includes bibliographical references and index.
   ISBN: 978-0-9819529-8-7

   1. Child rearing—Popular works. 2. Child care — Handbooks, manuals, etc. 3. Postnatal care — Popular works. I. Title.

HQ769 .K87 2010
649/.1

Printed in China

Disclaimer
The following information is for educational purposes only. The information on the following pages is not a substitute for a medical, psychological, or other professional evaluation, nor is it a substitute for the advice of a licensed medical physician or other professional.

*This book is dedicated to the woman of my dreams,
my soul mate and my wife forever,
Annette*

*It is also dedicated to my five wonderful and loving children
who have taught me about the limitless love
of a father for his children,
Matthew, Heidi, Mitchell, Mark, and Michael*

Thank you all for loving me so much.

I love you

Ron

CONTENTS

• ACKNOWLEDGMENTS •

This book could not have been written without the help of several key people. I want to sincerely thank everyone who reviewed the manuscript, offered their suggestions, and shared their expertise. I deeply appreciate their efforts in helping to bring this book to life.

Gary Strange, MD, FACEP, Professor and Chairman of the Department of Emergency Medicine at the University of Illinois Medical Center in Chicago, thoroughly reviewed each of the medical chapters in this book for accuracy. I am deeply indebted to Dr. Strange for the many hours he spent reviewing this manuscript and for his excellent comments and his expertise. Dr. Strange is the author of *Pediatric Emergency Medicine*, a textbook for emergency physicians.

Charles Nozicka, DO, FAAP, FAAEM, reviewed each of the medical chapters for content and accuracy. I sincerely appreciated Dr. Nozicka's enthusiasm for this project and for his many hours of work in bringing this book to fruition. Dr. Nozicka is the Medical Director of Pediatric Emergency Medicine at Condell Memorial Hospital in Libertyville, Illinois.

Sander Marcus, PhD, from the Illinois Institute of Technology's Institute of Psychology, provided an additional editing overview. Sander is the author of several books and articles on underachieving students. He was kind enough to share his expertise and review the chapters dealing with educational success, behavioral problems, and parenting.

Stanford T. Shulman, MD, the Chief of Infectious Disease at Children's Memorial Hospital of Chicago and the Virginia H. Rogers Professor of Pediatric Infectious Diseases at the Northwestern University Feinberg School of Medicine for reviewing and contributing to the chapter on fever.

Susan Fuchs, MD, FAAP, FACEP, a pediatric emergency specialist from Children's Memorial Hospital of Chicago, graciously reviewed the chapter on fever. Dr. Fuchs is the Associate Director of the Pediatric Emergency Medicine Division at Children's Memorial Hospital in Chicago.

Constantine Mavroudis, MD, a pediatric cardiovascular surgeon, reviewed the chapter on congenital heart problems. Dr. Mavroudis is the Surgeon in Chief and the Willis J. Potts Professor of Pediatric Cardiovascular

Surgery at Children's Memorial Hospital in Chicago and Northwestern University's Feinberg School of Medicine.

Carl Lewis Becker, MD, a pediatric cardiovascular surgeon, reviewed the chapter on congenital heart problems. Dr. Becker is the A. C. Buehler Professor of Pediatric Cardiovascular Surgery at Children's Memorial Hospital and Northwestern University's Feinberg School of Medicine in Chicago.

Peter Varga, MD, FAAP, FACC, a pediatric cardiologist, reviewed the chapter on congenital heart problems. I appreciated Dr. Varga's valuable input and expertise. Dr. Varga is an Associate Professor and the Director of Pediatric Cardiology at Loyola University Medical Center and the Ronald McDonald Children's Hospital.

Sapna Kansal Gupta, MD, shared his expertise and insights as a pediatrician by reviewing the chapter on ear, nose, and throat problems. Dr. Gupta is an instructor in pediatrics at the Northwestern University Feinberg School of Medicine in Chicago.

Dr. Ming Xu, the Medical Director of the Behavioral Health Department at Provena St. Mary's Hospital, reviewed the chapter on behavioral problems in children.

Dr. Albert Ma, MD, a child and adolescent psychiatrist from Rady Children's Hospital of San Diego, reviewed the chapters on autism, ADHD, and postpartum depression.

Dr. Michael Wahl, MD, FAAT, generously contributed his time and expertise to review the chapter on poisonings and overdoses. Dr. Wahl is the Director of the Illinois Poison Control Center.

Katrina Hubbard, RN, reviewed the chapter on preventable deaths in children. Katrina is an expert in injury prevention, a certified car-seat technician, and one of the instructors for our Total Parent Program.

Evelyn Lyons, RN, MPH, deserves a sincere note of thanks for reviewing the chapters on preventable deaths, keeping your child safe in the hospital, and finding a good doctor. Evelyn is the Co-Director of the Emergency Medical Services for Children for the Illinois Department of Public Health (affiliated with Loyola University Medical Center). One of Evelyn's key missions is to coordinate the review of emergency departments across the state of Illinois to certify that they have the appropriate equipment, training, and personnel to save critically ill children. I have been honored to serve as a physician reviewer and consultant alongside Evelyn as she and her team conducts pediatric certification visits at various emergency departments in Illinois.

Harriet Hawkins, RN, CCRN, FAEN, reviewed the chapter on CPR and cardiac arrest and shared valuable suggestions and insights. Harriet is the Resuscitation Education Coordinator at Children's Memorial Hospital in Chicago.

Tori Dixon reviewed and proofread all the chapters. Tori is the assistant editor for the Total Parent Web site.

A very special and sincere expression of gratitude and appreciation goes to my executive assistant, **Debbie Kreutzer.** Debbie has spent countless hours over the past ten years typing and retyping this manuscript in its various stages of development. I cannot say enough about Debbie's excellence, attention to detail, and commitment. Debbie is a highly talented individual who does everything in a very professional and outstanding manner.

To my medical illustrator, **Matthew Holt.** I was very impressed with the outstanding illustrations that Matthew created for this book. His unique talent for artistically capturing the key medical concepts of each topic is deeply appreciated. His superb illustrations have helped to create a book that is easy to understand and visually appealing.

And, above all, to my loving wife, Annette, and to our five wonderful children, Matthew, Heidi, Mitchell, Mark, and Michael. I deeply and sincerely thank them for their patience, understanding, love, and support. This book is a tribute to all of them for the wonderful life they have given me. They have made my life happier and more meaningful than I could ever have dreamed possible.

With sincere appreciation to all,
Ron Kurzejka, MD

Introduction

My inspiration for writing this book began over ten years ago when I realized how little the average parent knew about basic medical problems in children. I also became aware of an overall need for better parenting and communication skills, a greater emphasis on values, and a better understanding of the strategies for motivating children in school.

This book provides parents—and other child care providers—with information on the most common medical problems in children, along with the skills you need for raising healthy and educationally successful children with solid values and character. *The Total Parent* is a concise summary of more than ten years of personal research and more than twenty-five years of experience as an emergency medicine physician. It is also the product of my accumulated wisdom as a husband and father who is raising five wonderful children.

Other children's health books on the market tend to focus only on a single area, such as newborns, parenting, or only on medical issues. The Total Parent is different, for it is really several books in one. Yes, you will find up-to-the-minute medical information, tips, and treatments for all the common childhood illnesses and injuries, but this book also includes topics just as vital to your success as a parent: parenting skills, educational success, and character development.

I wrote this book for you and the children in your life, approaching each chapter as if I were having a one-on-one conversation with you. My goal was to ensure that the information presented is complete, concise, fascinating, and inspiring. Most important, I wanted to make sure that every chapter is easy to understand.

That's why I included several real-life examples and a summary of key points, which I call Total Parent Pointers, at the end of each chapter. Knowing how busy you are, I made it easy to read the key points of each chapter of the book in thirty minutes or less by just reading the Total Parent Pointers.

I've also included an extensive collection of over 250 photos and illustrations to complement the explanations of important medical concepts. The photos are real patients with real medical problems. The extensive medical illustrations make understanding and remembering each medical concept that much easier.

The information in this book is not just about teaching you to help your children but also about helping to motivate you to become a better parent, a better role model—and thus a better person.

Throughout this process, your children will respect you more and will be inspired to live up to your higher standards.

Since this book is also a handy reference, in a sense you may never finish it. Keep it around for those times when you could use a little medical or moral support and guidance. After reading this book, you'll absorb a vast amount of medical information, you will become a better parent, your children will do better in school, and you will have a positive impact on their personal character and values. And that is the greatest gift you can give your children and the finest measure of the total parent!

Ron Kurzejka, MD, FACEP

• LIST OF REVIEWERS •

CARL LEWIS BACKER, MD
Pediatric Cardiovascular Surgeon
A. C. Buehler Professor of Surgery
Children's Memorial Hospital
Feinberg School of Medicine
Northwestern University
Chicago, IL

SUSAN FUCHS, MD, FAAP, FACEP
Professor of Pediatrics
Feinberg School of Medicine
Northwestern University
Associate Director
Division of Pediatric Emergency
    Medicine
Children's Memorial Hospital
Chicago, IL

SAPNA GUPTA, MD
Instructor in Pediatrics
Feinberg School of Medicine
Northwestern University
Chicago, IL

HARRIET HAWKINS, RN, CCRN, FAEN
Resuscitation Education Coordinator
Children's Memorial Hospital
Chicago, IL

KATRINA HUBBARD, RN
Injury Prevention Specialist
Loyola University Medical Center
Maywood, IL

EVELYN LYONS, RN, MPH
Emergency Medical Services for
    Children
Division of EMS & Public Safety
Illinois Department of Public Health
Loyola University Medical Center
Maywood, IL

ALBERT MA, MD
Child and Adolescent Psychiatrist
Rady Children's Hospital
    of San Diego
UCSD Department of Child
    and Adolescent Psychiatry
San Diego, CA

SANDER MARCUS, PHD
Clinical Psychologist
Illinois Institute of Technology's
    Institute of Psychology
Consultant to Chicago Board of
    Education Gifted Children
    Program
Chicago, IL

CONSTANTINE MAVROUDIS, MD
Pediatric Cardiovascular Surgeon
Willis J. Potts Professor of Surgery
Surgeon in Chief
Children's Memorial Hospital
Feinberg School of Medicine
Northwestern University
Chicago, IL

CHARLES NOZICKA, DO, FAAP, FAAEM
Medical Director
Pediatric Emergency Medicine
Condell Medical Center
Libertyville, IL

STANFORD T. SHULMAN, MD
Virginia H. Rogers Professor of Pediatric Infectious Disease
The Feinberg School of Medicine
Northwestern University
Chief, Division of Infectious Disease
Children's Memorial Hospital
Chicago, IL

GARY STRANGE, MD, FACEP
Professor and Chair
Department of Emergency Medicine
University of Illinois Medical Center
Chicago, IL

PETER VARGA, MD, FAAP, FACC
Pediatric Cardiologist, Associate Professor, Director, Division of Pediatric Cardiology
Loyola University Medical Center
Maywood, IL

MICHAEL WAHL, MD, FAAT
Fellow American Academy of Toxicology
Director, Illinois Poison Center
Chicago, IL

MING XU, MD
Psychiatrist–Board Certified Director of Behavioral Health
Provena St. Mary's Hospital
Kankakee, IL

PART 1

New Baby Care

1

The First Year

Congratulations! You are now a proud parent of a wonderful baby boy or girl. You've made the long journey to this point and experienced the sacrifices and pains of pregnancy and the miracle of life and birth. Regardless of whether your delivery was easy or difficult, your baby is now with you, and you should have received information and instructions about the following:

1. Breast-feeding and bottle-feeding
2. Bathing your child
3. Taking a rectal temperature
4. Holding your child properly and supporting his head
5. Keeping the child warm with proper clothing and a warm hat
6. Understanding weight loss during the first five days
7. Watching for a yellowing of the skin (jaundice)
8. Making a follow-up appointment with your doctor

Your physician checked the child's eyes, ears, nose, throat, hips, heart, and lungs for any problems.

NEWBORN REVIEW

Your baby was given antibiotic eye drops to prevent an eye infection and was also given an injection of vitamin K, which helps your baby's blood to clot easier and stops any bleeding.

Your newborn received a sponge bath while in the hospital, and you learned how to give your child a sponge bath at home for the first three weeks. The stump of the umbilical cord may have been painted with a blue antibacterial dye to prevent infection. You were also shown how to clean the umbilical

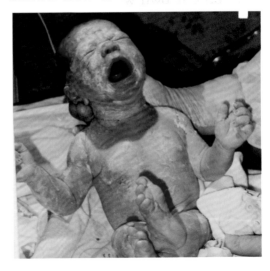

cord with alcohol and Q-tips to keep it clean and to prevent infection.

Your baby also had blood tests to check for certain genetic metabolic problems called phenylketonuria (PKU), thyroid diseases, and galactosemia.

THE NEW PARENT

If you haven't already, you will probably begin thinking about the amazing responsibility you have or are about to undertake. This small baby will be completely dependent on you, not only to protect her from harm, but also to feed, warm, and watch over her for any signs of medical illness.

It is normal for a new parent to feel scared, nervous, and overwhelmed. These feelings tell you that you are taking this beautiful little baby very seriously, as any good parent should.

I remember when my first child was born. My wife and I felt so overwhelmed and happy holding our son for the first time. But once we left the hospital, it dawned on us that we were on our own with a tiny, helpless infant who needed us nonstop, day and night. And we loved him so much that we were somewhat anxious about all the illnesses that can occur in an infant. What if our son developed a serious illness? What if our child became a victim of SIDS (sudden infant death syndrome)? What if he gets meningitis? (As a physician, I know that meningitis can sometimes result in hearing loss or permanent mental impairment.) What could my wife and I do to prevent any of these illnesses

from happening? Fortunately, this book will give you the answers to all of those questions and the information to deal with each of those issues with increased confidence.

The good news is that parents have been taking care of babies for thousands of years. Even in primitive rain forests and in cold and unfriendly climates, their infants have survived beautifully.

But as the baby's caregiver, you also need to be sure to take care of you.

The first few weeks after our firstborn arrived were especially tough for my wife. After all, she had just given birth and needed time to rest and heal, but how could she do this when the baby needed to eat every few hours? On top of sleep deprivation, physical discomfort, and feelings of uncertainty, she also had to cope with one of the hardest challenges for new parents—the loneliness of caring for an infant all day.

One of the best pieces of advice anyone gave us when we became new parents was to ask for and accept help from family and friends.

For advice and companionship, reach out to experienced mothers and caregivers whom you respect, such as your mother, mother-in-law, or good friend. They have been there and know what you're going through. That's why mothers you know (who are now your new colleagues) are such a great source of emotional support. And experienced moms enjoy helping new parents by sharing tried-and-true tips, such as how to soothe a fussy baby. There's also a good deal of comfort in having an experienced mom—rather than someone without kids—watch your baby while you take a walk around the block to restore your sanity.

Friends and family members who aren't parents can help you too. Your sister-in-law with no kids may not feel comfortable baby-sitting your newborn, but she may be happy to run an errand for you. Every bit of help you can receive during the first few weeks is priceless. Caring for a newborn is an overwhelming experience for all first-time parents, but it does get easier.

Finally, I strongly advise you to talk to your pediatrician or family doctor regarding any medical issues. Your pediatrician or family doctor knows that you will have many questions during the first few weeks and will be available to answer your questions and comfort you in times of need.

You also have access to the Total Parent Web site, which has many articles on newborns as well as videotaped descriptions about various childhood illnesses.

Let's discuss what you need to know to care for your new baby during the first year.

BREAST-FEEDING

Human milk is the best form of nutrition for an infant. Human breast milk has the optimal combination of sugar (lactose), easily digested proteins, and fat, which are naturally balanced for your infant.

Breast milk also contains antibodies to help fight infections, as well as vitamins and minerals. It even contains enzymes to help your baby digest the breast milk. Since it is such a well-balanced form of nutrition, it is almost completed absorbed. That is why breast-fed babies tend to have less frequent bowel movements than bottle-fed infants.

Breast-feeding will also enable you to lose weight easier since breast-feeding uses up about five hundred calories per day.

Breast-feeding

Important tips about breast-feeding

It is best to begin breast-feeding within the first hour of birth when the child is awake and alert. This is important not only because it initiates bonding between mother and child, but it also helps stimulate the production of a hormone (oxytocin) that will decrease your vaginal bleeding.

The first step to getting your infant to "latch on" is to hold your infant's face squarely facing your breast. Then gently rub or stroke your nipple against the infant's lower lip or cheek. This should cause the child to instinctively open his mouth and search for the nipple. This is called the rooting reflex. Your baby should latch on to your areola and not just the nipple. The child will then use his tongue to squeeze out the breast milk. If your baby doesn't latch on at first, just be patient. Your nurse will give you some tips on how to position your child properly for the best results. Be persistent and your baby will usually latch on after just a few tries.

Once your baby latches on, the sucking initiates the let-down reflex. This reflex causes the milk to start flowing through the milk ducts. Two hormones, prolactin and oxytocin, are also released at this time to help initiate and maintain the flow of milk.

The initial milk that flows during the first few days is called colustrum. This is actually a thin yellowish fluid that contains less calories then breast milk. However, colustrum is important because it is loaded with antibodies that help your child's body fight off infections. About three to five days later, your milk will change to the typical white-colored breast milk.

BOTTLE-FEEDING

Bottle-feeding may be an option for women who are unable to breast-feed for various reasons. It also enables the other parent to feed and bond with the child. Another advantage of bottle-feeding is that the parents know exactly how much formula is ingested each day.

The main disadvantages are cost and occasional contamination of the formula. This means germs or bacteria can get into the formula due to inadequate or improper strerilization techniques in the formula.

FORMULAS

There are three basic types of formulas on the market today.
1. Cow's milk (lactose)–based formulas
2. Soy-based formulas (contains soy protein)
3. Specialized formulas (for children with specific diseases)

Cow's milk–based formulas are the most common. They are available with or without iron. Children who cannot digest the cow's milk sugar, which is called lactose, are usually placed on a soy-based formula.

One of the most important things to keep in mind with formulas is to keep all of the rubber nipples and equipment as clean as possible. This means heat sterilizing the rubber nipples and using clean supplies at all times.

If you are using powdered formula, be sure to use water that has been brought to a boil for a full minute to kill any bacteria that could contaminate the formula. In addition, any formula that is left in the refrigerator and not used for over twenty-four hours should be discarded.

NEWBORN WEIGHT CHANGES
What do I need to know about my baby's weight changes?
The average weight of a newborn is approximately seven pounds. Your baby will lose weight during the first three to five days, due to the fact that the colustrum has fewer calories then breast milk. However, your child should return to her normal birth weight by approximately day number ten.

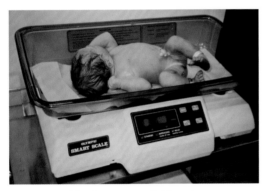

Newborn on weight scale

After this time, the child will gain approximately one-half to one ounce per day. The child who is not being breast-fed will take about two and one-half ounces of formula per day for every pound of body weight. Therefore, if the child is ten pounds, the child will probably take in ten × two and one-half ounces for a total of twenty-five ounces of formula per day. At about one month of age, babies usually take in approximately three to four ounces of formula per feeding. After the first month they will increase the feeding amount by approximately one ounce per month of age. This will continue until they reach eight ounces per feeding. In general, a baby will not drink more than thirty-two ounces of formula in a twenty-four-hour period. As a new parent, you will also be pleased to know that many babies do not usually require a middle-of-the-night feeding after approximately two to three months of age. However, some infants may not give up this feeding until they are four to six months old.

BURPING
How often should I burp my child?
In general, burping is recommended after the child takes in two to three ounces of formula. If the child is being breast-feed, he should be burped when you switch breasts.

CARING FOR THE UMBILICAL CORD STUMP
What do I need to know about caring for the umbilical cord stump?
The first thing to keep in mind is that the child should not be submerged in water while the cord stump is still in place. It will take approximately two to three weeks for the stump to fall off. Your pediatrician or hospital nurse will show you how to clean around the base of the stump using a cotton swab

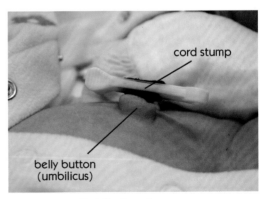

cord stump

belly button (umbilicus)

Umbilical cord stump

and alcohol. If the umbilical stump has not fallen off after two weeks, you should contact your doctor.

It is important to watch for any signs of infection at the cord stump because this can turn into a serious problem if not treated properly.

If you notice any redness or pus at the base of the stump, notify your pediatrician or family doctor immediately. This can be a sign of a serious infection called omphalitis. Also, if you notice any signs of infection, be sure to check your child's temperature. A rectal temperature of 100.4°F or more is considered a fever.

SLEEP PATTERNS

A newborn will typically sleep off and on during the day for a total of approximately sixteen hours. When you have a newborn in the house, one of the best ways to get enough rest and maintain your energy (not to mention your sanity!) is to try to take a nap whenever your child is sleeping.

What are some other changes that you need to be aware of during the first month?

As mentioned earlier, a child's weight will return to his birth weight by about ten days of age. After that, your child will gain approximately one-half to one ounce per day.

The child's face may also develop what is called baby acne. This usually occurs around the fourth or fifth week. Baby acne is a common occurrence, probably due to some of the mother's hormones that stimulate the oil glands in the baby's face.

The best way to care for baby acne is to simply wash the area with a mild soap and water.

NEWBORN REFLEXES

Babies have several reflexes or automatic responses that can be observed for the first few months. These reflexes are among the signs that your baby's nervous system is working properly. There are essentially six newborn reflexes:

1. Sucking reflex
2. Rooting reflex
3. Tonic neck reflex
4. Moro reflex
5. Walking and stepping reflex
6. Palmar grasp reflex

Rooting reflex

The rooting reflex occurs when you stroke one side of the child's cheek. When this occurs, the child will turn to that side looking for the nipple. The rooting reflex disappears at about four months.

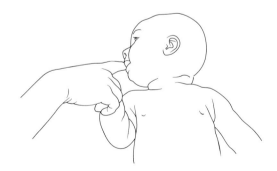

Rooting reflex

Tonic neck reflex

The tonic neck reflex occurs when the child's head is turned to one side. When you gently turn a child's head to one side, the child will stick one arm forward as if he is fencing with a sword. The tonic neck reflex disappears at about four to five months.

Moro reflex

The Moro reflex occurs when a child is suddenly startled or surprised. The Moro reflex is characterized by the child extending both of his arms and legs forward and then extending his neck and back. He then pulls his arms and legs inward. This reflex usually disappears at about two months of age.

Walking or stepping reflex

The walking or stepping reflex occurs when you hold the child up and touch his feet against a bed or flat surface. The child will tend to move his legs as if he is walking. This reflex occurs at approximately two months of age.

Palmar grasp reflex

The Palmar grasp reflex is a reflex that occurs when you place your finger in a child's hand and the child automatically grasps your finger. This disappears at approximately five to six months of age.

CRYING PATTERNS

Do different types of crying have different meanings?

Yes. Many mothers and fathers learn to appreciate the different kinds of cries their babies have. Moms and dads will soon begin to understand that certain cries can indicate one or more of the following:

1. The baby is uncomfortable because of a wet diaper.
2. The baby is hungry.

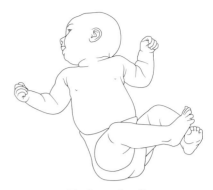

Tonic neck reflex

Moro reflex

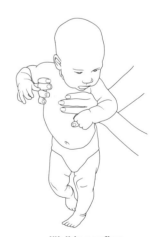

Walking reflex

Palmar grasp reflex

3. The baby is uncomfortable from some type of illness.
4. The child is crying due to something causing pain.

If your child is crying, focus on each potential reason to try to figure out why:

1. Pick up and comfort the child.
2. Check to see if the diaper is wet and change the diaper if necessary.
3. Feed the baby.
4. Burp the baby. (Perhaps a gas bubble in the stomach is causing the pain.)
5. Check the child's rectal temperature. (Fever is 100.4°F rectal or more.)
6. Check the fingers and toes to see if there are any hairs wrapped around them.

This last item might seem unusual. However, in the emergency room it is one of the things we look for in children who are persistently crying for no apparent reason. I have seen several children in the emergency room who have strands of hair wrapped around their toes. This causes a tight band of constriction and severe pain. Once these hairs are removed, the child stops crying.

Hairs wrapped around child's toes

You might be asking how these hairs get wrapped around the child's toes. It appears that the strands of hair simply fall into the child's crib and occasionally they end up getting wrapped around the toes as the child wiggles around.

COLIC

Colic is defined as excessive crying that occurs in healthy infants for over three hours a day at least three days per week. Babies with colic frequently have a slightly distended or enlarged belly and tend to hold their legs drawn up. Colic occurs in about one of every five children. It usually begins at about two to four weeks of age. It peaks at approximately six weeks and then decreases by about three months. Colicky crying usually occurs between the hours of 6:00 p.m. and midnight.

What causes colic?

As common as colic is, we are not sure what causes it, except that it seems that these children are unusually sensitive to any type of discomfort or stimulation. Occasionally colic can be due to sensitivity to certain foods that the mother has eaten if the mother is breast-feeding.

What can I do for my crying colicky baby to make her more comfortable?

One of the first things to do is comfort your child by picking him up. If you are breast-feeding, try to eliminate certain products from your diet that may be causing your child's discomfort. Some of the most common foods that have been associated with colic include milk products, cabbage, and caffeine.

If you are feeling overly stressed about your child's persistent crying, ask your spouse, family, or friends to give you a break. Persistent crying can be very stressful, especially when both mom and dad are already exhausted from lack of sleep during the first few months of having a new baby.

BOWEL MOVEMENTS

The first bowel movement that the child has is a blackish brown material called meconium, which consists of cells from the amniotic fluid that the child has swallowed while in the uterus. After the meconium stool has passed, the stools usually have a yellowish green color with the consistency of oatmeal. An infant's stool should never be hard. Children who are breast-fed usually only have one or two bowel movements per week. This is because the breast milk is so completely utilized by the body. In contrast, children who are formula fed have about one bowel movement per day.

URINATION

A typical infant should be urinating four to five times a day. Any less than four to five times a day indicates possible dehydration.

PACIFIERS

Pacifiers can be used for children. However, parents must never attach a pacifier to a cord wrapped around a child's neck. This can cause accidental choking.

SIDS (SUDDEN INFANT DEATH SYNDROME)

SIDS is the unexplained death of a child twelve months and under for no apparent reason. The incidence of SIDS seems to peak at four to sixteen weeks. Unfortunately, approximately one to two children out of every one thousand die every year from this syndrome. The cause of SIDS is still not known for certain. However, children who are at the highest risk for sudden infant death appear to have the following risk factors:

1. Low birth weight
2. A sibling who died of SIDS
3. Premature birth
4. Sleeping on their stomachs

What can I do to prevent SIDS?

The American Academy of Pediatrics started a "Back to Sleep" campaign several years ago. Research shows that infants who sleep on their backs have a decreased chance of dying of SIDS.

JAUNDICE

A yellowish orange discoloration of a child's skin and eyes during the first few days or weeks of birth is called jaundice. Jaundice is usually due to breast-feeding. However, jaundice can be a sign of a serious infection.

A child with jaundice and fever requires special testing and evaluation to rule out any potentially serious medical condition. If your child appears to have a yellowish orange discoloration in the skin and eyes during the first few days of life, call your pediatrician.

Child with jaundice—compare yellow tint of child's face to color of hand.

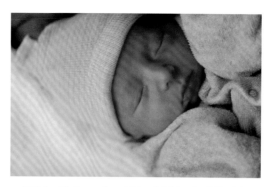

Child with jaundice. This child had a bilirubin level of 19. (Normal bilirubin is under 12) Diagnosis: Breast feeding jaundice.

Your pediatrician will order what is called a bilirubin blood test. Generally, the bilirubin level is considered abnormal if it is over the level of twelve in a full-term infant, but children who are premature can have abnormal levels lower than this. If your doctor feels that the bilirubin is simply from breast-feeding and not some other serious problem, phototherapy may be prescribed. This involves either home or hospital treatment with a bili-light (which the child wears around the body), or sometimes lights that are placed overhead in the crib. The light therapy usually continues for one to two days until the bilirubin drops to an acceptable level. The light therapy converts the bilirubin in the blood to a form that can be easily dissolved and removed from the body.

In children with serious illnesses and high bilirubin, an exchange blood transfusion may be needed, as well as treatment with antibiotics if infections such as meningitis are present. High bilirubin levels associated with serious infections can lead to deposits of bilirubin in the brain, which can cause permanent brain damage.

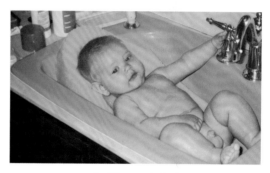

Bathing an infant

BATHING YOUR NEW BABY

As mentioned earlier, children under the age of three weeks should never, ever be submerged for a bath, because the umbilical cord stump may become infected. Children younger than three weeks should be given a sponge bath in an infant tub with mild baby soap. Make sure not to use any strong detergents on the baby's skin.

TAKING A RECTAL TEMPERATURE

Taking a rectal temperature is one of the most important skills a parent needs. Use a rectal mercury thermometer that has a shorter and wider tip than an oral thermometer. Take off the child's diaper. Hold the thermometer in your hand at the top and shake it down until the mercury column drops below 94°F. Put some lubricating jelly on the tip of the thermometer and insert it approximately one-half to one inch into the child's rectum. Hold it there for approximately one to one and a half minutes. Rotate the thermometer while you are taking the temperature to see how high the column of mercury is moving. A rectal temperature of 100.4°F or more is considered a fever. If your infant is one month or younger and has a rectal temperature of 100.4°F or more, contact your doctor immediately or bring your child immediately to a hospital emergency room.

THRUSH

Thrush is a yeast infection that occurs in a child's mouth as a result of the sugars that are in formula and breast milk. Thrush is characterized by white, cheesy-like patches on the inside portions of the mouth or on the tongue. Your doctor may prescribe an anti-yeast medicine such as nystatin. The

Child with thrush of tongue

doctor may recommend putting one drop on either side of the mouth four times a day.

VAGINAL DISCHARGE

Newborn girls may have vaginal discharge for a few weeks due to the high level of their mother's estrogen in their bloodstream. The estrogen stimulates secretions from the vaginal area in newborns. This condition usually disappears within a few weeks as the level of estrogen from the mother decreases in the child's bloodstream.

DIAPER RASH

What causes diaper rash?

Diaper rash is caused by either a fungus (yeast) or bacteria. Symptoms of diaper rash include a reddish inflammation on the skin in the diaper area. Your physician may prescribe a cream and/or an antibiotic and may also recommend frequent diaper changes to clear up the rash. Frequent diaper changes keep the area as dry as possible and help healing.

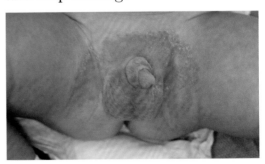

Diaper rash

CRADLE CAP (SEBORRHEA)

Cradle cap (seborrhea dermatitis) is characterized by scaly areas on a child's scalp. You may see this condition in the first few months. Your pediatrician may prescribe a special shampoo.

BIRTHMARKS

Some children have birthmarks on their faces, necks, or other parts of their bodies. These are sometimes called salmon patches or stork bites. These are of no real concern, and many of them clear up after a few years.

VOMITING

What are some of the causes of vomiting in the first thirty days of life?
Vomiting during the first thirty days of life requires careful evaluation by a physician. Spitting up a small amount of milk after feeding is not uncommon. However, persistent or projectile vomiting—vomiting that is forceful and projects out a few feet from the child—can indicate a serious medical problem.

PYLORIC STENOSIS

Projectile vomiting can indicate a congenital narrowing of the small intestine as it exits from the stomach. This is called pyloric stenosis, which occurs in one out of 150 male infants and one out of 750 female infants.

Pyloric stenosis usually occurs when the child is around two or three weeks old. It is a problem that requires surgery to enlarge the opening of the small intestine, called the duodenum. See the illustration for a picture of where the narrowing occurs. The vomiting usually happens just after or at the end of feeding.

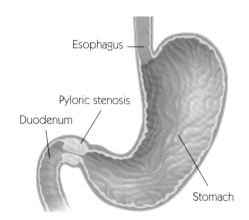

Pyloric stenosis

Another serious type of vomiting to watch for is a greenish vomit, which is called bilious vomiting. Call your doctor if your child has greenish vomit or vomit with blood in it.

MIDGUT VOLVULUS OF THE SMALL INTESTINE (GREEN VOMITING)

Vomiting green material in the first few weeks can be a sign of a sudden twisting and strangulation of the small intestine. This is called midgut volvulus. It usually occurs in the first few weeks of life. These children look acutely sick and appear to be in severe pain. The vomiting and stool may become bloody. Shock can occur within hours. The child will look ill and pale with diffuse tenderness of the belly (abdomen). This condition occurs twice as often in males than in females.

The diagnosis can be made by several means: x-rays of the abdomen, ultrasound, or upper GI x-rays after a swallow of barium dye. Treatment is abdominal surgery to untwist the bowel before it loses its blood flow and gangrene of the small intestine occurs.

INTUSSUSCEPTION

Intussusception (pronounced in-tuss-a-sép-shun) is a condition in which the small intestine becomes blocked because part of the small intestine has been pulled inside itself like a telescope. Intussusception causes a small bowel obstruction.

This problem usually occurs in children between three months and five years of age. (Most occur between five and nine months.) Males are affected four times more often than females. The chances of this occurring is about one to four out of a thousand children.

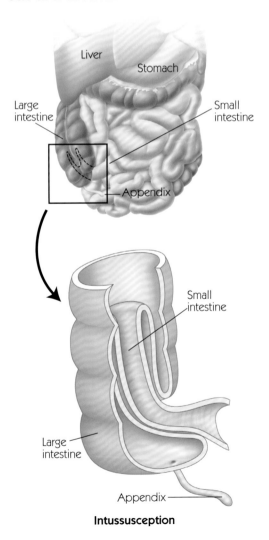

Intussusception

Intussusception symptoms may include:
1. Intermittent episodes of pain and vomiting alternating with the child feeling well and pain free.
2. Some children will have bloody stool or what looks like a "currant jelly stool."

How is the diagnosis of intussusception made?

A physician will examine the child's abdomen for a sausage-shaped mass that can sometimes be felt.

The diagnosis is made with either x-rays or ultrasound. Some cases are resolved by doing an air enema lower GI x-ray exam. Air is instilled in the rectum and x-rays are taken. In some cases this will cause the intestinal blockage to undo itself. In other cases, surgery may be required.

HERNIAS

Hernias are a protrusion of the intestines or other tissues through a weak area of the abdominal wall, the inguinal area or the femoral area. (The inguinal and femoral areas are in or near the crease between the belly and the upper thigh.) Umbilical and inguinal hernias are the most common. Parents will sometimes notice these hernias when they see a bulge in these areas while the child is crying, coughing, or straining. Hernias should be surgically corrected in children before they cause an incarcerated hernia as decribed below.

See the illustration for the most common locations of hernias.

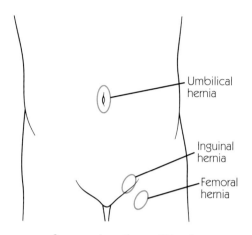

Common Locations of Hernias

Umbilical hernia

Inguinal hernia

Femoral hernia

INCARCERATED HERNIAS

The key point you need to know is how to tell when a simple hernia turns into an incarcerated hernia. An incarcerated hernia occurs when the contents of the hernia become twisted and caught in a hole in the abdominal wall, which results in more swelling and cuts off the blood flow to the intestines.

The signs of an incarcerated hernia are:

1. Vomiting
2. Abdominal pain and/or pain at the site of the hernia
3. Tenderness and firmness of the bulging hernia
4. Inability to push the hernia back into place with gentle pressure

An incarcerated hernia is a surgical emergency

In some cases, the physician or surgeon may be able to push the contents of the hernia back into place. If not, the hernia must be surgically corrected within a few hours for a good outcome.

SHAKEN BABY SYNDROME

Shaken baby syndrome is a condition in which the child's brain has been traumatized due to a forceful back-and-forth shaking by a caregiver or parent. It is actually considered child abuse. In many cases, a fatigued and tired parent loses control and shakes the child back and forth. With this shaking, the child's head swings forward and backward. This forward and backward shaking of the child's skull causes the brain to move back and forth within the skull and bruise itself against the inside of the skull.

Shaken baby syndrome can lead to small, medium, or large areas of bleeding within the brain, as well as contusions of the brain. Children who are victims of shaken baby syndrome may develop permanent developmental problems if it is not diagnosed early. These children can also have seizures due to brain trauma. Tragically, a certain percentage of children who have this condition can die.

Shaken baby syndrome

TOTAL PARENT POINTERS
THE FIRST YEAR

1. **Newborns decrease their weight during the first few days** after they are born, but they usually regain their original birth weight by approximately the tenth day. Thereafter, children typically gain one-half to one ounce per day.

2. Children usually take approximately three to four ounces of formula per feeding during their first few weeks. You can increase this by one ounce per month until they reach approximately eight ounces per feeding. Normally a child will not need more than thirty-two ounces per day.

3. **Know how to take a rectal temperature.**

4. **Note that a fever is defined as a temperature of 100.4°F rectally** or more in a child. Any infant under the age of one month with a temperature of 100.4°F needs to be evaluated immediately by your pediatrician, family doctor, or a doctor at the nearest emergency room.

5. Do not ever, ever submerge a child's body in water for the first three weeks, or until the umbilical stump falls off. Keep the umbilical stump clean with alcohol or whatever cleaning routine is recommended by your pediatrician.

6. **Projectile vomiting** is a serious problem in infants and should be evaluated immediately by your physician.

7. **Pyloric stenosis** can cause **projectile vomiting** and usually occurs at two to three weeks of age.

8. **Intussusception** occurs in children between three months to five years of age. Part of their small intestine is pulled up into the intestine, like a telescope, which can result in a bowel obstruction. The clues to intussusception are episodes of **severe belly pain** that comes and goes, **vomiting**, and **bloody stool**. The stool may sometimes have a dark purple color like currant jelly.

9. A **hernia** occurs when a portion of the intestine pushes through a small hole or gap inside the abdominal wall, scrotum, or thigh. An **incarcerated hernia** occurs when the intestine becomes stuck inside this gap of tissue. The loop of intestine that is caught in the hernia becomes painful because of the resulting intestinal blockage and progressive loss of blood flow. This is an **emergency condition** that requires **immediate evaluation** by a physician. (See the diagrams on page 29 that highlight the most common sites for hernias.) The signs of an incarcerated hernia are:
   - Vomiting
   - Abdominal pain and/or pain at the site of the hernia
   - Tenderness, firmness, and/or swelling of the bulging hernia
   - Inability to push the hernia back into place with gentle pressure

10. **Colic** usually occurs under the ages of three months of age. General guidelines for treating colic include walking with the child, rocking the child, changing the child's diaper, placing the child in a comfortable position, checking to see if the child is hungry, and making sure your child has had enough sleep.

2

Fever

When is a fever dangerous?

Fever is one of those good news, bad news events. The good news is that it signals that something is up with your child, and it's the body's natural defense system kicking in to fight infection. But as a parent, the unsettling or bad part is that it's worrisome for you and not very pleasant for your child, either.

You might think, Is this just a cold, a virus, or something more serious that I need to really pay attention to, call the doctor, and snap into action about? Be assured that these are all very normal and real concerns. Read on and you will learn about fever, get help deciding when it might be serious, and find tips on when you should call your doctor or bring your child to the hospital.

What is a fever?

Fever is one of the body's most important warning signs. It's a red flag that something is wrong. Knowing how to interpret that warning sign and what symptoms and clues play a role in fever-related illnesses can help you decide when to call your doctor. Learning this information now, before you're in crisis mode with a sick child in the middle of the night, may even help you save your child's life some day in the future.

Over the past twenty-five years as an emergency room physician, I've seen thousands of children with fever. My mission is to give you the knowledge and confidence to deal with your child's fever effectively, safely, and quickly.

Fever explained

Fever reflects the body's natural defense against infection. When an infection occurs, the body's immune system revs up, sending white blood cells and antibodies to fight the infection. In addition, the body releases chemicals that tell the brain to increase the body's normal temperature to help fight the infection. Researchers believe that many or most viruses and bacteria may have difficulty surviving at higher temperatures, so this is one of the ways the body tries to wipe out those bad guys.

In an attempt to cope with the actual heat caused by a fever, the body adapts by increasing the heart rate, the breathing rate, and the blood circulation to the skin. As a result, a child who has a fever will feel hot and will look flushed (much like they do when they come in from playing a sweaty game of catch or after running around on a playground).

What causes a fever?

Fever is often the first symptom of an infection caused by a virus or bacteria. Virus-caused illnesses (such as the common cold or chicken pox) are not helped by treatment with antibiotics, while bacteria-caused illnesses (such as strep throat) benefit from treatment with antibiotics.

How high does a temperature have to be to be called a fever?

Fever is defined as the following:
- Rectal Temperature: 100.4°F (38°C) or higher
- Oral Temperature: 99.5°F (37.5°C) or higher
- Armpit (Axillary) Temperature: 98.6°F (37°C) or higher

If you are using an ear thermometer, note whether it is set to the oral or rectal mode.

Which method is the most accurate way of taking a temperature in an infant?

The most reliable way to get an accurate temperature of a child under the age of two years is rectally (with a good quality thermometer). Although mercury thermometers have traditionally been the most accurate, good quality digital thermometers are now available and produce results more quickly. (The American Academy of Pediatrics recommends not using mercury thermometers due to the potential of mercury exposure.)

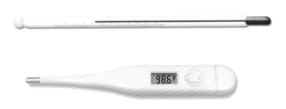

Standard nonmercury and digital thermometer

A rectal temperature is the only true reading of the body's core temperature. You should get comfortable taking your child's temperature rectally because it's simple and accurate. And if you treat it naturally, so will your kids. Here are some tips to make it even easier:

- Position your child on his or her back with legs raised—as if you were going to change a diaper.
- Insert the thermometer one-half inch into the rectum. If you are using a non-mercury thermometer, wait about a minute for the reading. If you are using a digital thermometer, it will usually beep when the temperature reading is complete. Check the instructions on the package to make sure you are using and reading it correctly. If you use a digital thermometer, make sure it is of high quality.

- Pediatricians recommend a rectal temperature if the child is age two or less. The younger the child, the more important it is to ensure an accurate temperature. Over the age of two to three years, an oral thermometer can be used. Keep in mind that the child must be able to keep it under his tongue long enough to take the temperature.
- Forehead thermometers: Because skin temperatures can be unreliable, forehead thermometer strips should be used ONLY as a screening thermometer for children over the age of one.

- Ear (tympanic) thermometers: My personal experience in our emergency room indicates that unless you are an experienced health professional, you will find that these are not reliable for parents or untrained people to use in children. An unreliable temperature measurement is sometimes worse than no temperature reading at all.

IMPORTANT CAUSES OF FEVER

Let's discuss the importance of taking a temperature in a child under the age of three years.

The critical diagnoses that physicians definitely do not want to

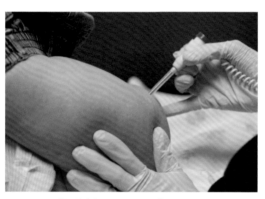

Rectal temperature by nurse

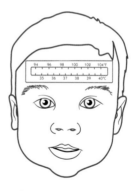

Forehead thermometer strip

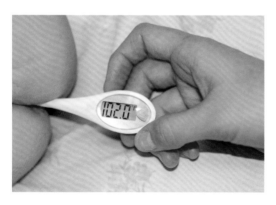

Rectal temperature by digital thermometer

Ear (tympanic) thermometer
being used on a child

miss when we evaluate an infant with a fever are:

1. Meningitis (an infection of the spinal fluid and the lining around the brain)
2. Sepsis (an overwhelming infection due to bacteria in the bloodstream that can cause a high fever or a low body temperature [hypothermia] in infants or young children)
3. Pneumonia or other lung infections
4. A severe urinary or kidney infection
5. Severe flu
6. Appendicitis or some other serious abdominal emergency that may require surgery
7. A severe skin infection or an abscess (Note: An abscess is a collection of pus—a boil)
8. Bone or joint infections (osteomyelitis or septic arthritis)

CLUES TO THE CAUSE OF FEVER

Observe your child for clues to the cause or the source of the fever.

The older the child, the better she is at communicating the details of her symptoms. It's tougher to tell with children too young to talk. Try to let their bodies do the communicating for you. Watch for specific symptoms or clues that localize the source of the infection.

You now have an opportunity to have one of those heroic parental roles—the chance to become a "Sherlock Holmes medical detective." Sherlock Holmes, of course, was the most famous of all fictional detectives. He used his powers of observation and logic to figure out all kinds of things about people and to solve many mysterious crimes. Let's see how you can become like Sherlock Holmes and use your powers of observation and logic to look for medical clues to figure out the cause of your child's fever.

CLUES TO THE SOURCE OF YOUR CHILD'S FEVER

Does your child have any of the following?

1. Cough
2. Runny nose
3. Difficulty breathing
4. Wheezing
5. Frequent urination (a sign of a urinary tract infection) or decreased urination (a sign of dehydration)
6. Diarrhea
7. Vomiting
8. Rash
9. Headache
10. Abdominal pain
11. Stiff Neck (can be a sign of meningitis)

As you'll see in the following real-life examples of parents with children just like yours, the way you'll want to respond has a lot to do with the child's age and his symptoms. Let's take a look at how fever is evaluated at various ages: birth to three months, three months to three years, and over three years of age.

FEVER—AGE UNDER THREE MONTHS

What should you do IF . . . you wake up at 2 a.m. and hear your three-week-old baby girl crying, she has a 101°F rectal fever?

Fever in infants under three months of age is potentially serious. Call your pediatrician or go to the nearest emergency room immediately. Fever in children who are younger than twenty-eight days of age is even more likely to be serious. Infants at this age do not have well-developed immune systems, and they can become extremely sick very quickly. They can even die from certain infections (such as meningitis) or from a blood infection (called sepsis). These children need to be seen by a doctor immediately. In general, any child under the age of three months (and especially under twenty-eight days) who has a fever of 100.4°F rectally or more should be seen by a doctor immediately.

FEVER—FROM THREE MONTHS TO THREE YEARS

Children in the three-month to thirty-six-month age group should be seen within twenty-four hours of the onset of a fever. But if they are lethargic or look sick, they need to be seen by a physician immediately. While very young infants are difficult to diagnose because they do not show the typical signs of illness, children in this three- to thirty-six-month age group can be evaluated more reliably by a physician.

What are some of the signs that my five-month-old baby with a fever of 101.0°F is probably sick and needs to be seen right away by a doctor?

The fact that the child with a fever is more than three months old makes me (and your doctor) feel more comfortable because your child's symptoms will correlate more with (or be a clearer sign of) how sick she is. However, your physician will still be very thorough examining your infant under the age of one year because the signs of illness are still not a completely reliable indication of what the illness is. Here are some clues and physical signs that I look for while examining a three- to thirty-six-month-old child with a fever.

PROBABLY SICK SIGNS (AGE THREE TO THIRTY-SIX MONTHS)

- Excessive sleepiness
- Decreased appetite (The infant will not bottle-feed or breast-feed because he is too uncomfortable, too sleepy, or has trouble breathing.)
- Fussiness
- Inconsolable crying (The child keeps crying no matter how much you try to comfort her, such as by feeding or changing a diaper.)
- Decreased alertness
- Difficulty breathing or rapid breathing with flared nostrils
- Pale or dusky skin color
- Decreased urination (Most infants should urinate four to five times in a twenty-four-hour period. Any less than this amount may be a sign of dehydration.)
- Poor eye contact with parents (in children more than three or four months old)

Signs that decrease the chances of a serious illness

- Smiling, happy, and playful

- Good eye contact (infants over three to four months)
- Alert
- No breathing problems (no flared nostrils, no inner rib retractions, no rapid breathing)

KEY POINTS ABOUT FEVER IN THE THREE-MONTH TO THIRTY-SIX-MONTH AGE GROUP

1. Fever (a rectal temperature 100.4° F or more) in a child between three months and twelve months of age needs to be carefully evaluated. Children in this age group should be carefully observed for signs of being probably sick. The younger the child, the more cautious you need to be. If they have any of the probably sick signs, or your gut instincts tell you that he is not acting right, you should bring your child to your pediatrician or to an emergency room.

2. Children in the twelve- to thirty-six-month age group usually need to be seen by a physician within twenty-four hours, unless they have any of the signs of being probably sick (as noted above). If they have signs of being probably sick, they should be seen immediately by your doctor or by an emergency medicine physician.

Now, taking on the role of Sherlock Holmes, let's use your powers of observation and see what you think about the appearance of the following four children (see below). Which of these four children look to be probably sick?

WHICH CHILD LOOKS PROBABLY SICK?

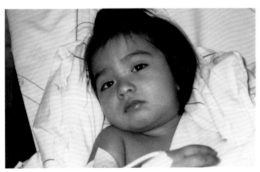

The clue is the child without the smile (lower left corner). This girl had a 103.5°F rectal temperature.

She didn't want to take any fluids and had trouble turning her head. Talking was difficult (because it hurt too much). She had a severe sore throat, which was a bacterial infection that progressed to an abscess (collection of pus) behind her upper airway. An x-ray of the abscess is below. This is called a retro-pharyngeal abscess.

The most common signs of a retropharyngeal abscess are fever, pain with swallowing, a sore throat for several days, and a muffled voice. The voice is muffled because the child has severe throat pain when speaking.

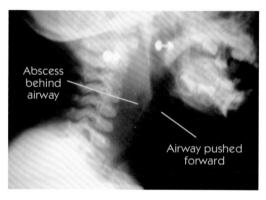

x-ray of Retropharygeal Abscess
Note how the abscess pushes the airway (trachea) forward. This required drainage by a pediatric ear, nose, and throat surgeon in the operating room (as well as IV antibiotics)

What are the most common causes of fever in the three to thirty-six-month age group?

- Common cold or upper respiratory tract infection
- Bronchiolitis (caused by the RSV virus)
- Pneumonia
- Gastroenteritis (diarrhea, vomiting, and abdominal pain)
- Croup—(viral infection of the smaller bronchial airways of the lung—"barking seal" cough)
- Pharyngitis (sore throat)
- Urinary Tract Infection (bladder or kidney infection)
- Influenza (during the flu season—the winter months)

COMMON COLD (UPPER RESPIRATORY TRACT INFECTION)

Otherwise known as the common cold, an upper respiratory tract infection often has a runny nose, cough, sneezing, fever, fatigue, and nasal congestion. Please understand that a child who appears healthy but who has a fever, cough, and a runny nose does not need an antibiotic for this illness. This is because a cold or upper respiratory tract infection is caused by a virus, not a bacterium. Viruses are not killed by antibiotics, only bacteria are.

Please talk with your doctor about this and come to an understanding that the overuse of antibiotics is not a good thing for your child (or for any of us) in the long run. Overuse of antibiotics causes bacteria that are normally present in the body to become resistant. This means that eventually the person needs more and more powerful antibiotics to fight the resistant bacteria if they later cause an infection. We are already experiencing some problems with certain bacteria which have multiple antibiotic resistance.

BRONCHIOLITIS (RSV)

Slight fever, cough, wheezing, rapid breathing, and sometimes inner rib retractions in children under the age of three years. Bronchiolitis is usually caused by a virus called RSV (respiratory syncytial virus). See our Total Parent Breathing Checklist at the end of this chapter for information and visual clues to assess your child's breathing.

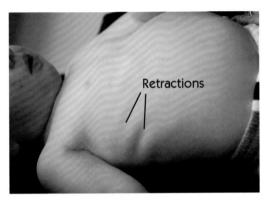

Inner rib retractions

PNEUMONIA

Children who have pneumonia typically have a fever, shortness of breath, rapid breathing, and a cough. They may also have inner rib retractions.

STOMACH FLU (GASTROENTERITIS)

Acute gastroenteritis often includes diarrhea, vomiting, and abdominal pain and can be caused either by viruses or bacteria.

CROUP

Croup is a viral infection associated with a nagging cough that typically sounds like a barking seal. Children who have croup usually have a slight fever (around 100.5°–101°F) and varying degrees of difficult breathing. Croup can be mild, moderate, or severe.

SORE THROAT

Sore throat (acute pharyngitis) symptoms include fever, pain in the throat (especially when swallowing), and enlarged lymph nodes in the neck. A sore throat can be caused by the familiar strep (streptococcus) bacteria, infectious mononucleosis, or another virus. About 70 percent of cases are due to a virus and do not need an antibiotic. About 20–25 percent are due to strep bacteria, and 5 percent are due to infectious mono (also called infectious mononucleosis).

URINARY TRACT INFECTION (UTI)

The main symptoms of a urinary tract infection are: burning pain when urinating, frequent urination, occasional blood in the urine, sometimes fever. All female infants and uncircumcised males younger than one year old should be checked for a urinary tract infection if no other cause for a fever is found. Some children may not have any symptom except fever. Vomiting is a common sign of a urinary tract infection under the age of one.

FLU (INFLUENZA)

Children with the flu (influenza A or B) typically have fever, muscle aches, fatigue, sore throat, cough, diarrhea, nausea, and vomiting.

The flu can last for several days to more than a week.

While flu vaccines are effective at preventing infection with some strains of flu virus, they do not protect against all strains of the flu virus. In addition, vaccines may not be effective against certain strains of flu each year because the flu virus actually can change. This is called "drift." By the time a particular flu virus vaccine finally reaches the market, the flu virus proteins may have drifted and changed, and that particular strain of flu may have become a significantly different viral protein than the one that existed when the vaccine was made. That is why some flu vaccines are not as effective as scientists expected during a particular flu season.

Check with your physician each year to see if you or your child need the flu vaccine during the fall. Traditionally, the flu vaccine is usually recommended for children six months or less, adults age sixty-five or more, and those with chronic illnesses. However, more recent guidelines are now recommending vaccination for all ages. Keep in mind that flu vaccines are needed every year due to the changes in flu viruses. Check with your doctor for the latest recommendations for the flu vaccine or go to the Centers for Disease Control Web site (www.cdc.org).

BABY SAMANTHA'S STORY— FEVER IN A THREE-WEEK-OLD

Kim and Tom are parents of a baby, now three weeks old, named Samantha. Her birth weight was eight pounds, two ounces.

Kim noticed that Samantha's appetite had changed. Normally, baby Samantha took in sixteen ounces of fluids per day. This day, as of 8 p.m. Samantha had taken in only ten ounces of fluids. She didn't appear to be ill—no cough, runny nose, vomiting, or diarrhea. She just had a decreased appetite, was crying, and was fussy.

Kim put Samantha to bed at the baby's usual time. But when Samantha woke for her 2 a.m. feeding, Kim noticed that Samantha was slightly warm.

She checked Samantha's rectal temperature with a good digital thermometer. It read 100.9°F. Kim knew that a rectal temperature of 100.4°F or higher indicated a fever and that children who have a fever and are one month old or younger should be seen immediately by a pediatrician or family physician. Samantha's pediatrician told Kim to take Samantha to the emergency room immediately.

When Kim and Tom arrived at the emergency room, they told the triage nurse that Samantha was three weeks old and had a 100.9°F rectal temperature.

I immediately examined the baby and spoke with the parents in an examining room. My primary goal was to find the source of the baby's fever. Was it one of the usual causes . . . a cold, an ear infection, a urinary tract infection, stomach flu, pneumonia, or some other viral illness? Or was it a more serious cause, such as meningitis or sepsis (an infection in the bloodstream)? In addition, I wanted to see if Samantha had any of the signs of being probably sick or probably not sick.

After a thorough history and physical exam, I could not find an obvious source for Samantha's infection. Samantha did, however, have several signs of being probably sick. These included a decreased appetite, fussiness, and crying more than usual. I ordered blood tests, blood cultures, a urine test, and a chest x-ray.

In addition, I told Samantha's parents that since their child was only three weeks old and there was no readily identifiable source of the fever, I would need to do a spinal tap. I clearly explained the risks and benefits of doing a spinal tap, and they agreed to the procedure. (A spinal tap is performed by inserting a very small needle in the child's lower back to obtain a small amount of spinal fluid. This is done to make sure the child does not have meningitis.) Samantha was also promptly started on intravenous antibiotics.

One hour later, the lab test on the spinal fluid showed that there were more than one hundred white blood cells in the spinal fluid. Having more than fifteen to twenty-two white blood cells in this age group is considered abnormal. This confirmed that Samantha had meningitis. She was admitted to the hospital and continued on IV antibiotics.

Two days later, the cultures of the spinal fluid and of the blood revealed a germ or bacterium called group B strep (referred to as GBS). Fortunately, Samantha was receiving the correct antibiotic to kill this bacteria. If the parents had refused the spinal tap, we would not have had a sample of fluid to grow the GBS germ. We would not have been able to test different antibiotics against it to see which ones would work. That could have meant valuable time would have been lost in treating baby Samantha.

DOCTOR'S NOTE ABOUT SPINAL TAPS

Why is a spinal tap so important in infants with a fever?
A spinal tap is done to collect a sample of the spinal fluid for several reasons. First, it is used to determine if an infection is present in the fluid surrounding the brain and the spinal cord (meningitis). In addition, the spinal fluid can be used to grow a bacteria culture. The culture can tell us if we are using the correct antibiotic to treat the illness. It takes approximately forty-eight hours to grow the bacterial culture in the lab.

Take-away message: treating fever in children thirty-six months and younger
You should know that an infant's fever is defined as any rectal temperature of 100.4°F or higher. Oral and axillary (armpit) temperatures are not an accurate measurement for babies age twelve months or less and should not be used. Whenever an infant feels warm, his temperature should be checked with a good quality rectal thermometer.

Any child three months old or younger who has a rectal fever of 100.4°F or more should be evaluated immediately by your pediatrician, family physician, or an emergency room physician. Babies can become seriously ill within hours of developing a fever. Prompt action and medical attention is critical for a positive outcome, as it was in Samantha's case.

In addition, it is difficult for a physician to assess the signs of illness in young babies because they do not have the same signs of illness as older children. Babies cannot tell us where they hurt. So physicians look for additional indications of illness such as a decrease in activity, excessive sleepiness, inconsolable crying, fever, a decrease in appetite, and/or increased irritability or fussiness. That's where parents can help us. After all, you know your baby best; you live with your baby, we don't. You can be our eyes and ears. So never hesitate to tell us what you think and what you have observed. What you see helps us to ferret out the correct diagnosis and treatment.

A spinal tap is a fairly easy and safe procedure for infants when done by trained physicians. It is extremely helpful in diagnosing a life-threatening infection in children called meningitis.

COUGHING AND DIFFICULTY BREATHING

What should you do if, as you are putting your three-year-old daughter to bed, you notice that she has a 102°F fever, a cough, a runny nose, and some trouble breathing.

How do you know if this is—or isn't—pneumonia or some other serious illness?

Take a look at the Fever Checklist at the end of this chapter (on page 44) and review the symptoms related to difficulty breathing. The following questions are designed to help you to assess your child's breathing:

- Does your child have difficulty breathing?
- Do your child's rib muscles get pulled in when she breathes in?
- Does your child have dilated (flaring of the) nostrils with each breath taken in?
- Does your child have deep or abdominal breathing? (That is, does the belly protrude quite a bit in and out with each breath?)

Let's say you discover that your child has flaring of the nostrils with each breath, and her rib muscles get pulled in with each breath. She also seems to have deep or abdominal breathing. What should you do?

If the answer to any of the questions above is "yes," the child should be seen by a doctor immediately. Use our Total Parent Breathing Checklist to remember the signs of difficult breathing in your child (see page 43).

Fever, headache, and neck stiffness are signs of what?

Let's take a look at a real-life example and see if you can figure out this one.

What should you do if your twelve-year-old son has a fever of 102.5°F, a headache, vomiting, a stiff neck, fatigue, and the lights hurt his eyes? It is 10 p.m.

Should you call your doctor?

Yes, it could be meningitis. The main symptoms of meningitis include:

- Fever
- Headache
- Neck stiffness
- Bright lights bother the eyes
- Confusion (occasionally)
- Severe fatigue
- Vomiting
- Hallucinations

KAWASAKI DISEASE

Kawasaki disease is a rare illiness (three thousand cases per year in the United States) that typically occurs in a child under five years of age with a fever for more than five to twelve days (with no known source), severe pink eyes, red lips, and a rash of the trunk, palms, and soles.

The most serious complication of the disease is a weak and bulging area (aneurysm) in an artery to the heart. This aneurysm can become blocked and cause a heart attack in a child.

The treatment is aspirin, IV administration of an antibody called gamma globulin and close monitoring for abnormal heartbeats and weakness of the heart muscle.

For more details about the symptoms of Kawasaki disease, see chapter 18, "Rashes and Skin Diseases."

YOUR FEVER CHECKLIST

Remember that fever is only one sign of illness. There are other symptoms that you need to check for and make a note of before you talk to your doctor. To make this easier for you, we have developed a Fever Checklist, which can be found on page 44. This checklist reminds you about the other important symptoms to look for and also gives you tips about the signs of being probably sick versus probably not sick. For a free downloadable and printable copy, go to our Web site at *TheTotalParent.com* to look for the Quick Facts section. Click on the Fever Checklist.

What temperature qualifies as a fever?

Fever is defined as a rectal temperature of 100.4°F or more or an oral temperature of 99.5°F or more. Only rectal temperatures should be done in children under the age of two.

If your child has a fever, your doctor will want to know about other symptoms associated with the fever. Please review the questions on the Fever Checklist and have your answers ready when you speak to your doctor or go to the emergency room.

TOTAL PARENT BREATHING CHECKLIST©

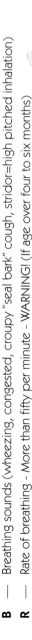

THETOTALPARENT.com
Dr. Ron Kurzejka, M.D.
Call 920–PARENTS
(920–727–3687)

B — Breathing sounds (wheezing, congested, croupy "seal bark" cough, stridor=high pitched inhalation)
R — Rate of breathing - More than fifty per minute - WARNING! (If age over four to six months)
E — Eye contact (focuses on you or looks away)
A — Abdominal breathing and appearance (pink or blue lips)
T — Temperature
H — Heavy breathing
I — Inner rib retractions
N — Nasal flaring
G — Grunting

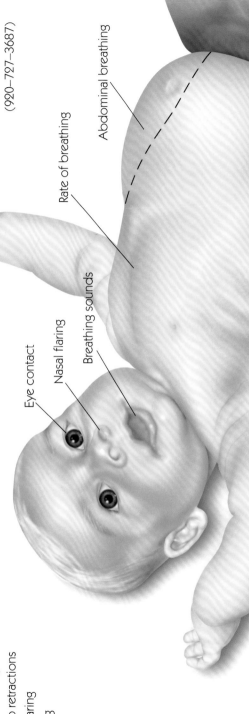

Abdominal breathing

Rate of breathing

Breathing sounds

Nasal flaring

Eye contact

Inner rib retractions

100.4°F (rectal) = Fever

38°C (rectal) = Fever

Age	Pounds	Kg	Normal Breathing Rate
Newborn	6–14	3–6 kg	30–50
6 month–1 yr	15–23	7–10 kg	30–40
2–4 yrs	24–35	12–16 kg	20–30
5–8 yrs	36–55	18–26 kg	14–20
8–12 yrs	55–110	26–50 kg	12–20
Over 12 yrs	>110	>50 kg	12–20

TOTAL PARENT FEVER CHECKLIST

TheTotalParent.com

YES	NO	**High Risk Checklist for Infants**
❏	❏	Is your child under three months of age?
		Does your infant have any of the following signs?
❏	❏	• Inconsolable crying (crying that does not stop, no matter what your do, in spite of feeding, changing diaper, or holding child)
❏	❏	• Excessive sleepiness (consider infection, sepsis, meningitis, low glucose, low sodium, dehydration)
❏	❏	• Excessive fussiness
❏	❏	• An inability to focus on your face or other objects. Does your child appear to be too irritated to fixate or focus on anything due to irritability?
❏	❏	Is there a change in your child's level of alertness?

YES	NO	**Coughing and Difficulty Breathing**
❏	❏	Does your child have difficulty breathing?
❏	❏	Do your child's rib muscles get pulled in when he breathes in?
❏	❏	Does your child have dilated or flaring nostrils with each breath in?
❏	❏	Does your child have deep or abdominal breathing? (That is, does the belly move in and out quite a bit with each breath?)

YES	NO	**Dehydration**
❏	❏	Has your child urinated less than four to five times in the past twenty-four hours?
❏	❏	Does you child have sunken-looking eyes?

YES	NO	**Urinary Tract Infections**
❏	❏	Has your child urinated excessively—over six or seven times in the past twenty-four hours?
❏	❏	Does your child seem to have any abdominal pain?
❏	❏	Does your child have back pain?
❏	❏	Were there any prior urinary or bladder infections?
❏	❏	Has your child been vomiting?
❏	❏	Does your child seem to have pain when urinating (either drawing his legs up when urinating or signs of pain during urination)?

YES	NO	**Rash**
❏	❏	Many causes: viruses (roseola, chicken pox), scarlet fever, MRSA* *methicillin-resistant Staphylococcus aureus (resistant to many antibiotics)

YES	NO	**Premature-Delivery Questions**
❏	❏	Was your child born prematurely (more than two weeks early)?
❏	❏	Was your delivery a normal delivery or were there complications? What was your child's birth weight? _____

Symptoms for children over the age of three:

YES	NO	**Does your child complain of any of the following?**
❏	❏	Severe headache (consider meningitis—although headache is common with many fever-related illnesses)
❏	❏	Earache (consider external or middle ear infection)
❏	❏	Sore throat (consider viral pharyngitis, strep throat, mono, epiglottitis)
❏	❏	Neck stiffness or neck pain (consider meningitis)
❏	❏	Stomach pain (many causes). Where is it located? Upper/lower/right/left
❏	❏	Pain with urination (consider urinary tract infection)
❏	❏	Back pain (could be a possible kidney infection)
❏	❏	Eye pain from bright lights (consider meningitis and migraine)

TOTAL PARENT POINTERS
FEVER

1. Keep a thermometer in your house and know how to take a rectal and oral temperature. Only rectal temperatures should be done if the child is age one year or younger.
2. **Fever is defined as:**
   a. **Rectal temperature of 100.4°F or higher (38°C or more)**
   b. **Oral temperature of 99.5°F or higher (37.5°C or more)**
   c. **Armpit temperature of 98.6°F or more (37°C or more)**
3. Infants who are younger than three months and who have a fever (100.4°F rectal temperature or higher) can become seriously ill. They need to be evaluated by a doctor as soon as possible.
4. If your child is **less than a month old** and has a rectal temperature of 100.4°F or more, bring your child to the nearest emergency room immediately and call your family doctor. **Children four weeks of age and less have poorly developed immune systems to fight infections.**
5. Children over the age of three months must go to the emergency room or see a physician immediately if they have a fever and any of the following symptoms:
   a. Change in their level of alertness, severe headache, lethargy, and/or neck stiffness
   b. Trouble breathing
   c. Progressively worsening abdominal pain

TOTAL PARENT POINTERS
FEVER

d. Excessive lethargy, sleepiness, or "looking sick"
e. If your gut instincts tell you that something is wrong with your child, bring your child to a doctor. Your instincts will often be right.

6. **The most common causes of fever are:**
   a. The common cold (upper respiratory tract infection)
   b. Sore throat (pharyngitis caused by viruses or bacteria such as group B strep or infectious mono)
   c. Croup
   d. Gastroenteritis
   e. Urinary tract infection
   f. Pneumonia
   g. Viral illnesses
   h. Influenza

7. **Meningitis** is an infection of the fluid that is inside the skull and that surrounds the brain. It can be caused by viruses or by bacteria. Here are the symptoms of meningitis.
   a. Children age one and younger: Fever over 100.4°F (rectally), decreased appetite and alertness, and increased fussiness.
   b. Children age one and older: **Fever, headache, stiff neck, fatigue, eye pain from bright lights,** and **change in behavior,** and **lethargy** or **confusion.**

8. **Urinary tract infection** symptoms include fever, **frequent urination, painful urination,** and an urgent need to go to the bathroom. Infants may have only a fever, fussiness, and frequent urination. (Remember also that urinary infections are more common in girls.) Vomiting may be a sign of a urinary infection in infants under the age of one.

9. **Abdominal pain** (especially **progressively severe abdominal pain**) and **fever** can be signs of a serious condition that requires immediate medical attention.

10. **Teething does not cause fever.** If a tooth is coming in and the child has a fever, then there is probably some other reason for the fever, such as a viral illness or the beginning of a cold.

11. Talk with your doctor and come to an understanding that **antibiotics are not necessary for all children with a fever. Children with viral colds and other viral illnesses do not need antibiotics.**

12. The **symptoms of pneumonia** are the following:
   a. Fever
   b. Cough
   c. Trouble breathing
   d. Rapid breathing
   e. Nasal flaring
   f. Inner rib muscle retractions (in infants). See our Total Parent Breathing Checklist.
   g. Grunting
   h. Poor eye contact if the child is not getting enough oxygen

3

Finding a Good Doctor

Finding the right doctor for your child is one of the most important decisions that you need to make regarding your child's health care. This chapter offers several suggestions about how to do this as well as some tips on being an informed patient.

To find a good doctor:

1. Ask your friends and family who they use. Get their opinions and recommendations about other pediatricians and family doctors.

2. Talk to nurses who work at local hospitals, especially pediatric nurses. They will usually have a good idea as to which pediatricians and family doctors have the best reputations around the hospital.

3. Ask the physicians you know who they use or who they would recommend.

4. If you do not have relationships with any of the above people, call a local hospital's pediatric unit and ask one of the nurses on duty, or the charge nurse, if she can recommend a good pediatrician.

5. Call the operator and ask for a hospital's physician referral service. Tell the person that you are looking for a particular type of doctor with good communication skills and a good bedside manner. Sometimes, physician referral services just go down a list of staff physicians and refer you to the next one on the list or the closest one to you. They can be very helpful if you prefer a certain type of physician, such as male or female, etc. They also can help you find a doctor who has a special interest in a particular area such as autism, ADHD, etc.

Once you have two or three physician referrals, you can go online and Google their names to find out where they went to medical school and where they did their residency (specialty) training. A hospital may also have a Web site that lists their physicians and their educational background as well as any specialty interest (as noted above).

TIPS ON BEING AN INFORMED PATIENT

The second aspect to having a positive doctor-patient relationship is your being an informed patient. When you go to a doctor's office with your child, you should be prepared with several questions about your child's condition. (It's good to write these down ahead of time so that you don't forget something.) The key things that you want to ask are:

1. Child's diagnosis
2. What is the treatment for this condition?
3. How long does this condition usually last?
4. If medications are prescribed, ask about any significant side effects from the medications.
5. Tell your doctor about any allergies the child may have to medications, foods (such as eggs or shellfish), and dyes used for x-ray procedures.
6. Will the medications interact with any medications your child is already on?
7. Ask about any school restrictions.
8. Get a note for school and/or physical education absences.
9. Is the condition contagious?
10. What can you do to prevent other children in the home from becoming sick?
11. Are there any special dietary restrictions?
12. Ask the doctor or nurse if they have any preprinted materials that describe your child's diagnosis. (Studies have shown that patients only remember a small percentage of what they are told.) You can also search our Web site at *TheTotalParent.com.* (Look at the Quick Facts section or search for your topic of interest.)
13. Ask about how to contact the doctor or his partners after office hours if you have any questions.
14. Repeat the instructions back to your doctor or nurse to make sure that you fully understand what they said.
15. Go to *TheTotalParent.com* Web site for our easy-to-use parent to doctor questions form, which lists the questions to ask. Search for parent to doctor questions or doctor visits.

TOTAL PARENT POINTERS
FINDING A GOOD DOCTOR

1. **Ask nurses or doctors you know** who work at your local hospital who they would recommend as a good doctor for your child.

2. **Call the pediatric unit a local hospital** and ask one of the nurses which doctors they would recommend or who they use.

3. **Use the parent-to-doctor questionnaire** at TheTotalParent.com to help you remember what questions to ask during your visit.

4. **Ask for written materials about your child's illness** so you can read up on it and become more knowledgeable. (You can also go to our Web site and read up on your child's diagnoses.)

5. **Repeat your instructions back to your doctor and/or nurse** to make sure that you fully understand everything.

6. Ask about any school absence duration and **obtain a written school excuse.**

7. Tell you doctor about your child's **allergies** to medications or foods.

8. **Ask your doctor how to get in touch with him/her after office hours.**

4

Immunizations

Immunizations are as important today as ever. Proper immunizations are a critical component of disease prevention and must be followed on a prescribed timetable to protect your child against disease.

Here are a few important facts about how vaccines have improved the lives of our children:

1. In the United States, paralytic polio decreased from 16,316 children in the early twentieth century to zero cases in 2007 as a result of the polio vaccine.
2. We eliminated rubella (German measles) in the United States in 2004 and no longer have congenital rubella syndrome birth defects (such as hearing and heart defects).
3. Did you know that over 200,000 deaths due to measles (rubeola) occur worldwide every year in countries that do not have the strict vaccine guidelines we have here in the United States?

Does my child need immunizations?

Immunizations are important because they help prevent your child from getting the following fourteen major diseases:

- Polio
- Measles (rubeola)
- Mumps
- Chicken pox
- Rubella (German measles)
- Pertussis (whooping cough)
- Diphtheria
- Tetanus
- Haemophilus influenza
- Hepatitis B
- Human papilloma virus (HPV)
- Meningococcal illness
- Pneumococcal illness
- Influenza

What immunizations does my child need?

A list of recommended immunizations is included at the end of this chapter. Here are some of the more common vaccines:

DTaP VACCINE

The DTaP vaccine protects your child from diphtheria, tetanus (lockjaw), and pertussis (whooping cough). The American Academy of Pediatrics strongly recommends that all children receive the complete series of DTaP vaccinations. Currently the DTaP vaccine is recommended over the older DTP vaccine. The DTaP vaccine is different from the previous DTP vaccine because it uses only part of the original pertussis bacteria rather than the whole bacteria.

The DTaP vaccines are given at two, four, and six months. The fourth dose is given at twelve months and the fifth dose is given at eighteen months. The child receives another booster before school between the ages of four and six.

Some children experience side effects from immunization injections. These may include a low-grade fever under 102°F and some mild redness at the injection site. The child may be somewhat less active than normal and may cry a bit after the injection.

POLIO VACCINES

Polio is an illness that can cause paralysis on one side of the body or one arm or leg or both arms and legs. Your parents and grandparents may remember the days before the polio vaccines, when polio was one of the most feared of diseases. And most of us know, of course, that this disease paralyzed President Franklin Delano Roosevelt and the great violinist Itzhak Perlman. Today we take the absence of polio almost for granted, thanks to the worldwide efforts of organizations such as Rotary International and the World Health Organization. But polio is still a potential threat, and there is

proven protection from it, thanks to immunizations.

The polio vaccine may be given orally or as an injection. It is given at two, four, twelve, and eighteen months and again between the ages of four and six.

There are advantages and disadvantages associated with both forms of the vaccine. In some cases, children who receive only the oral polio vaccine can develop vaccine-associated paralytic polio. This can occur in a child who has a less than adequate immune system. The other disadvantage with the oral polio vaccine is that it contains a weakened poliovirus. The advantage of the oral polio vaccine is that the child avoids injections. In addition, the oral polio vaccine is more effective than the injected as far as preventing the spread of the poliovirus.

In some cases, your pediatrician may recommend two doses of oral polio vaccine followed by two injections of the polio vaccine. In this case, the child will have the advantage of fewer injections and less chance of getting a vaccine associated with paralytic polio. Discuss the options with your doctor to make the best choice for your child.

MMR (MEASLES-MUMPS-RUBELLA) VACCINE

The MMR vaccine is used to protect your child against mumps, measles, and rubella. These immunizations will be given between the ages of twelve and fifteen months. Typical reactions to these injections are:

- Some mild soreness at the site of injection
- A low-grade fever

The child will receive a second MMR injection before twelve years of age. One thing that parents need to be aware of is that egg protein is used in making the vaccine. Therefore, if your child is allergic to eggs, you should inform your pediatrician.

HAEMOPHILUS INFLUENZA TYPE B VACCINE (HIB)

Children should receive a vaccine for Haemophilus B at two months of age. The use of this vaccine has resulted in a significant decrease in serious infections such as epiglotitis, infections of the bloodstream, and pneumonia caused by this bacterium.

CHICKEN POX VACCINE

This vaccine (a virus) is given to prevent or decrease the severity of chicken pox. It is given to children between the ages of twelve and eighteen months who have never had chicken pox. Some children may still get a mild case of chicken pox even though they have had the vaccine.

HEPATITIS B VACCINE

Children are immunized for hepatitis B at birth, two months, and between sixteen and eighteen months. Children who are allergic to yeast should not receive the vaccine.

HPV (HUMAN PAPILLOMA VIRUS) VACCINE

This virus can cause cervical cancer in women. It can also cause genital warts in both men and women. The presence of the HPV virus in the cervix has been shown to correlate with the development of cervical cancer later in life. Many people have asymptomatic infections (infections without any obvious symptoms). About twenty-five million people in the United States have HPV infections that can cause genital warts and related lesions. HPV infections can be diagnosed with a Pap smear. Keep in mind that women over the age of thirty should have a Pap test every two to three years if the prior Pap tests have been normal for three consecutive years.

The first dose of the HPV vaccine is given to girls around age eleven to twelve. The second dose is two months later. The third dose is six months after the first dose.

MENINGOCCAL VACCINE

This vaccine can prevent your child from getting certain types of meningitis. As I mentioned in an earlier chapter, meningitis is an infection in the fluid surrounding the brain. This vaccine is given to most children at age eleven to twelve. However, certain children who have a problem with their immune systems or who have no spleen may be given this vaccine as early as age two. (Check with your doctor if you think your child is in a high-risk group due to a chronic illness or condition.)

INFLUENZA VACCINE

The influenza vaccine is usually modified each year based on the current viruses that are most likely to cause the flu illness. This vaccine is only given to certain high-risk individuals based on recommendations of the Centers for Disease Control.* Talk to your doctor about the current year recommendations before the flu season begins in the late fall. Keep in mind that the flu vaccine only protects against some types of flu viruses, not all of them.

RECOMMENDED IMMUNIZATION SCHEDULE
for Persons Aged 0 Through 6 Years—United States • 2009

Vaccine	Age										
	Birth	1 month	2 months	4 months	6 months	12 months	15 months	18 months	19–23 months	2–3 years	4–6 years
Hepatitis B [1]	HepB	HepB		see footnote 1		HepB					
Rotavirus [2]			RV	RV	RV [2]						
Diphtheria, tetanus, pertussis [3]			DTaP	DTaP	DTaP	see footnote 3	DTaP				DTaP
Haemophilus influenzae type b [4]			Hib	Hib	Hib [4]	Hib					
Pneumococcal [5]			PCV	PCV	PCV	PCV				PPSV	
Inactivated poliovirus			IPV	IPV		IPV					IPV
Influenza [6]						Influenza (Yearly)					
Measles, mumps, rubella [7]						MMR		see footnote 7			MMR
Varicella [8]						Varicella		see footnote 8			Varicella
Hepatitis A [9]						HepA Series (2 doses)				HepA Series	
Meningococcal [10]										MCV	

	Range of recommended ages		Certain high-risk groups

1. **Hepatitis B vaccine (HepB).**
   (Minimum age: birth)
   At birth:
   - Administer monovalent HepB to all newborns before hospital discharge.
   - If mother is hepatitis B surface antigen (HBsAg)-positive, administer HepB and 0.5 mL of hepatitis B immune globulin (HBIG) within 12 hours of birth.
   - If mother's HBsAg status is unknown, administer HepB within 12 hours of birth. Determine mother's HBsAg status as soon as possible and, if HBsAg-positive, administer HBIG (no later than age 1 week).

   After the birth dose:
   - The HepB series should be completed with either monovalent HepB or a combination vaccine containing HepB. The second dose should be administered at age 1 or 2 months. The final dose should be administered no earlier than age 24 weeks.
   - Infants born to HBsAg-positive mothers should be tested for HBsAg and antibody to HBsAg (anti-HBs)

*The current recommendation from the Centers for Diease Control is that all children receive the flu vaccine.

after completion of at least 3 doses of the HepB series, at age 9 through 18 months (generally at the next well-child visit).

4-month dose:

- Administration of 4 doses of HepB to infants is permissible when combination vaccines containing HepB are administered after the birth dose.

2. **Rotavirus vaccine (RV).**
(Minimum age: 6 weeks)

- Administer the first dose at age 6 through 14 weeks (maximum age: 14 weeks 6 days). Vaccination should not be initiated for infants aged 15 weeks or older (i.e., 15 weeks 0 days or older).
- Administer the final dose in the series by age 8 months 0 days.
- If Rotarix® is administered at ages 2 and 4 months, a dose at 6 months is not indicated.

3. **Diphtheria and tetanus toxoids and acellular pertussis vaccine (DTaP).**
(Minimum age: 6 weeks)

- The fourth dose may be administered as early as age 12 months, provided at least 6 months have elapsed since the third dose.
- Administer the final dose in the series at age 4 through 6 years.

4. ***Haemophilus influenzae* type b conjugate vaccine (Hib).**
(Minimum age: 6 weeks)

- If PRP-OMP (PedvaxHIB® or Comvax® [HepB-Hib]) is administered at ages 2 and 4 months, a dose at age 6 months is not indicated.
- TriHiBit® (DTaP/Hib) should not be used for doses at ages 2, 4, or 6 months but can be used as the final dose in children aged 12 months or older.

5. **Pneumococcal vaccine.**
(Minimum age: 6 weeks for pneumococcal conjugate vaccine [PCV]; 2 years for pneumococcal polysaccharide vaccine [PPSV])

- PCV is recommended for all children aged younger than 5 years. Administer 1 dose of PCV to all healthy children aged 24 through 59 months who are not completely vaccinated for their age.
- Administer PPSV to children aged 2 years or older with certain underlying medical conditions (see MMWR 2000;49[No. RR-9]), including a cochlear implant.

6. **Influenza vaccine.**
(Minimum age: 6 months for trivalent inactivated influenza vaccine [TIV]; 2 years for live, attenuated influenza vaccine [LAIV])

- Administer annually to children aged 6 months through 18 years.
- For healthy nonpregnant persons (i.e., those who do not have underlying medical conditions that predispose them to influenza complications) aged 2 through 49 years, either LAIV or TIV may be used.
- Children receiving TIV should receive 0.25 mL if aged 6 through 35 months or 0.5 mL if aged 3 years or older.
- Administer 2 doses (separated by at least 4 weeks) to children aged younger than 9 years who are receiving influenza vaccine for the first time or who were vaccinated for the first time during the previous influenza season but only received 1 dose.

7. **Measles, mumps, and rubella vaccine (MMR).** (Minimum age: 12 months)
   - Administer the second dose at age 4 through 6 years. However, the second dose may be administered before age 4, provided at least 28 days have elapsed since the first dose.

8. **Varicella vaccine.**
   (Minimum age: 12 months)
   - Administer the second dose at age 4 through 6 years. However, the second dose may be administered before age 4, provided at least 3 months have elapsed since the first dose.
   - For children aged 12 months through 12 years the minimum interval between doses is 3 months. However, if the second dose was administered at least 28 days after the first dose, it can be accepted as valid.

9. **Hepatitis A vaccine (HepA).**
   (Minimum age: 12 months)
   - Administer to all children aged 1 year (i.e., aged 12 through 23 months). Administer 2 doses at least 6 months apart.

- Children not fully vaccinated by age 2 years can be vaccinated at subsequent visits.
- HepA also is recommended for children older than 1 year who live in areas where vaccination programs target older children or who are at increased risk of infection. See MMWR 2006;55(No. RR-7).

10. **Meningococcal vaccine.**
    (Minimum age: 2 years for meningococcal conjugate vaccine [MCV] and for meningococcal polysaccharide vaccine [MPSV])
    - Administer MCV to children aged 2 through 10 years with terminal complement component deficiency, anatomic or functional asplenia, and certain other high-risk groups. See MMWR 2005;54(No. RR-7).
    - Persons who received MPSV 3 or more years previously and who remain at increased risk for meningococcal disease should be revaccinated with MCV.

This schedule indicates the recommended ages for routine administration of currently licensed vaccines, as of December 1, 2008, for children aged 0 through 6 years. Any dose not administered at the recommended age should be administered at a subsequent visit, when indicated and feasible. Licensed combination vaccines may be used whenever any component of the combination is indicated and other components are not contraindicated and if approved by the Food and Drug Administration for that dose of the series. Providers should consult the relevant Advisory Committee on Immunization Practices statement for detailed recommendations, including high-risk conditions: http://www.cdc.gov/vaccines/pubs/acip-list.htm. Clinically significant adverse events that follow immunization should be reported to the Vaccine Adverse Event Reporting System (VAERS). Guidance about how to obtain and complete a VAERS form is available at http://www.vaers.hhs.gov or by telephone, 800-822-7967.

RECOMMENDED IMMUNIZATION SCHEDULE
for Persons Aged 7 Through 18 Years—United States • 2009

Vaccine	Age		
	7–10 years	11–12 years	13–18 years
Tetanus, Diphtheria, Pertussis [1]	see footnote 1	Tdap	Tdap
Human papillomavirus [2]	see footnote 2	HPV (3 doses)	HPV Series
Meningococcal [3]	MCV	MCV	MCV
Influenza [4]	Influenza (Yearly)		
Pneumococcal [5]	PPSV		
Hepatitis A [6]	HepA Series		
Hepatitis B [7]	HepB Series		
Inactivated poliovirus [8]	IPV Series		
Measles, mumps, rubella [9]	MMR Series		
Varicella [10]	Varicella Series		

Range of recommended ages Certain high-risk groups Catch-up immunization

1. **Tetanus and diphtheria toxoids and acellular pertussis vaccine (Tdap).**
   (Minimum age: 10 years for BOOSTRIX® and 11 years for ADACEL®)
   - Administer at age 11 or 12 years for those who have completed the recommended childhood DTP/DTaP vaccination series and have not received a tetanus and diphtheria toxoid (Td) booster dose.
   - Persons aged 13 through 18 years who have not received Tdap should receive a dose.
   - A 5-year interval from the last Td dose is encouraged when Tdap is used as a booster dose; however, a shorter interval may be used if pertussis immunity is needed.
2. **Human papillomavirus vaccine (HPV).**
   (Minimum age: 9 years)
   - Administer the first dose to females at age 11 or 12 years.
   - Administer the second dose 2 months after the first dose and the third dose 6 months after the first dose (at least 24 weeks after the first dose).
   - Administer the series to females at age 13 through 18 years if not previously vaccinated.
3. **Meningococcal conjugate vaccine (MCV).**
   - Administer at age 11 or 12 years, or at age 13 through 18 years if not previously vaccinated.
   - Administer to previously unvaccinated college freshmen living in a dormitory.
   - MCV is recommended for children aged 2 through 10 years with terminal complement component deficiency, anatomic or functional asplenia, and certain other groups at high risk. See MMWR 2005;54(No. RR-7).
   - Persons who received MPSV 5 or more years previously and remain at increased risk for meningococcal disease should be revaccinated with MCV.

4. **Influenza vaccine.**
   - Administer annually to children aged 6 months through 18 years.
   - For healthy nonpregnant persons (i.e., those who do not have underlying medical conditions that predispose them to influenza complications) aged 2 through 49 years, either LAIV or TIV may be used.
   - Administer 2 doses (separated by at least 4 weeks) to children aged younger than 9 years who are receiving influenza vaccine for the first time or who were vaccinated for the first time during the previous influenza season but only received 1 dose.

5. **Pneumococcal polysaccharide vaccine (PPSV).**
   - Administer to children with certain underlying medical conditions (see MMWR 1997;46[No. RR-8]), including a cochlear implant. A single revaccination should be administered to children with functional or anatomic asplenia or other immunocompromising condition after 5 years.

6. **Hepatitis A vaccine (HepA).**
   - Administer 2 doses at least 6 months apart.
   - HepA is recommended for children older than 1 year who live in areas where vaccination programs target older children or who are at increased risk of infection. See MMWR 2006;55(No. RR-7).

7. **Hepatitis B vaccine (HepB).**
   - Administer the 3-dose series to those not previously vaccinated.
   - A 2-dose series (separated by at least 4 months) of adult formulation Recombivax HB® is licensed for children aged 11 through 15 years.

8. **Inactivated poliovirus vaccine (IPV).**
   - For children who received an all-IPV or all-oral poliovirus (OPV) series, a fourth dose is not necessary if the third dose was administered at age 4 years or older.
   - If both OPV and IPV were administered as part of a series, a total of 4 doses should be administered, regardless of the child's current age.

9. **Measles, mumps, and rubella vaccine (MMR).**
   - If not previously vaccinated, administer 2 doses or the second dose for those who have received only 1 dose, with at least 28 days between doses.

10. **Varicella vaccine.**
   - For persons aged 7 through 18 years without evidence of immunity (see MMWR 2007;56[No. RR-4]), administer 2 doses if not previouslyvaccinated or the second dose if they have received only 1 dose.
   - For persons aged 7 through 12 years, the minimum interval between doses is 3 months. However, if the second dose was administered at least 28 days after the first dose, it can be accepted as valid.
   - For persons aged 13 years and older, the minimum interval between doses is 28 days.

This schedule indicates the recommended ages for routine administration of currently licensed vaccines, as of December 1, 2008, for children aged 7 through 18 years. Any dose not administered at the recommended age should be administered at a subsequent visit, when indicated and feasible. Licensed combination vaccines may be used whenever any component of the combination is indicated and other components are not contraindicated and if approved by the Food and Drug Administration for that dose of the series. Providers should consult the relevant Advisory Committee on Immunization Practices statement for detailed recommendations, including high-risk conditions: http://www.cdc.gov/vaccines/pubs/acip-list.htm. Clinically significant adverse events that follow immunization should be reported to the Vaccine Adverse Event Reporting System (VAERS). Guidance about how to obtain and complete a VAERS form is available at http://www.vaers.hhs.gov or by telephone, 800-822-7967.

The Recommended Immunization Schedules for Persons Aged 0 Through 18 Years are approved by the Advisory Committee on Immunization Practices (www.cdc.gov/vaccines/recs/acip), the American Academy of Pediatrics (http://www.aap.org), and the American Academy of Family Physicians (http://www.aafp.org).

TOTAL PARENT POINTERS
IMMUNIZATIONS

1. Your child needs **immunizations** to prevent disease. Take the immunization schedule and preventive nature of the immunizations very seriously.

2. Immunizations are important because they help prevent your child from getting the following **fourteen major diseases**:
   - Polio
   - Measles
   - Mumps
   - Chicken pox
   - Rubella (German measles)
   - Pertussis (whooping cough)
   - Diphtheria
   - Tetanus
   - Haemophilus influenza
   - Hepatitis B
   - Human papilloma virus (HPV)
   - Meningococcal illness
   - Pneumococcal illness
   - Influenza

3. The following important facts show **how vaccines have improved the lives of our children**:
   - In the United States, **paralytic polio decreased** from 16,316 children in the early twentieth century to no cases in 2007 as a result of the polio vaccine.
   - **Rubella has been eliminated** in the United States, which has also eliminated congenital rubella syndrome birth defects (such as hearing and heart defects).
   - **Over 200,000 deaths due to measles** (rubeola) **occur** every year **in countries that lack** the **strict vaccine guidelines** we observe in the United States.
   - The **human papilloma virus** (HPV) vaccine **protects girls** from this virus, which can cause cervical cancer in women.

4. Talk to your child's doctor about any **allergies** you believe your children may have.

5. Talk to your doctor about any other **options** or any **concerns** you may have regarding immunizations for your children. **Side effects from many immunizations include a low-grade fever and soreness at the injection site**. Your children may also be a little fussy after their immunizations.

6. For a complete list of the timing of all vaccines for children, visit TheTotalParent.com and search for immunizations.

5

Postpartum Depression

Postpartum depression is a problem that affects one in five new mothers. This is quite a shocking statistic because many mothers ignore or do not report this form of depression. It is estimated that between 400,000 to 580,000 women in the United States suffer from postpartum depression every year. In fact, celebrities such as Brooke Shields and Courtney Cox have suffered from this condition in the past.

Postpartum depression is not the same as what is known as the "baby blues." The baby blues is more common and actually affects four out of five new mothers, although it is less serious than postpartum depression. It is characterized by frequent crying, exhaustion, and irritability, rather than the deeper and more serious depression seen in postpartum depression.

Who is at risk for postpartum depression?

Postpartum depression can affect any woman, whether she is a marathon runner or an easygoing mother with no prior history of emotional problems. New fathers can also suffer from feelings of sadness or depression after the baby arrives.

According to the National Mental Health Association, there are several factors that can increase the chances that someone may develop postpartum depression. These include:

1. Young or single mothers
2. History of mental illness or substance abuse
3. Financial or marital difficulties or other stressful life event
4. Previous pregnancy, birth, or postdelivery difficulties
5. Low self-esteem as a parent
6. Medical problems involving a child
7. A major life change at the same time as the birth of the baby—divorce, change of job, etc.
8. Lack of supportive environment to help with the baby

What is the treatment for postpartum depression?

The key to treating postpartum depression involves four main areas:

1. Psychological
2. Physiological (examples: thyroid problems, sleep deprivation)
3. Social support
4. Medications (antidepressants)

The key to psychological treatment is to provide a supportive environment and determine if there are any prior emotional traumas or unresolved emotional issues. The physiological or biological concerns may be, for example, a thyroid problem that can cause depression or a drug or alcohol problem. Third, in terms of the social aspects, a lack of a social support system, a negative home environment, or a negative family environment may exacerbate this condition.

What should you do if you think you have postpartum depression?

First, call your OB gynecologist to discuss the issue. In many cases your doctor can refer you to a local support group or, in some cases, prescribe medication. In addition, talk to a close friend who can provide emotional and social support during this time of crisis. This may include:

1. Helping with watching the baby so you can get an adequate amount of sleep.
2. Helping with various chores around the house, such as cleaning and laundry.
3. Being there and having someone to talk to during this difficult period.

In many cases it is good to seek out a mom who has two or more children who can share with you her concerns of when her children were first born. Many mothers, however, are uncomfortable sharing their lack of confidence to care for their children when they were first born.

As a personal note, I can tell you that when we had our first child I, too, felt somewhat anxious about having this tiny infant to care for twenty-four hours a day. As an emergency physician I was certainly aware of all the potential illnesses that could occur, and perhaps that's what made it even more stressful. However, as each day passed, my wife and I grew more comfortable and confident in our new role as parents.

What is postpartum psychosis?

An extreme form of postpartum depression is called postpartum psychosis. This only affects one to two women out of one thousand. Women who have postpartum psychosis need to be aware that there is a 5 percent chance of suicide and a 4 percent possibility of killing their child.

The signs of postpartum psychosis include hallucinations, manic (hyperactive) or very lethargic behavior, and delusional thoughts. Suicidal thoughts are also common. If you notice your loved one has any of the signs listed above, contact your physician immediately.

Other Resources for Postpartum Depression

If you would like to read other articles about postpartum depression, you can contact any of the following sources via the Internet:

1. Visit TheTotalParent.com and search for postpartum depression. Start with "Mom's Support" on top of the home page.

2. National Mental Health Association (www.nmha.org)

3. Postpartum Support International (www.postpartum.net)

TOTAL PARENT POINTERS
POSTPARTUM DEPRESSION

1. **Postpartum depression** occurs in one out of five new mothers. **Frequent crying, exhaustion**, and **irritability** characterize postpartum depression.
2. According to the National Mental Health Association, **several factors can increase the chances that a mother may develop postpartum depression**:
   - Young or single mothers
   - History of mental illness or substance abuse
   - Financial or marital difficulties or other stressful life event
   - Previous pregnancy, birth, or postdelivery difficulties
   - Low self-esteem as a parent
   - Medical problems involving a child
   - A major life change at the same time as the birth of the baby (divorce, change of job, etc.)
   - Lack of supportive environment to help with the baby
3. **Treating postpartum depression addresses four areas**:
   - Psychological (providing a supportive environment)
   - Physiological (identifying medical reasons for depression, such as a thyroid problem, sleep deprivation, or substance abuse)
   - Social support (enlisting the help of friends and relatives with childcare, running errands, and shopping; sharing your feelings with mothers you respect and trust)
   - Medications (antidepressants)
4. **Postpartum psychosis is an extreme form of postpartum depression**. The signs of postpartum psychosis include: **hallucinations, manic (hyperactive) or very lethargic behavior**, and **delusional thoughts. Suicidal thoughts are also common**. If you notice your loved one has any of the these symptoms, contact your physician immediately. Women with postpartum psychosis need to be aware that there is a 5 percent chance of suicide and a 4 percent chance of killing their child.
5. **A hotline number** for women with depression is available through the National Women's Health Information Center at **1-800-994-9662**. Visit TheTotalParent.com and search for postpartum depression. Start with "Mom's Support" at the top of the home page. Other helpful Web sites are offered by the National Mental Health Association (www.nmha.org) and Postpartum Support International (www.postpartum.net).

PART 2

When Your
Child Is Sick
or Injured

6

Abdominal Pain, Vomiting, and Diarrhea

Diagnosing the cause of abdominal pain in children is sometimes a challenge. Is it just a stomach ache that will go away on its own, or is it something more serious? The myriad of symptoms associated with stomach pain and the different organs in the abdomen make these diagnoses, at times, very challenging. Add to this the fact that young children often cannot even tell us about the details involving their abdominal pain, and it becomes even more taxing for all of us.

In the emergency room (ER), my most immediate concerns are signs of appendicitis, a twisted testicle (testicular torsion), a bowel obstruction, or a tubal pregnancy (in older girls). Keep in mind that lower abdominal pain in boys can indeed be caused be a twisted testicle (testicular torsion). In teenage girls with lower abdominal pain, we perform tests to rule out a tubal pregnancy (a pregnancy in the fallopian tube), which can cause severe bleeding and shock if the tubal pregnancy ruptures.

Here is the information that can help you sort it all out:

What are some of the most important causes of abdominal pain?

The most important causes of abdominal pain include:
- Appendicitis
- Urinary tract infections or kidney infections
- Stomach flu (acute gastroenteritis)
- Acid reflux (GERD or gastroesophageal reflux disease)
- Stomach irritation (gastritis)
- Bowel obstruction

How can I tell whether my child's abdominal pain is serious?

Any abdominal pain that is progressively worsening should be evaluated immediately by your physician. A pain that gets more intense might indicate a serious problem, such as appendicitis or a bowel obstruction.

What are the symptoms of appendicitis?

If your child has appendicitis, he will have right lower abdominal pain, loss of appetite, nausea, vomiting, and sometimes a low-grade fever. The

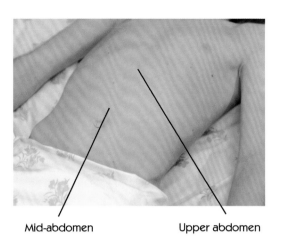

Mid-abdomen   Upper abdomen

Pointing to pain location in appendicitis

abdominal pain typically begins in the upper abdomen or mid-abdomen (as noted in the photo above).

The pain gradually progresses to the lower right side of the abdomen or the right lower quadrant (RLQ) over the next twelve to twenty-four hours.

Children with appendicitis will complain that it hurts in their lower right side when they cough, walk, or sneeze. A bumpy car ride to your

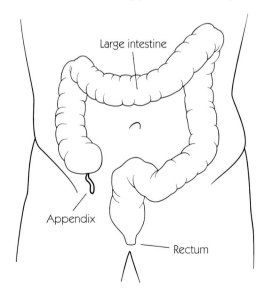

Location of appendix in right lower quadrant of abdomen

doctor's office or the hospital will sometimes also cause pain, which is typically accompanied by nausea and vomiting. Children with appendicitis often lose their appetite or have a decreased appetite.

When I am evaluating a child with right lower abdominal pain and considering appendicitis, I will ask them the following questions: "What's your favorite food to eat? If I gave you that food right now, do you think you could eat it?" If they answer no to this, it increases my suspicion of appendicitis.

In addition, I'll ask them to cough and point with one finger where they feel the pain. If they point to the spot noted in the diagram, this makes me more concerned about a diagnosis of appendicitis.

Then, I will press on that sore area to see if they are very tender and if their muscles tighten up when I press there. If they will not let me press there and their abdominal muscles tighten, this is called "guarding." If they have this sign, I will immediately call a surgeon to evaluate the child.

Unfortunately, there is no test to prove with 100 percent certainty that the child does or does not have appendicitis. However, a CT scan can frequently help with the diagnosis. But even a CT scan is not 100 percent accurate for appendicitis.

KIDNEY AND URINARY INFECTIONS

What are the symptoms of kidney infections and urinary tract infections?

Children with kidney or urinary infections have pain when they urinate and have to urinate more frequently than normal. They also tend to have a feeling that they have to get to the bathroom quickly and that they cannot "hold it." They also may have a fever and pain in the lower abdomen or pain in the right or left side of the back. Girls are more likely to have urinary tract infections than boys because of the shorter urethra leading from the bladder to the outside. Children who have had a urinary tract infection in the past are also more likely to have urinary infections in the future.

STOMACH FLU (GASTROENTERITIS)

What are the symptoms of acute gastroenteritis? (Stomach flu)

Symptoms of acute gastroenteritis include fever, vomiting, diarrhea, and abdominal pain. Children with frequent episodes of watery diarrhea and vomiting usually have gastroenteritis, often referred to as stomach flu. The illness typically lasts about five to seven days and usually occurs during the winter months.

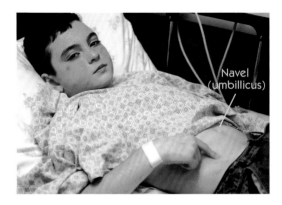

Child with appendicitis pointing to location of pain

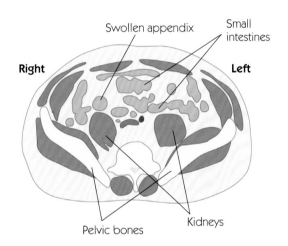

One of the views taken by a CT scanner for appendicitis

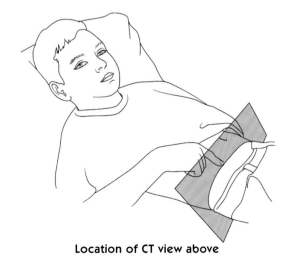

Location of CT view above

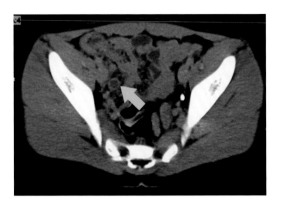

CT scan of appendicitis
The arrow points to an enlarged tubular appendix in the child's lower right side. This is diagnostic of appendicitis.

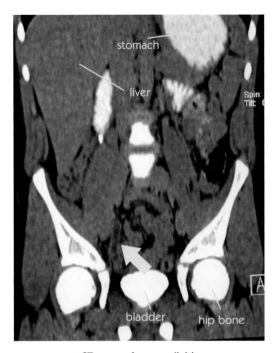

CT scan of appendicitis
The arrow points to a dilated appendix. This is a vertical scan that takes a view in the body which separates it into front and back halves.

What causes acute gastroenteritis?

Acute gastroenteritis (symptoms include vomiting, diarrhea, abdominal pain, and fever) is caused by a virus in 80 percent of cases. The most common virus is called the rotavirus. The rotavirus accounts for about 30 to 35 percent of episodes of diarrhea in children. The usual age is between three and fifteen months.

How should I treat gastroenteritis at home?

Begin by encouraging your child to eat, and more important, drink fluids. Home treatment of stomach flu should include an over-the-counter fluid such as Pedialyte, fruit juices, or noncarbonated and caffeine-free beverages. Popsicles are a very good and popular alternative if your child refuses other liquids. If your child is nursing, breast milk is still fine. Also, your doctor may sometimes prescribe a rectal suppository or a quick-dissolving oral medication to help decrease your child's vomiting.

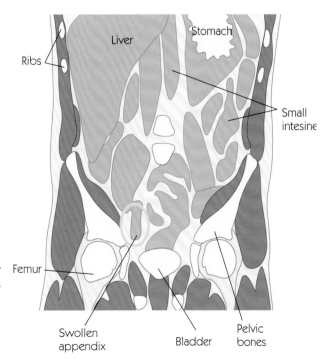

Organs and appendix in adject CT scan

However, avoid giving ONLY water to young children with gastroenteritis (see secret doctor info below).

How is gastroenteritis treated in a hospital?

If your child is significantly dehydrated or cannot take liquids by mouth, your physician may decide to put her in the hospital and treat the dehydration with IV fluids. The reason for this is to make sure the child's dehydration improves. In some cases, the doctor may prescribe medications to ease the vomiting.

DEHYDRATION

How do you know if your child is dehydrated?

With young children, I'll ask parents if their child is urinating at least five times a day. If a child under the age of one is urinating five times a day, I know that he is not dehydrated. A child who is urinating less than four to five times a day is becoming dehydrated.

Children with severe dehydration can develop tenting of their skin. In the child discussed below, I pulled up the skin on the abdomen, and the skin stayed in a tentlike position due to severe dehyration.

When should I bring my child to a doctor?

Bring your child to the doctor if he is unable to take in enough liquids and is becoming dehydrated. Keep in mind that the younger the child, the sooner he will become dehydrated and the less clear the symptoms will be. The main signs to look for include:

- A child who is not playful
- A child who is acting very tired or listless, sleeping a lot, acting lethargic
- A child who is urinating less than five times in twenty-four hours
- A child whose eyes look sunken

 SECRET DOCTOR INFO
Complications of Water-Only Feeding for Infants

It's not widely known that young children who drink only water for as little as one day can develop a lowering of sodium in their bloodstream, which can in fact cause seizures. Plain water does not contain any salt or electrolytes, and because of this a child's body can become depleted of salt and the sodium level in the blood can decrease. I've seen several infants in our emergency room have seizures because of this. When we measure the sodium level in their blood, we often find that it's very low. Typically, the well-meaning parent, grandparent, or caregiver has only been offering the child water for the past one to two days.

If your child has gastroenteritis, after receiving an adequate amount of oral fluids, push easily digested foods such as those found in the BRAT diet, the mnemonic acronym for bananas, rice, applesauce, and toast. (However, several studies have shown that gradual resumption of a regular diet is just as effective as the BRAT diet.)

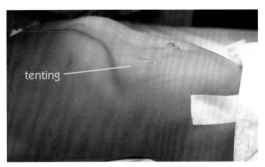

Tenting of skin of child's abdomen in severe dehydration

- A child lacking tears when crying
- A child whose breathing rate seems faster than normal
- A child whose mouth and lips look dry

In some cases, your doctor may order lab tests to evaluate the severity of your child's dehydration and to determine the cause. These tests may include a blood count, electrolytes, stool culture, stool exam for parasites, and stool tests for rotavirus. If your child has bloody diarrhea, the physician may be concerned about other bacteria that can cause bloody diarrhea.

GERD (GASTROESOPHAGEAL-REFLUX DISEASE)

What is GERD?

GERD stands for gastroesophageal reflux disease. This is another common cause of upper abdominal pain in children and adults. This illness occurs when acid from the stomach flows backward (refluxes) into the esophagus. (See diagram in the righthand column.)

The esophagus becomes irritated from the acid, and the child feels pain or heartburn in the upper abdomen and lower sternal area.

What is the treatment for GERD?

The treatment is usually a medication, such as Pepcid, which blocks or decreases the production of stomach acid. Over-the-counter antacids such as Mylanta and Tums can also be used.

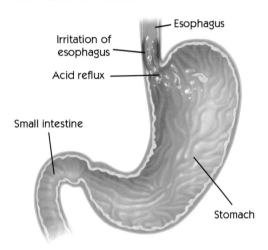

Esophagus

Irritation of esophagus

Acid reflux

Small intestine

Stomach

Gastroesophageal-reflux disease

What are gastritis and peptic ulcer disease?

Gastritis and peptic ulcer disease are caused by the irritation of the stomach lining by the acid produced in the stomach. Some patients have a bacteria called H pylori, which causes their stomach to ulcerate. Gastritis is a milder form of stomach irritation than a peptic ulcer.

What is the treatment for gastritis and peptic ulcer disease?

These are both treated with medications that decrease stomach acid, as well as with antacids. Children with an H pylori infection are also treated with antibiotics to kill the bacteria causing the stomach ulcer.

Can any foods cause abdominal pain in children?

In older children, abdominal pain can sometimes be caused by caffeine products such as sodas and coffee. These products can cause intestinal cramping and gas pains.

BOWEL OBSTRUCTION

A child with a bowel obstruction will often have persistent vomiting, abdominal pain, and an abdomen that seems to be enlarging.

Who is at risk for a bowel obstruction?

Children are more likely to have a bowel obstruction if they have had prior abdominal surgery

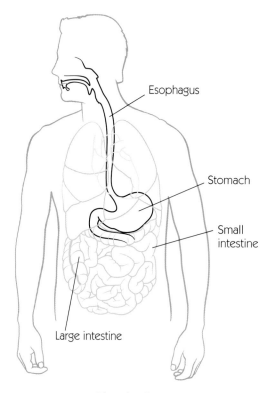

Digestive System showing esophagus and stomach

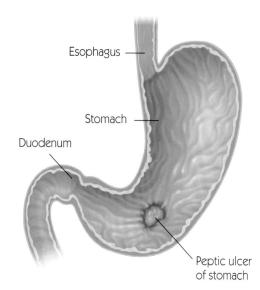

Peptic Ulcer disease

INTUSSUSCEPTION

Intussusception (pronounced in-tuss-a-sep-shun) is a condition in which the small intestine becomes blocked because part of the small intestine has been pulled inside itself like a telescope. Intussusception causes a small bowel obstruction.

This problem usually occurs in children between three months and five years of age. (Most occur between five to nine months.) Males are affected four times more often than females. The chance of this occurring is about one to four out of a thousand children.

An illustration of intussusception is included on the next page.

Intussusception symptoms may include:

1. Intermittent episodes of pain and vomiting alternating with the child feeling well and pain free.
2. Some children will have bloody stool or what looks like a currant jelly stool (four out of ten children).

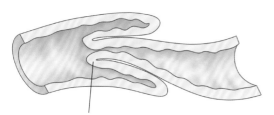

Intussusception of small intestine

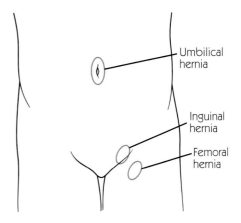

Common locations for hernias

How is the diagnosis of intussusception made?

The physician will examine the child's abdomen for a sausage-shaped mass that can sometimes be felt.

The diagnosis is made with either x-rays or ultrasound. Some cases are resolved by doing an air enema lower-GI x-ray exam. Air is instilled in the rectum, and x-rays are taken. In some cases this will cause the intestinal blockage to undo itself. In other cases, surgery may be required.

HERNIAS

Hernias are a protrusion of the intestines or other tissues through a weak area of the abdominal wall, the inguinal area, or the femoral area. (The inguinal and femoral areas are in or near the crease between the belly and the upper thigh.) Umbilical and inguinal hernias are the most common. Parents will sometimes notice these hernias when they see a bulge in these areas while the child is crying, coughing, or straining. Hernias should be surgically corrected in children before they cause an incarcerated hernia as decribed below.

See the illustration in the next column for the most common locations of hernias.

INCARCERATED HERNIAS

The key point that you need to know is how to tell when a simple hernia turns into an incarcerated hernia. An incarcerated hernia occurs when the contents of the hernia become twisted or have their blood supply cut off because of sudden worsening due to swelling, etc.

THE SIGNS OF AN INCARCERATED HERNIA ARE:

1. Vomiting
2. Abdominal pain and/or pain at the site of the hernia.
3. Tenderness, firmness, and/or swelling of the bulging hernia.
4. Inability to push the hernia back into place with gentle pressure.

An incarcerated hernia is a surgical emergency. In some cases, the physician or surgeon may be able to push the contents of the hernia back into place. If not, the hernia must be surgically corrected within a few hours for a good outcome.

MIDGUT VOLVULUS OF THE SMALL INTESTINE (GREEN VOMITING)

Vomiting green material in the first few weeks can be a sign of a sudden twisting and strangulation of the small intestine. This is called midgut volvulus. It usually occurs in the first few weeks of life. These children look acutely sick and appear to be in severe pain. The vomiting and stool may become bloody. Shock can occur within hours. The child will look ill and pale with diffuse tenderness of the belly (abdomen). This condition occurs twice as often in males than in females.

The diagnosis can be made by several means: plain x-rays of the abdomen, ultrasound, or upper-GI x-rays after a swallow of barium dye. The treatment is abdominal surgery to untwist the small intestine before it loses its blood flow and gangrene of the small intestine occurs.

TESTICULAR TORSION

Testicular torsion is a twisting of the testicle that results in a lack of blood flow to the testicle. If this lasts for more than six to twelve hours, the testicle may die and will not produce sperm.

The key symptoms of a twisted testicle (testicular torsion) are:

1. Sudden onset of severe pain in one testicle in a child or adolescent (this is most common in teenagers, but it can occur at any age).
2. The boy may complain of pain in the lower abdomen, flank, or testicle.

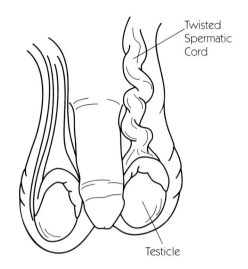

Testicular torsion

3. Nausea and vomiting may occur.
4. Swelling and tenderness of one testicle.
5. If the diagnosis is made in the first four hours of pain, the save rate of the testicle is around 96 percent. If the diagnosis is not made for twelve hours, the save rate of the testicle is only 20 percent.

CAUSES OF ABDOMINAL PAIN IN TEENAGE GIRLS

Some of the more serious causes of abdominal pain that parents should know about in teenage girls are:

1. Tubal pregnancy (a pregnancy that occurs in the fallopian tube instead of the uterus)
2. Rupture of an ovarian cyst (mittleshmertz)

What are the signs of an early pregnancy?

1. Lower abdominal pain
2. A missed period (although this is not 100 percent accurate. I have

seen teenagers and women who have had up to three menstrual periods who are later found to be three months pregnant.)

3. Breast tenderness
4. Frequent urination
5. Morning sickness (nausea and/ or vomiting in the morning hours or all day)
6. Positive home pregnancy test

What are the signs of a tubal or ectopic pregnancy?

A tubal pregnancy may have all of the signs noted above. In addition, the girl may have:

1. Pain localized to the lower right or lower left abdominal area.
2. The pain usually begins about six weeks after the last menstrual period.
3. There may be signs of low blood pressure such as dizziness, lightheadedness, or fainting.
4. Other signs of pregnancy include fatigue, morning sickness, breast tenderness, missed period.
5. Positive home pregnancy test.

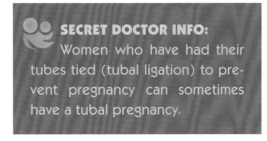

The diagram below illustrates the location of a tubal pregnancy.

Note how the fetus has begun to grow in the fallopian tube instead of the uterus. The growth of the fetus in the fallopian tube results in pain caused by stretching of the fallopian tube. Eventually, the tube ruptures, causing moderate to severe bleeding in the mother. Some cases result in the mother's death due to shock and severe blood loss.

The diagnosis is usually made by an ultrasound exam and by the level of a pregnancy hormone called Beta-HCG (human chorionic gonadotropin). The level of this hormone doubles every two days in a normal pregnancy. Therefore, if the Beta-HCG level is 500 units

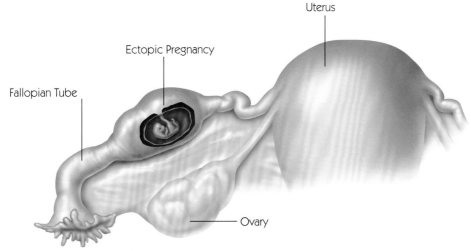

Tubal pregnancy

today, it should be 1,000 units in two more days in a normal uterine pregnancy. A tubal pregnancy will usually show a slower increase of this hormone. (Keep in mind that these are general guidelines and not absolute numbers.)

RUPTURED OVARIAN CYSTS

The signs of a ruptured ovarian cyst are:

1. Sudden pain in the lower abdomen that may be localized to the lower right or lower left abdomen in a girl who is capable of becoming pregnant. (Keep in mind that pain in the lower right side can also be a sign of appendicitis.)

2. Worsening abdominal pain with coughing, walking, or movement.

3. The pain begins about two weeks after the last menstrual period.

4. The pain usually lasts for twenty-four to forty-eight hours and then goes away.

Pain in the lower abdomen in a girl or woman of childbearing age can be due to a tubal pregnancy, a ruptured ovarian cyst, or if the pain is in the lower right abdomen, possibly appendicitis.

What is Mittleschmertz?

Mittleschmertz is the medical name for a ruptured ovarian cyst that occurs two weeks after the last menstrual period. The normal follicle or cyst that releases the egg (or ovum) two weeks after the last period may sometimes cause moderate bleeding to occur. This results in sudden pain from the blood irrigatating the abdominal cavity. The blood is eventually reabsorbed, and the pain goes away in about twenty-four to forty-eight hours. The symptoms can mimic a tubal pregnancy, appendicitis, kidney stones, a twisted fallopian tube, and other abdominal problems.

TOTAL PARENT POINTERS
ABDOMINAL PAIN, VOMITING, AND DIARRHEA

The most serious causes of abdominal pain include appendicitis and bowel obstruction. Parents need to be concerned about abdominal pain and have a physician evaluate the child if any of the following are present:

1. The pain is **gradually progressive** over a twelve- to twenty-four-hour period.
2. The pain is **very severe.**
3. The child **vomits blood.**
4. There is **blood in the stool.**
5. The **abdomen is becoming larger** or distended.
6. The child is becoming dehydrated and is **urinating less than four to five times in twenty-four hours.**
7. The **pain is in the lower right side of the abdomen** and associated with nausea, loss of appetite, and sometimes vomiting. Any vomiting that accompanies fever over 100.4°F rectal in a child under the age of three months should be evaluated immediately by a physician.
8. The key signs of **testicular torsion** (twisted testicle) are:
   a. Sudden onset of pain in one testicle
   b. Nausea, vomiting, lower abdominal pain, or flank pain
   c. Swelling and tenderness of one testicle.
9. **Appendicitis** is characterized by:
   a. Pain in the right lower quadrant of the abdomen that is worse with coughing, sneezing, bumps in the road during car rides, or by shaking the child's abdomen. (However, the pain usually begins in the upper or midabdomen and over twelve to twenty-four hours moves down to the right lower portion of the abdomen.)
   b. Loss of appetite (Kids won't even eat their favorite food.)
   c. Nausea and sometimes vomiting
   d. Sometimes a low-grade fever of 99.6°–100.6°F oral or 100.4°–101.4°F rectal will be present.
10. **Intussusception** is a condition in which the small intestine becomes blocked because part of the small intestine has been pulled inside itself like a telescope. Intussusception causes a small bowel obstruction.
    Intussusception symptoms may include:
    • Intermittent episodes of pain and vomiting alternating with the child feeling well and pain free.
    • Some children will have bloody stool or what looks like a currant jelly stool (four out of ten children)
11. **Hernias** are a protrusion of the intestines through a weak area of the abdomen, scrotum, or the inguinal area.
    The signs of an incarcerated hernia are:
    • Vomiting
    • Abdominal pain and/or pain at the site of the hernia
    • Tenderness, firmness, and/or swelling of the bulging hernia
    • Inability to push the hernia back into place and make it disappear with gentle pressure

TOTAL PARENT POINTERS
ABDOMINAL PAIN, VOMITING, AND DIARRHEA

12. **Signs of a tubal pregnancy include:**
    a. A missed period (pain typically occurs six to eight weeks after the last period)
    b. Pain in lower right or lower left abdomen
    c. Symptoms of pregnancy such as: fatigue, breast tenderness, frequent urination, morning sickness (nausea and vomiting)

13. Mittleschmertz is the medical name for **a ruptured ovarian cyst** that usually occurs two weeks after the last menstrual period. It includes sudden onset of pain in the right or left lower quadrant, pain with coughing and walking, and no fever. Keep in mind that pain in the right lower quadrant of the abdomen is always suspicious for appendicitis and should be evaluated by your doctor or an emergency physician as soon as possible.

7

Bites, Bugs, Worms, and Stings

Active children are very likely to interact with animals in their play and life explorations. Not surprisingly, along with good old-fashioned fun sometimes comes the possibility that an injury, like an animal or insect bite, may occur. The most common bites come from dogs, cats, spiders, and (unfortunately) even other children.

Dog bites can be minor in children or they can be devastating. Frequently a toddler or young child will unintentionally irritate a dog, causing a hostile response by a normally well-behaved and friendly dog. Dogs respond by biting the child in various parts of the body. The results can be minor or severe.

You may be surprised to learn that dog bites are considerably less likely to get infected than cat or human bites. However, a common recommendation is to use prophylactic antibiotics only for hand or foot wounds and for those wounds that have a significant amount of associated crush injury.

DOG BITES

Parents need to know that young children do not know how to behave around friendly dogs. Young children may pull their tail because it is moving and it looks like a fun thing to do. Here are a few commonsense guidelines for young children near dogs:

- All young children should be supervised while they are near dogs. (This includes friendly dogs that are "great with kids.")
- Dog bites on the hands or feet can cause very serious infections.
- Dog bites on the face can sometimes require plastic surgery.
- Notify the county animal commissioner about the dog bite and the name and address of the owner, if known. (Emergency rooms do this routinely when someone has an animal bite.)

If a dog bite has occurred, the animal commissioner will usually quarantine an unimmunized animal for ten days to watch and observe it for any signs of rabies. Bats are at extremely high risk for carrying rabies. Other animals that can carry rabies include cats and ferrets. Certain animals that should be considered to be infected with rabies include skunks, raccoons, and foxes. Livestock have also been known to carry rabies. Another important item to consider in assessing risk is whether there have been know cases of rabies in the state over the past few years.

RABIES

Rabies is an infection of the nervous system that causes progressive paralysis, bizarre behavior, and even death in untreated cases. Patients frequently cannot drink water because it causes severe spasms of their swallowing muscles. Hence, many believe the notion that patients with rabies fear water.

People who travel to countries where rabies is more common need to be immunized. Any bites or scratches from infected animals while in foreign countries should be reported to your doctor and the local health department. The incubation period can be anywhere from twenty to ninety days. However, some cases have been diagnosed more than one year after a bite. Once a person has rabies, the disease is usually fatal.

Can my child get rabies from a dog or cat bite?

Rabies can occur from dog or cat bites in the United States, but the chances are very low due to high rates of animal vaccinations in this country. The animals that most commonly carry rabies include bats, coyotes, foxes, raccoons, skunks, and some livestock. Any child who has been bitten by any of these animals should receive the rabies vaccine. Whenever a dog bites a child, the local ER is required to fill out a heath department form. In these cases, the animal commissioner will follow up to make sure that the dog's rabies shots are up to date. In the case of a stray dog, it is important to determine why the dog bit the child. If this was an unprovoked attack by a dog running around wildly and acting strangely, then the child may need to receive the rabies vaccine series.

Several key questions that a physician will ask if your child has been bitten by a stray dog include:

- Was the dog acting abnormally just before biting your child?
- Did the dog seem to be acting in an inappropriate or aggressive manner?
- What was your child doing just before the dog bit him?
- Has anyone seen the dog since the time of the bite, and does anyone know the whereabouts of the dog?

What do I need to know about rabies shots?

There have been several misconceptions about the rabies vaccine in the past. Many years ago this vaccine required more than ten injections. However, we now have a new vaccine that requires only five injections over twenty-eight days. The first day is called day zero. The child receives the remaining injections on days zero, three, seven, fourteen, and twenty-eight. The child will also receive an injection of rabies immunoglobulin (rabies antibody) on the first day of the rabies vaccine series.

Keep in mind that although rare, rabies can be a fatal illness if not treated. Therefore, if your physician recommends that the child receive the rabies vaccine series, please follow your doctor's recommendation.

Which home pets are usually free of the risk of rabies?

Bites from gerbils, chipmunks, mice, domesticated rabbits, hamsters, and guinea pigs almost never require rabies treatment. Squirrels and rats do not carry rabies either.

CAT BITES

Cat bites usually cause puncture wounds and a high likelihood (50 percent or more) of infection. Most cat bites require thorough cleaning with high-pressure saline in a doctor's office or emergency room. The child will need to be treated with an antibiotic that is effective against bacteria found in the mouth of cats.

What you need to know about cat bites

It is very important for the child to finish the entire course of antibiotics recommended by a physician. In addition, parents should watch for signs of infection within the first twenty-four to forty-eight hours.

Any symptoms such as redness, warmth, fever, swelling, or pus from the area should prompt a call or visit to a physician.

The patient's last tetanus shot should be known. If the last shot has been longer than five years ago, then a repeat tetanus booster needs to be given.

HUMAN BITES

Human bites also tend to become infected. Human bites should be treated with a thorough cleansing by a physician in an emergency room, along with prescribed antibiotics. Human bites, especially of the fingers or toes, tend to cause more complicated infections.

WORM INFECTIONS

Worm infections that occur in children include:
- Roundworms
- Pinworms
- Whipworms

ROUNDWORMS

The roundworm is called ascaris. This worm is picked up when a child ingests foods that have been contaminated. The worms are ingested on unclean vegetables or other sources and eventually lead to worms in the intestines. These worms can cause abdominal pain, fever, and symptoms related to the lungs, such as coughing up blood. Roundworms can be diagnosed by having the physician order a test of a stool specimen to check for the ova and parasites of these worms. This worm can be treated with a single dose of an anti-worm medication.

Below is a photo of a worm that was expelled from the anus of a young child in an emergency room.

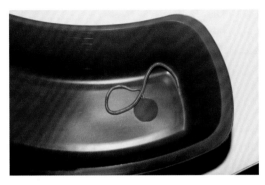

Roundworm

PINWORMS

A child with pinworms typically has rectal itching. Children will frequently have itching at night, which may result in severe scratching of the skin around the rectum. The eggs can be found by doing a tape test. To do a tape test, place a piece of cellophane tape over the rectal area in the morning to see if any small ova or eggs become attached to the tape. Parents may sometimes see the small, moving, white, threadlike worms. These worms are approximately one-third of an inch long and several of them can usually be seen moving around the rectal area. If these are seen, a piece of tape can be applied over the worms to immobilize them so you can show your pediatrician or family doctor the next day. One dose of an anti-worm medication usually kills the worms and cures the problem.

WHIPWORMS

Whipworms occur in children in the Appalachian areas and other warm areas of the United States. Children with this worm infestation can have bloody diarrhea and have trouble absorbing certain foods. Children also can become anemic and develop learning deficits from an inability to absorb B complex vitamins.

DIAGNOSIS OF WORM INFECTIONS

The diagnosis is made by finding worms or ova (eggs) in a stool specimen. (This usually takes a few days.) The treatment consists of an oral medication.

TRICHINOSIS (PORK TAPEWORM)

This type of worm is found primarily in the Northeast and mid-Atlantic states. Children with pork tapeworm infections can develop muscle pains, swelling around the eyes, and sometimes fever.

The diagnosis is made by a blood test or by obtaining a sample (biopsy) of muscle.

TREATMENT OF PORK TAPEWORM INFECTIONS

Treatment is with an oral anti-worm medication. Sometimes steroids are also used.

SPIDER BITES

The two most serious types of spider bites include:
- Black widow spiders
- Brown recluse spiders

BLACK WIDOW SPIDERS

The black widow spider is characterized by its famous hourglass pattern on the underside of its abdomen.

In 1999, almost 600 persons were bitten by black widows and 135 were bitten by brown recluse

Black widow spider
(photo courtesy of the Centers for Disease Control
and the Public Health Image Library)

spiders. There was only one death reported, and that was from the brown recluse spider.

What you need to know about black widow spider bites

A bite from a black widow spider may cause a halo-shaped target lesion within a few hours. The bite may become red and sometimes looks like hives.

The child may then develop symptoms in the abdomen and in the lower back. The abdominal pain can become very severe, and the pain may extend down the child's legs. Some will complain of a burning sensation in the soles of the feet. The overall chance of death is under 5 percent.

Treatment of black widow spider bites

Apply ice to the area. If the symptoms are more severe, the doctor may prescribe muscle relaxants for the muscle spasms. Antivenom may be considered for severe cases, although this generally is not recommended because other treatments are quite effective and death is rare.

BROWN RECLUSE SPIDERS

Brown recluse spiders release a toxin that causes the skin surrounding the bite to die. Within a few hours to a few days the area becomes swollen, red, and tender. It then becomes a blue gray color that is surrounded by a whitish ring. In about three to four days, the area becomes black. In about two weeks, there is a hole, which is left from the dead skin.

In some cases the child may develop a severe reaction within the first twenty-four to forty-eight hours that includes fever, muscle aches, and joint pains. The child may develop severe bleeding and convulsions.

It is important to observe your child carefully for any signs of fever, bleeding, kidney damage, or shock. If the child does not have any serious symptoms, such as fever or bleeding, the wound can be reevaluated every few days until the toxin has left his system. Surgical treatment of the wound may be recommended within a few weeks based on how much dead tissue is present.

BEE, HORNET, AND WASP STINGS

About 50 to 150 people die each year in the United States due to stings from bees, hornets, or wasps. Honeybees are less aggressive than wasps or hornets. They bite when irritated or stepped on. When a honeybee stings, the stinger comes off with a small venom sac attached. Although U.S. honeybees are not easily provoked, a very aggressive hybrid of African honeybees is known as killer bees or Africanized bees. These were imported to Brazil over fifty years ago to increase honey production, and now they can be found in Arizona, New Mexico, Texas, and Southern California. All wasps and hornets, however, tend to be aggressive. They will sting with minimal irritation. Wasps tend to build their nests under the eaves of buildings.

Avoid disturbing the hives of bees, wasps, or hornets. Their response is to protect their hive. If you accidentally disturb a hive, and a swarm of bees attacks, the best thing to do is to run away and place a shirt or cloth over your face. Many believe that bees are attracted to the carbon dioxide that we exhale. Covering your face should protect this area from being stung. Swarms of Africanized bees may pursue their victims for up to a quarter of a mile.

Reactions to stings from bees, hornets, and wasps

- Localized pain and burning
- Localized allergic reaction with hives and/or swelling of the area but no shortness of breath, wheezing, hoarseness, or throat swelling
- Severe allergic reaction with hives and/or swelling of the area plus shortness of breath, tightness of the throat, wheezing, swelling of the face, and sometimes shock (a severe drop in blood pressure)

Treatment of bee, hornet, and wasp stings

The treatments for **mild reactions** include:
- Apply ice to the affected area
- Antihistamine medications, such as Benadryl
- Over-the-counter pain medications

Treatment of **moderate reactions** that include significant hives or swelling of the stung site include:
- Calling an ambulance if there is any shortness of breath, wheezing, facial swelling, hoarseness, or history of severe reactions
- Apply ice to the affected area
- Antihistamine medications such a Benadryl and Pepcid
- Some children may need an epinephrine injection by a physician, nurse, or other qualified healthcare professional (patients with a prior history of significant reactions may self-administer epinephrine using an autoinjector in a thigh muscle). Severe reactions require immediate ambulance transport to the nearest ER or medical center.

Signs of a **severe allergic reaction** to a sting include:
- Difficulty breathing
- Hives
- Wheezing
- Hoarseness
- A sensation of throat swelling or closing off of the airway
- Low blood pressure due to shock, which may cause dizziness, sweats, or lightheadedness
- Swelling of the face, lips, and/or eyelids
- Swelling or hives at the site of the bite

TOTAL PARENT POINTERS
BITES, BUGS, WORMS, AND STINGS

1. **Bites can become infected in the first twenty-four hours.** Any child with a human or cat bite should be seen by a doctor within the first few hours. The doctor will sometimes prescribe antibiotics to prevent infection and will evaluate dog bites for the risk of rabies. Dog bites are less prone to infection than are cat bites. Antibiotics are usually reserved for bites to the hands or feet, deep puncture wounds, and wounds with significant tissue trauma.

2. **Rabies** can occur after bites from **bats, skunks, raccoons, coyotes, foxes, and sometimes cattle. Dogs and cats** can cause rabies, but this is uncommon in the United States. Stray dogs (who cannot be captured and observed) that were behaving strangely or attacked the child without being provoked are of concern. Rabies injections may be indicated in these cases. Bites from animals in other countries can have a much higher risk of having rabies.

3. **Pinworms** are small, white, threadlike worms that cause itching in the anal area. Put a piece of cellophane tape over the rectal area in the morning to obtain eggs to show your family doctor. The same technique can be used at night to trap the pinworms.

4. **Roundworms** are larger, pale white worms that live in the child's intestines. These worms can cause abdominal pain, fever, and coughing up blood. Ascaris eggs are present in fertilizers and on some unwashed vegetables.

5. **Pork tapeworms** can cause muscle pains, fever, and swelling around the eyes.

6. **Black widow spider bites** can cause severe abdominal pain. The bite area looks like a target. Black widow spiders have an hourglass pattern on their abdomen.

7. **Brown recluse spider bites** can cause the child to develop a severe, deep area of tissue loss over several days.

8. Bee, hornet, and wasp stings have **three possible reactions**:
   - Localized pain and burning
   - Localized allergic reaction with hives and/or swelling of the area but no shortness of breath, wheezing, or throat swelling
   - Severe allergic reaction with hives and/or swelling of the area plus shortness of breath, tightness of the throat, wheezing, swelling of the face, and shock (a severe drop in blood pressure)

9. **Treatment of moderate reactions** to stings by bees, hornets, and wasps with hives or swelling of the stung area include:
   - Calling an ambulance if there is any shortness of breath, wheezing, facial swelling, or hoarseness
   - Icing the affected area
   - Antihistamine medications such a Benadryl and Pepcid
   - Some patients may require an injection of epinephrine by a physician, nurse, or other qualified healthcare professional (patients with a prior history of significant reactions may self-administer epinephrine using an autoinjector in a thigh muscle)

TOTAL PARENT POINTERS
BITES, BUGS, WORMS, AND STINGS

10. **Severe reactions** to stings by bees, hornets, and wasps **require immediate ambulance notification**. Signs of a severe allergic reaction to a sting include:
    - Difficult breathing
    - Hives
    - Wheezing

    - A sensation of throat swelling or the closing off of the airway
    - Low blood pressure due to shock may occur
    - Swelling of the face, lips, and/or eyelids
    - Swelling or hives at the site of the bite

8

Bone and Muscle Injuries

FRACTURES, SPRAINS, STRAINS, AND JOINT PAINS

Kids, as you know, are relatively fearless. Their personal goal is to run, jump, and play, usually without any concern they could hurt themselves if they're not careful. But sometimes this fun-filled play results in an unfortunate injury. And, as parents, it's hard for us to know when it's a fracture and when it's only a sprain. Even I, as an emergency physician, can't know for sure without the benefit of an x-ray (unless, of course, my x-ray vision is working . . . Ha, ha. Actually, I don't really have x-ray vision, but some of my students have thought I did).

This chapter contains tips for parents, based on my experience in treating these injuries for over twenty years in the emergency room. You will learn:

1. The difference between a fracture, sprain, and strain.
2. The most common childhood fractures and their complications.
3. The complications of fractures that go through the growth plate of growing bones.
4. The key symptoms to look for if your child has a limp for no reason.
5. The signs of a "nursemaid's elbow" injury.
6. The symptoms of juvenile rheumatoid arthritis in children.

FRACTURES

A fracture is a broken bone. A fracture and a break are the same thing. A fractured bone can also be classified as:

1. Aligned versus angulated fractures.
2. Open fracture versus closed fracture. An open fracture is one in which the bone protrudes through the skin. This allows bacteria to get in and infect the bone and is much more serious.
3. Simple versus comminuted fracture—simple means only one fracture whereas a comminuted one involves several fractures.

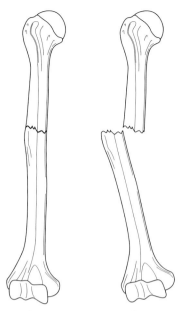

Aligned vs. **angulated** fractures

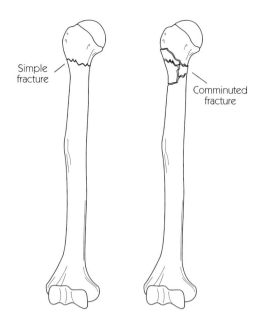

Simple fracture

Comminuted fracture

Comminuted fracture—Compare the simple fracture of the humerus on the left versus the comminuted fracture of the humerus on the right

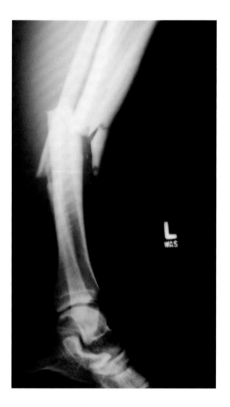

x-ray of angulated fracture

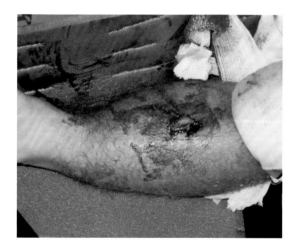

Open fracture
Note the open wound on the front of the lower leg. The tibia bone pushed through and caused this open fracture wound.
See x-ray of fractures of lower leg to the left.

What is a dislocation?

A dislocation is a malalignment of the bones in a joint usually due to trauma. It can occur in any joint. The most common joint dislocations are the fingers, shoulder, kneecap (patella), elbow, knee, and hip.

See the photo (below) of a finger dislocated during a football game.

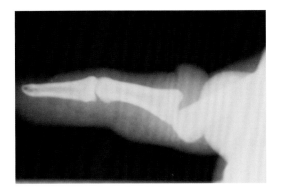

x-ray of dislocated little finger

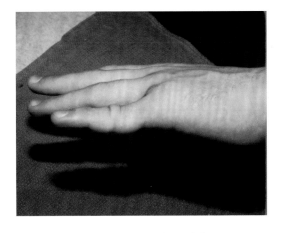

Dislocation of little finger joint
This is called a dislocation of the metacarpal-phalageal joint (MCP joint) because it occurs at the joint between the metacarpal bone of the hand and the phalanx bone at the base of the little finger.

What is the treatment for a dislocated finger if this occurs at a football game or some other sports event?

In general, only a physician should care for these types of injuries. On the field, a coach cannot possibly know if this is a dislocation or a more complex fracture and dislocation. The coach should send the player to an ER where x-rays should be taken first. The physician will then know exactly what type of injury is involved. The child will usually be given a pain reliever and/or a numbing medication. Then the dislocated finger will be gently moved back into place.

Can you guess what bone is dislocated in this photo?

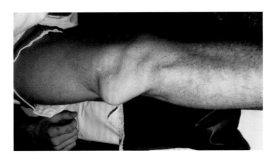

If you guessed kneecap (patella), you are correct. Patellar dislocations usually slip back in place on their own when the child straightens out his knee. However, some children are not that lucky. In this case, we gave the boy some IV pain medication and a muscle relaxant, and then gently pushed the patella back into place.

He went home with a knee immobilizer and crutches. He was sent to an orthopedic doctor during the next few days for further follow-up and reevaluation.

SPRAIN

A sprain is a torn ligament. The ligament holds the joints together. It can be either a partial or a complete tear.

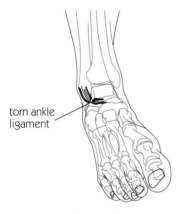

torn ankle ligament

ankle sprain

STRAIN

A strain is a torn muscle. For example, when you get sudden pain in your calf muscle after you started to run, you tore the muscle and have a muscle strain.

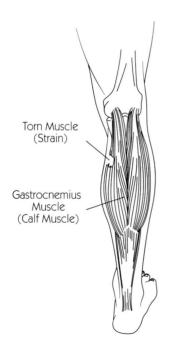

Torn Muscle (Strain)

Gastrocnemius Muscle (Calf Muscle)

Calf muscle strain (gastrocnemius muscle strain)

What are the most common fractures in children?

The most common fractures are:
- Collarbone fractures (clavicle)
- Wrist fractures
- Ankle fractures
- Forearm fractures
- Elbow fractures
- Knee fractures

Fractures of the clavicle are the most common fractures in children. They usually result from a fall on a shoulder. They usually heal well after several weeks in a sling.

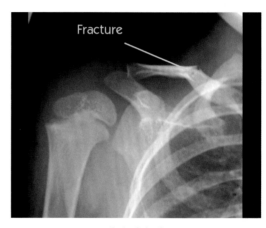

Fracture

x-ray of clavicle fracture

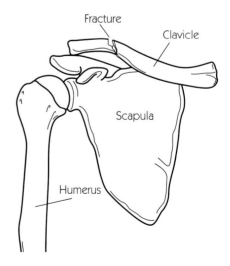

Fracture

Clavicle

Scapula

Humerus

Fracture of the clavicle (collar bone)

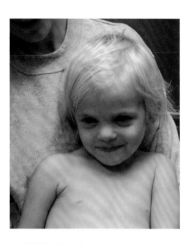

Child with clavicle fracture

Child in figure eight strap
used for clavicle fracture

WRIST INJURIES

Sprains, fractures, and dislocations are the most common wrist injuries.

A sprain is a torn ligament in the wrist. A fracture is a broken bone. A dislocation is the displacement of a bone relative to another, with disruption of the intervening joint.

Wrist injuries with swelling

The wrist should be splinted with a small board or placed on a pillow for comfort. A thin phone book can also be wrapped around the child's wrist and taped closed.

The child should then be brought to your doctor or an emergency room for x-rays. The wrist should be x-rayed to determine if there is one of the following:

- Fracture of one or both bones of the forearm (radius and ulna)
- Greenstick or bending fracture of the forearm bones
- Wrist sprain

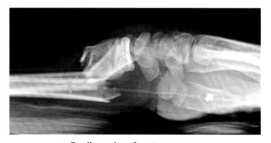

Radius-ulna fracture x-ray

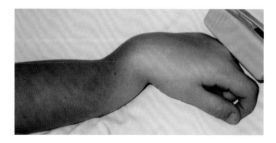

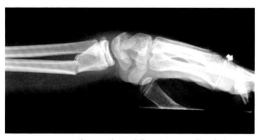

x-ray of angulated fractures of wrist

How will the physician correct the alignment of severely angulated fractures?

Correcting the bone alignment is usually achieved by giving the child some IV pain medications or by injecting the area of the fracture with some numbing medicine such as Lidocaine. The physician will then manipulate the bones to get the ends of the broken bones lined up correctly. A repeat x-ray will then be done to make sure that the bones are in good position.

The child will then be sent home with a splint or a cast.

GREENSTICK (TORUS) FRACTURES

A greenstick fracture occurs in young children because their bones can bend instead of break due to the flexibility of the bones. It is called a greenstick fracture because it is similar to a young, green tree branch that can bend before it breaks. A bending or greenstick fracture of the radius in the forearm is shown below.

GROWTH PLATE INJURIES OF BONES

Let's talk about injuries to the growth plate of the bones in children. The end of the long bones in children has a growth plate, illustrated on the facing page. This growth plate is made of cartilage being turned into bone. Certain injuries to the growth plate can cause the bone to grow at an angle or to grow abnormally. There are five grades of severity for growth plate injuries. Type I is the least serious and Type V is the worst. The diagrams on the facing page show the five types of growth plate fracture injuries.

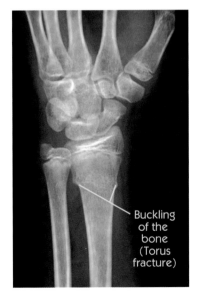

Torus (greenstick) fracture of radius

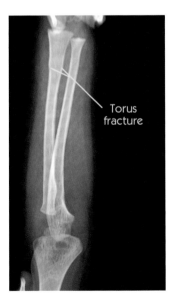

Another torus fracture of the radius. Note buckling of the bone

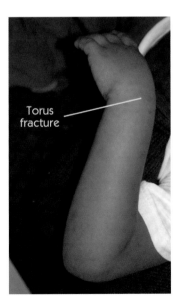

Child with torus fracture of radius

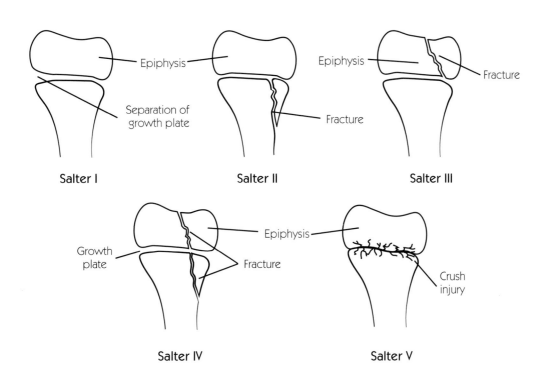

Salter I

Epiphysis

Separation of growth plate

Salter II

Fracture

Salter III

Epiphysis

Fracture

Salter IV

Growth plate

Epiphysis

Fracture

Salter V

Crush injury

Classification of growth plate injuries (Salter Class I–V)
Note: Class I is the least severe. Class V is most severe.

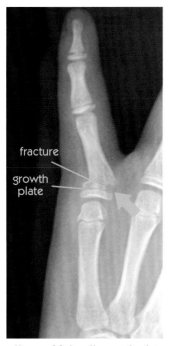

fracture

growth plate

X-ray of Salter II growth plate fracture of the little finger

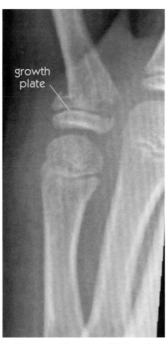

growth plate

Closeup of x-ray of Salter II growth plate fracture

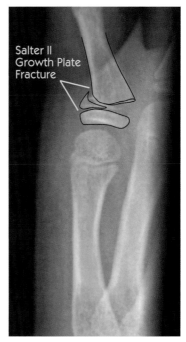

Salter II Growth Plate Fracture

Growth plate fracture of the little finger

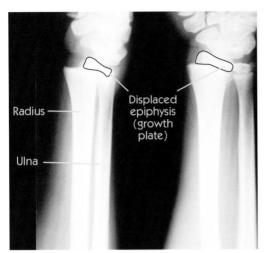

X-ray of displaced epiphysis (growth plate).
Note how the end of the radius bone has
been pushed out of position. This occurs
because the growth plate is made of
cartilage and is weaker than the bone.

ELBOW FRACTURES

Elbow fractures are among the most serious fractures in children. These fractures require very careful orthopedic management and follow-up. Whenever a child falls on an elbow

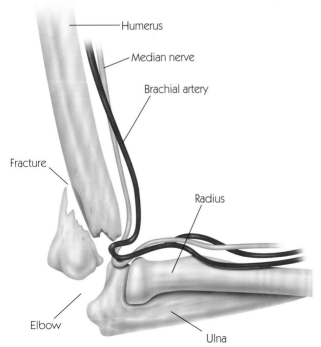

Artery and nerve near an elbow fracture

and the elbow is swollen, parents need to be concerned about a possible elbow fracture. If a splint is not available, the arm should be carefully supported on a pillow for comfort.

The child should then be brought to the emergency room. The emergency physician or family doctor will order x-rays to determine whether the injury is a fracture and/or a dislocation. If there is a fracture above the elbow joint, it's called a supracondylar fracture. These fractures need to be handled very carefully to make sure that the sharp edge of the broken bone does not damage or cut through one of the nerves or arteries of the forearm.

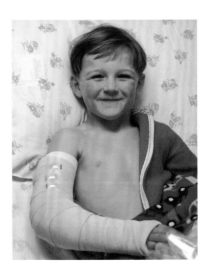

Boy in long-arm splint

Elbow fractures can result in complications, even with the best doctors and the best orthopedic care. Some children with severe elbow fractures can lose the ability to fully extend their elbow joint. This is called Volkman's ischemic contracture.

NURSEMAID'S ELBOW

A nursemaid's elbow is a dislocation of the radial bone in the elbow. This injury usually occurs in children under the age of five when someone suddenly pulls on the child's outstretched arm. It may also occur when a child hangs from something. This is a common injury and can occur with relatively little force. In itself, this injury is not a reason for concern regarding child abuse.

Child with nursemaid's elbow

What are the signs of nursemaid's elbow?

Children with nursemaid's elbow have a mild to moderate, vague pain in the forearm and elbow. They do not want to use that arm and typically support it with their other arm on their lap. When they are standing, the arm is held at their side with the palm turned toward the back. We sometimes call this the waiter's hand, as if a waiter is looking for a tip with his hand turned backwards. One of the key signs is that the child is unable to bend his elbow. You can determine this by holding a shiny keychain or the child's favorite toy for the child to reach for. You will notice that your child will not use the injured arm to reach for the keys or toy because of the pain in the elbow.

What should I do if my child has nursemaid's elbow?

- Keep the child's arm supported in a position of comfort (we don't know if the child has a fracture). Use a pillow or have the child rest the arm on her lap.
- Bring the child to your nearest emergency room or doctor's office.
- Apply ice to the injured area.

What is the treatment for nursemaid's elbow?

The main goal is to make sure that a fracture or dislocation is not present. In some cases, an x-ray may be required. However, in cases in which there is a clear history of someone pulling on the child's arm without any history of a fall, no deformity, and no swelling, x-rays may not be necessary.

First step in the reduction of a nursemaid's elbow

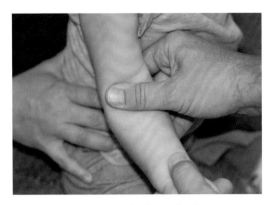

**Second step in the reduction
of nursemaid's elbow**

Last step in the reduction of nursemaid's elbow

To treat a nursemaid's elbow, the physician will do a special maneuver with the child's arm to move the dislocated head of the radius bone back into place. I usually tell parents that this will cause some pain for just a few seconds or minutes.

To do this, the physician will first turn the patient's palm up and then flex the elbow by bringing the child's hand up toward that shoulder.

Frequently a pop will be felt by the physician's finger over the forearm near the elbow. After this maneuver, the child will usually be able to use the arm completely within a few minutes and can go home. The key sign that the radius is back in place is that the child can flex his elbow. I usually offer something for the child to reach for, which requires him to flex his elbow and confirms that the radius bone is back in place.

KNEE INJURIES

Knee injuries can be divided into:
1. Knee fractures and dislocations
2. Knee sprains and contusions
3. Internal tears of the knee ligaments and cartilage

Knee fractures are characterized by swelling, pain, and deformity of the knee area. Several examples of knee fractures are diagrammed on pages 97 and 98.

Knee ligament sprains

Knee ligament sprains usually have pain on one side of the knee, limping, and no significant swelling.

Internal injuries of the knee's ligaments or cartilage

Internal injuries of the knee include:
1. Torn cartilage (torn meniscus)
2. Rupture of the cruciate ligaments (anterior or posterior)

Injuries to the outside ligaments of the knee can by mild, moderate, or severe. A severe injury is a complete rupture of the ligament.

The illustration on page 97 shows a complete tear of both the anterior cruciate ligament and the lateral knee ligament (lateral collateral ligament).

Internal injuries of the knee (tears of the cartilage or the cruciate ligaments) are characterized by:

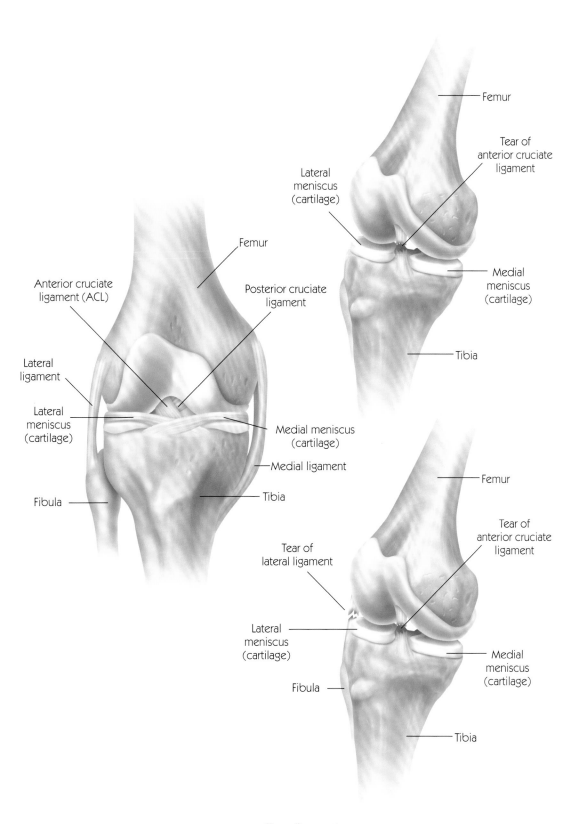

Knee ligaments

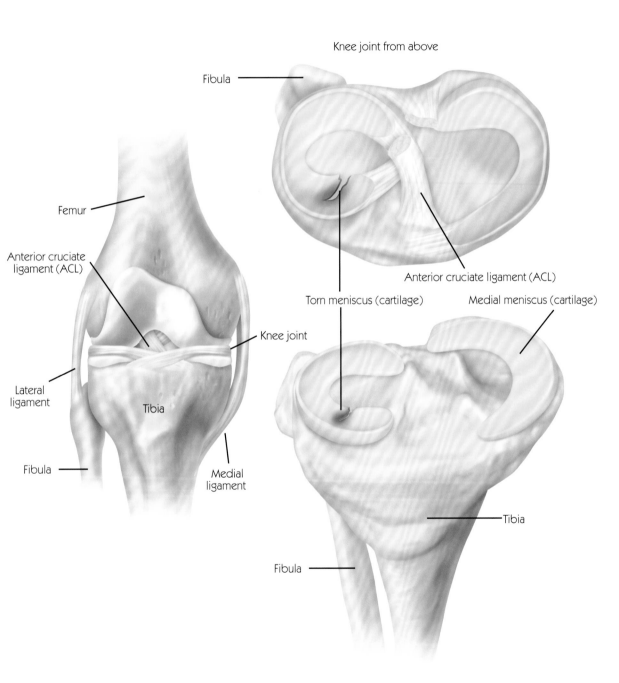

Knee joint from above

Fibula

Femur

Anterior cruciate
ligament (ACL)

Lateral
ligament

Tibia

Fibula

Medial
ligament

Knee joint

Anterior cruciate ligament (ACL)

Torn meniscus (cartilage)

Medial meniscus (cartilage)

Tibia

Fibula

Torn knee cartilage (Meniscus)

1. Knee swelling (the knee is filled with fluid)
2. Inability to bear weight on the knee
3. The knee feels like it wants to give out when the child walks on it

These injuries can sometimes be diagnosed by a physician experienced in sports injuries. However, these injuries frequently require an MRI (magnetic resonance imaging) scan to confirm the diagnosis. The MRI scan gives the orthopedic surgeon a much better idea of what he will be dealing with if the child requires knee surgery. Fortunately, many knee surgeries can now be performed through an arthroscope. This means a large incision is not needed and the recovery time is much shorter.

SHOULDER INJURIES

The most serious shoulder injuries include:
1. Fractures
2. Dislocations

Shoulder fractures usually result from a fall on the shoulder. They usually heal well when treated in a sling for several weeks.

Shoulder dislocations are usually caused by sports injuries or a fall.

Patients with a loose shoulder due to prior dislocations may redislocate after relatively minor stresses.

Treatment consists of getting the shoulder back in place after intravenous pain medication and sedation.

This is usually done in the emergency room.

A shoulder separation occurs when the ligament that connects

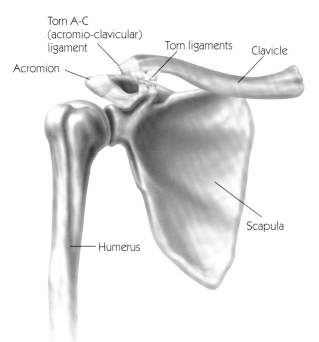

A-C separation
(acromio-clavicular or shoulder separartion)

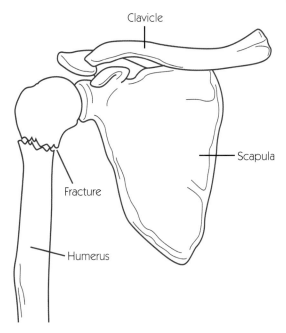

Fracture of humerus

the two bones in the shoulder area is torn. This is called the A-C (acromio-clavicular) ligament.

Look carefully at the photo below and see if you can find where the acromio-clavicular ligament is torn.

Shoulder separations can be first, second, or third degree. A third degree is the worst and implies a complete tear of the A-C ligament.

Mild separations are treated with a sling. Complete tears frequently require surgery in otherwise healthy children.

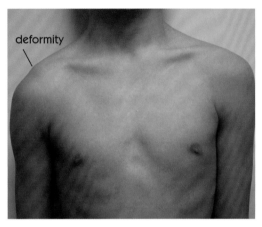

deformity

A-C separation
Note slight deformity at site of A-C ligament

LIMPING

Limping due to trauma is often easier to deal with than limping not associated with trauma. A child who is limping due to a fall will usually have one of the following:

- Bruising of the hip area or swelling
- Hip fracture
- Hip bone growth plate slippage

X-rays will determine which of the above are present.

Hip pain or limp not associated with trauma

The first step is to determine whether the child has a fever. A fever of 99.5°F or higher oral, or 100.4°F or higher rectal, raises the suspicion of an infected hip joint (called a septic arthritis) or a viral infection. This most frequently affects the hip and the knee joints. A child who has a painful joint, whose pain increases with any movement of that joint, and who has a fever needs to be seen by a doctor and evaluated immediately.

The physician may order an x-ray to determine if there is slippage of the growth plate in the hip. The physician will also look for other causes of hip pain, such as inflammation of the hip joint (synovitis, due to a virus), a bacterial infection of the joint, or arthritis of the joint such as juvenile rheumatoid arthritis (JRA). A septic hip joint is an infection caused by bacteria.

If the child has a fever, the physician may order tests to determine if a hip joint infection is present. In some cases, the physician or orthopedic surgeon will insert a needle into the hip joint and withdraw some joint fluid. Cloudy fluid indicates an infection. Clear, light yellow fluid is usually a good sign. The lab analysis of the joint fluid provides the final diagnosis about whether an infection is present. If the joint is infected, the child will be placed on IV antibiotics and admitted to the hospital. An infection can cause permanent damage to the hip if not diagnosed and treated early.

Viral synovitis of the hip

Some children may also have a limp due to a viral inflammation of a joint. This is called a viral synovitis. It is not as serious as a bacterial infection (which is called a septic joint). Children with a viral synovitis may limp and have variable degrees of pain in the hip joint. Although other joints can be affected, the joint with a viral synovitis usually clears up with anti-inflammatory medications such as ibuprofen.

However, the physician may need to do certain tests and procedures to make sure that there is no bacterial infection. This may include inserting a needle in the joint to analyze the fluid.

COMPLICATIONS OF JOINT INFECTIONS

Long-term complications can include:
- Chronic arthritis of the joint
- Gradual destruction of the joint
- Need for joint replacement at some time in the future
- Hip pain or limp without trauma or fever

If my child has a limp, but no fever or trauma, what else could it be?

If the child does not have an infected joint, there are other conditions that can cause limp, such as a slipped growth plate of the ball of the hip.

Another problem is impaired blood flow to the ball of the hip. This is called Legg-Calvé-Perthes disease (LCP disease). Let's discuss both of these.

SLIPPED GROWTH PLATE OF HIP (SLIPPED EPIPHYSIS)

A slipped growth plate of the hip is a condition that can cause hip pain, thigh pain, or sometimes only knee pain. This is one of the few conditions in which a hip problem can cause knee or thigh pain instead. It usually occurs in adolescents who are overweight. However, it can also occur in teenagers who are growing very rapidly. The pain may be felt in the hip, knee, thigh, or only the knee. Physicians and parents need to have a high index of suspicion when a child complains only of knee or thigh pain and has a slight limp. The real problem may be in the hip instead of the knee. Physicians are well aware of this condition in teenagers. Your doctor will obtain x-rays of both the knee and the hip if this is suspected.

The diagram on page 102 illustrates how the slipped hip growth plate looks compared to a normal hip. In some cases, children in this condition may require surgery. This is sometimes referred to as a SKIF-EE by orthopedic surgeons and other physicians. This is based on the medical term "slipped capital femoral epiphysis," which is abbreviated to SCFE.

Complications of a slipped hip growth plate (slipped capital femoral epiphysis):
- Lack of adequate blood flow to the hip, causing damage to the ball of the hip.
- Chronic arthritis of the hip.

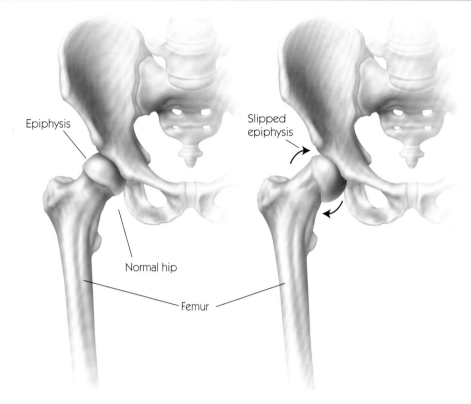

Epiphysis

Slipped epiphysis

Normal hip

Femur

Slipped epiphysis of hip

- Impaired growth of the hip and femur can result in one leg being shorter than the other.

What should I do for my teenager with hip or knee pain with a limp?

Have your child evaluated by a physician within the first twenty-four hours. If a fever is present, the child should see a doctor as soon as possible.

A physician will obtain x-rays of the hip and determine if a slipped hip growth plate is present.

LEGG-CALVÉ-PERTHES (LCP) HIP PAIN OR LIMP WITHOUT FEVER OR TRAUMA

Another condition that can cause a limp or hip pain in children is a condition called Legg-Calvé-Perthes (LCP) disease. This is due

to impaired blood flow to the round bone (femoral head) of the hip joint and damage to the bone because of a lack of blood flow. This condition usually occurs in children between the ages of four and nine and is more common in Caucasian children. It is also more common in children with sickle-cell anemia.

What are the symptoms of LCP disease?

Children with this condition may have hip pain, thigh pain, or sometimes only knee pain. This can make it difficult to diagnose. The pain is usually worse with exercise.

How is LCP disease treated?

The physician will order x-rays to determine if there are signs of damage to the round bone of the femur or a wide joint space. In some cases, the physician will order a bone scan or an MRI (magnetic resonance imaging) scan to confirm the diagnosis. These children require close follow-up by an orthopedic surgeon.

What are the complications of LCP disease?

Some of these children may require a hip replacement as they get older. Other complications include arthritis and intermittent hip pain.

OSGOOD-SCHLATTER'S DISEASE KNEE PAIN IN TEENAGERS NOT ASSOCIATED WITH TRAUMA

Adolescent children who have knee pain, especially between the ages of fourteen and sixteen, may have a problem due to inflammation of the bone right under their knee joint. This condition is called Osgood-Schlatter's disease. This is due to repeated pulling on the bone by the quadriceps (thigh) muscle, which attaches to the tibia, located just under the knee. There is a small bump called the tubercle on the bone where the muscle attaches. (See diagram below.)

Repetitive pulling due to jumping, running, or rapid growth results in this bone becoming inflamed. There is usually tenderness over the tibial tubercle and the patellar tendon (as noted in the diagram). The tibial tubercle area may also be swollen occasionally.

WHAT IS THE TREATMENT FOR OSGOOD-SCHLATTER'S DISEASE?

Parents should have their children refrain from any strenuous physical activity. The child should be evaluated by a doctor in one to two days. The use of Tylenol or Motrin and ice is helpful.

ANKLE INJURIES

Ankle sprains are one of the most common injuries in children and usually occur on the outside of the ankle. Ankle injuries can range from mild to moderate to severe.

It is an interesting fact that, in children, the ankle ligaments are usually stronger than the bones and growth plate. Therefore, children with ankle injuries may damage their growth plate before they tear their ligaments.

Severe ankle injuries occur when there is a complete tearing or disruption of the ankle ligaments. Some of these may require surgery. Most minor and moderate ankle injuries heal when the child keeps her weight off the affected ankle, sometimes with the use of crutches.

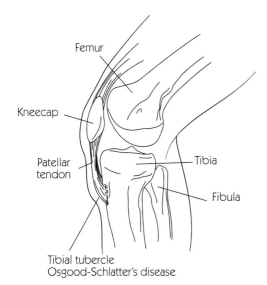

Knee and tibial tubercle and Osgood-Schlatter's disease

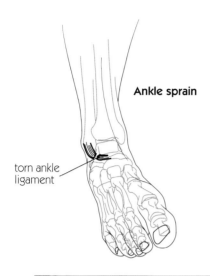

Ankle sprain

torn ankle ligament

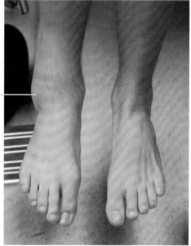

Swollen ankle

Ankle sprain

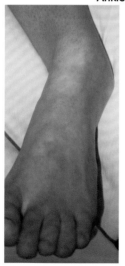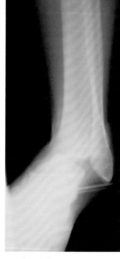

(left)—Dislocated ankle
(right)—x-ray of ankle dislocation

What should I do for my child's ankle injury?

Any ankle injury associated with significant swelling, tenderness, and inability to bear weight should be evaluated by your physician as soon as possible. Of course, significant deformity or swelling of the ankle should be evaluated immediately in the emergency room.

The key to having a good result is rest and no weight-bearing activity, as directed by your physician.

ANKLE DISLOCATIONS

Ankle dislocations are characterized by severe deformity of the ankle. Splint the ankle with a pillow and bring your child to the ER immediately. Ankle dislocations can result in poor blood flow to the foot. These need to be reduced or put back in place as soon as possible.

FOOT INJURIES

Foot injuries usually require an x-ray to determine if a fracture is present. Treatment is rest and use of crutches or sometimes a specialized walking shoe until the fracture or sprain is healed.

SUBUNGUAL HEMATOMA BRUISING UNDER A TOENAIL OR FINGERNAIL

Bruising under a toenail or fingernail is called a subungual hematoma. This is usually due to a crushing injury such as if a child catches his fingers in a car door. If the x-rays obtained by the physicians do not indicate a fracture, then frequently the pain is due to pressure underneath the nail causing pain. Many times the physician will drain this blood under pressure from under the nail by making a small hole in the nail with a hot wire or cautery. By relieving this pressure, the pain usually improves significantly.

What is the home care for a subungual hematoma?

Usually the parents will be instructed to have the child soak her finger or toe in peroxide once or twice a day to help the blood continue to dissolve and drain. The area around the nail should be watched for any signs of redness, swelling, or infection.

ARTHRITIS

Arthritis means a painful joint. Arthritis in children can be due to several conditions:

- Juvenile rheumatoid arthritis (JRA)
- Infection of a joint (septic arthritis or septic joint)
- Arthritis from viral infections

What are the symptoms of juvenile rheumatoid arthritis?

Juvenile rheumatoid arthritis, or JRA, is characterized by inflammation in two or more joints. The pain is increased with any movement of the joint. The same joints on each side of the body are usually affected in JRA.

These joints are usually slightly warm. The parents can determine whether the area is warm by placing the backs of their fingers against the area to see if it feels warm. The backs of the fingers are very sensitive to temperature. That is why

parents know to use the backs of their fingers to feel a child's forehead to see if they have a temperature.

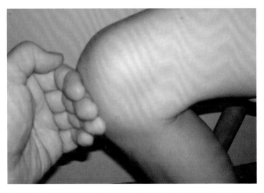
Checking warmth of joint with the back of fingers

Parents should also find out if there are any members of the family who have rheumatoid arthritis, since JRA is an inherited disease.

If my child has a warm, painful joint, what else should I do?

The child should also be checked for a fever (a temperature of 99.5°F oral or 100.4°F rectal or more) to determine if an infection is present. The child should be evaluated by a physician or an emergency physician immediately if there is a fever. If there is no fever, then call your doctor for a recommendation.

What kinds of tests can tell if my child has JRA or a joint infection?

If the physician suspects juvenile rheumatoid arthritis, she will order blood tests such as the following:

- Rheumatoid factor
- Erythrocyte sedimentation rate (ESR)
- CBC (complete blood count)

If the rheumatoid factor is positive and the ESR is elevated, this indicates that the child probably has rheumatoid arthritis.

If the doctor suspects a joint infection, she may order blood cultures. The doctor will also obtain fluid from the joint to see if it shows signs of infection.

What is the treatment for JRA?

The mainstay treatment for JRA is usually aspirin or an anti-inflammatory medication such as ibuprofen or naproxen.

BONE TUMORS

Fortunately, malignant (malignant means cancer) bone tumors only occur in about seven children out of every one million children under age fifteen. Most bone tumors occur between the ages of ten to twenty years of age (the time of the growth spurt).

The most common symptoms of malignant bone tumors are the following:

1. Deep bone pain that awakens the child at night.
2. Persistent bone pain that does not go away after a reasonable period of time.
3. Bone pain associated with a lump or swelling of the bone in the area of pain.

Your doctor will order an x-ray if there is a suspicion of a bone tumor. The x-rays of malignant bone tumors show characteristic signs, which can aid in the early diagnosis. Malignant bone tumors require surgery and chemotherapy.

TOTAL PARENT POINTERS
BONE AND MUSCLE INJURIES

1. **Elbow injuries (fractures) can be very serious.** Keep the child's arm and elbow immobilized. Support the child's arm with a pillow and bring the child to your doctor or the local emergency room.
2. **Nursemaid's elbow** occurs in children under the age of five. The child typically has his arm pulled by someone and then cannot bend his elbow. The bone called the radial head has been pulled out of a round ligament. The bone can be repositioned by a doctor using a special maneuver.
3. A **limp** in a child can be a serious problem. The first thing to do is check for a fever. If the child has a fever, the doctor will do tests to check for an **infected joint (septic joint).** Other causes of a limp can be a simple strain, a viral infection (viral synovitis), or a more serious problem such as a lack of blood flow to the hip joint (LCP disease).
4. **Ankle sprains** are one of the most common injuries that we see in the ER The best treatment is the mnemonic RICE, which stands for rest, ice, compression (with a bandage), and elevation
5. **Clavicle (collarbone) fractures** are the most common fractures in children.
6. **Knee injuries** can be difficult to diagnose. x-rays of the knee only show the bone—they do not show the ligaments. Children with significant knee cartilage or cruciate ligament injuries may have the following signs:
   a. **Inability to bear weight** on that leg due to pain in the knee or a feeling that the knee is giving out.
   b. **Swelling of the knee**
   c. **A sensation of a "pop"** and sudden pain in the knee during the sports game or activity.
   d. A sensation of **locking of the knee** with range of motion.
7. **Juvenile rheumatoid arthritis** is characterized by:
   a. Pain in several joints associated with warmth in the joint
   b. Pain with range of motion in the affected joints
   c. A family history of rheumatoid arthritis
   d. Relief with aspirin or ibuprofen
8. Some of the most serious bone problems in children are:
   • Elbow fractures and dislocations
   • Slippage of the bones in the hip **(slipped capital femoral epiphysis—SCFE)**
   • **Loss of blood flow to hip** (avascular necrosis) Legg-Calvé-Perthes disease
   • Knee injuries (fractures, dislocations and ligament injuries)
   • Shoulder injuries (fractures, dislocations, and rotator cuff tears)
   • **Fractures to the growth plate of bones**

9

Burns

If you've ever burned your finger on a stove, you know how painful even a simple burn can be. Burns are also one of the most preventable injuries we see in the emergency room. Burns happen to kids when they get a sunburn, when they are cooking or near the stove unsupervised, when they play with matches, or unfortunately when a fire occurs in the home. Most burns will require your doctor's attention or an immediate trip to the ER, depending on the severity. Here are some points to keep in mind:

TYPES OF BURN INJURIES

1. A first-degree burn is the mildest type of burn. Symptoms include redness and pain. No blisters are present. A typical example is a mild sunburn.
2. A second-degree burn is characterized by blisters, pain, and weeping fluid from the burned area.
3. Third-degree burns are deep burns that affect all layers of the skin. Third-degree burns frequently require skin grafting.

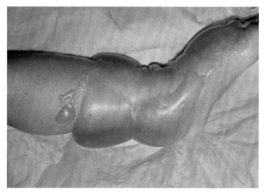

Second-degree burn of foot and ankle

Will a first-degree burn heal by itself?
Yes. First-degree burns will heal by themselves because they have not damaged the skin significantly.

Will a second-degree burn heal by itself?
Most second-degree burns will heal by themselves if they are relatively superficial. You can frequently tell if a second-degree burn will heal by itself if you see new skin growing at the sites of the hair follicles a few days after the burn. If new skin is starting to grow at the hair follicles, this is a sign of a superficial second-degree burn. However, a small percentage of second-degree burns

are deep second-degree burns. These may require skin grafting.

Case study

Here is a young girl who accidentally knocked over a very hot cup of coffee from the kitchen table onto her arm and left side. The photo below shows second-degree burns of her left arm, left chest wall, and left side of abdomen.

Children who have significant burns such as this are best treated in a burn center. Burns that usually require a burn center are:

- Burns involving the hands and feet, especially if they completely go around the finger or toe, are significant. This also includes burns that go all the way around an arm or leg. (These are called circumferential burns. These are more serious because they can swell and cut off the blood flow to the finger, toe, arm, or leg.)

Second-degree burns of left arm and left side of chest due to hot coffee

- Burns of the genital area are serious and should be treated at a burn center
- Any burn that involves more than 10 percent of the body should be treated at a burn center.

How can I tell if the burn involves more than 10 percent of the body?

This is called estimating the body surface area of the burn. You can easily estimate the body surface area of a burn by using the child's

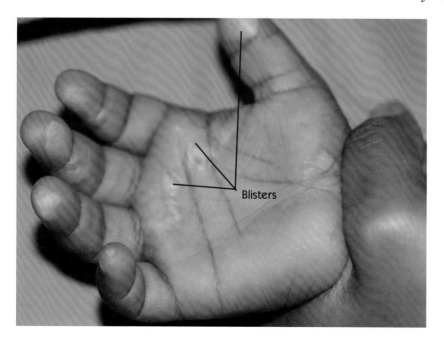

Blisters

Second-degree burns of hand

hand. Place the child's hand with the fingers closed near the burned area. The area of the child's hand is about 1 percent of the child's body surface area. Try to figure out how many of the child's hands would be needed to cover the burned area.

Let's take a look at the photo on page 109 again and pretend we are using the imagined size of the child's palm to determine the percent of body surface that is burned. What do you think it is?

I estimated about 10–12 percent.

The child was given IV pain medicine, IV fluids, and transported to our local burn center. The child did very well and was discharged several days later.

Do third-degree burns heal by themselves?

Usually not, unless they are very small. A third-degree burn has burned through all levels of the skin and will usually not heal by itself. Third-degree burns frequently require skin grafting.

What is the most common type of burn injury in children?

Scalding by hot liquids is the most common type of burn injury seen in young children. The key issue for this type of injury is prevention. All parents, baby-sitters, and caregivers of young children should be instructed to keep pot handles on the stove turned inward so that a child cannot grab them and tip them over. A child should never be left alone in the kitchen when food is cooking on the stove. In addition, all home hot-water heaters should be set to heat the water no higher than 120°F.

What is the treatment for a hot water scald burn injury?

All burn injuries can be treated with lukewarm to cool tap water. Do not place butter or any other creams on the burn before the burn is evaluated by a physician. Any creams will limit the physician's ability to completely visualize the degree of burn injury. Other medications, such as butter or aloe, are not needed in the early stages of a burn injury.

Go to *TheTotalParent.com* to view more pictures of first-, second-, and third-degree burns as well as charts to determine percentage of body surface affected by the burn.

HOUSE FIRES

The best way to prevent injuries from house fires is through prevention and education. This involves having smoke detectors in or near all bedrooms as well as carbon monoxide detectors in key locations throughout the house. Smoke detectors decrease your chances of dying in a house fire by 50 percent!

House fires account for approximately 45 percent of all deaths due to burns. Deaths due to house fires can occur through smoke inhalation and toxic chemical inhalation, as well as the burn injury itself. Although advances in medicine have resulted in fewer deaths from severe burns, a significant number of deaths still occur every year in children with severe burn injuries.

Every house should have at least one fire extinguisher to be used for kitchen or electrical fires. Every family should also practice what to do in the event of a house fire. Many schools and local fire departments teach young children how to stop, drop, and roll if their clothing is on fire. Children should be instructed how to call 911 and also taught how to get out of the house safely via a preplanned escape route in the event of a house fire.

TOTAL PARENT POINTERS
BURNS

1. **Every house must have smoke detectors near each bedroom. Smoke detectors decrease the chances of dying in a house fire by 50 percent.** (Battery-powered smoke detectors need to be checked every month. Replace batteries yearly.)

2. **Carbon monoxide detectors should also be a must for every house.** A blocked furnace may not cause a fire but it may cause everyone to be exposed to the risk of carbon monoxide poisoning. Symptoms of carbon monoxide poisoning are headache, confusion, and sleepiness.

> **SECRET DOCTOR INFO**: Suspect **carbon monoxide intoxication** if everyone in the house has a headache and fatigue and the furnace is being used at the beginning of the fall-winter season.

3. **Turn down the temperature of your hot water heater to 120°F** to prevent hot water burns to infants and children.

4. **Practice fire drills twice a year.** Teach your children how to get out of the house if there is a fire. Make it a game. See if they can get out of their room blindfolded and make it out of the house by walking and also by crawling on the floor. Crawling along the floor is important if the house is filled with smoke.

5. Have **fire extinguishers** near the stove and on each floor where people are sleeping.

6. Teach you children about the dangers of matches and fires. Keep your matches, butane candle lighters, etc. locked and away from children. Be very careful around campfires.

7. **What are the three types of burns?**
   a. **First-degree burn**—mild, skin is red and painful.
   b. **Second-degree burn**—blisters and painful. May be superficial or deep.
   c. **Third-degree burn**—white or charred skin, no pain, may require skin grafting because the skin will not grow back by itself.

8. **Body surface area of burn**—Estimate the percent of body surface affected by the burn. Use the child's hand with the fingers closed. Lay this near the burn. The area covered by the child's hand is about 1 percent of the body surface area. Figure out how many hands it would take to cover the burned area. If it takes five hands, this is a 5 percent body surface burn.

9. **Burns that usually require a burn center are:**
   - **Burns involving the hands and feet,** especially if they completely go around the finger or toe, are significant. This also includes burns that go all the way around an arm or leg. (These are called circumferential burns. These are more serious because they can swell and cut off the blood flow to the finger, toe, arm, or leg.)
   - **Burns of the genital area** are serious and should be treated at a burn center
   - **Any burn that involves more than 10 percent of the body** should be treated at a burn center.

10

Difficult Breathing and Cough

These two topics are so broad that we could fill an entire book discussing them. However, let's focus only on emergency factors. These are the key points that you need to know as a parent caring for a sick child with difficult breathing or a cough in the middle of the night.

DIFFICULT BREATHING

One of the most important skills you can develop is the ability to evaluate your child's breathing. The Total Parent Breathing Checklist uses the word BREATHING to help you remember the key points that you should check.

Take a look at the Total Parent Breathing Checklist on page 114. Let's go through each of these individually and discuss how to evaluate your child's breathing.

B—BREATHING SOUNDS

Abnormal breath sounds indicate some form of lung problem or airway constriction and include

B	Breathing sounds
R	Rate of breathing
E	Eye contact
A	Abdominal breathing and appearance (pink or blue lips)—Is the belly moving in and out?
T	Temperature
H	Heavy breathing—Is the child breathing deep and fast?
I	Inner rib retractions
N	Nasal flaring—dilation of the nostrils with each breath.
G	Grunting

wheezing, a croupy barking-seal cough, congestion, and stridor. Stridor is a high-pitched sound that you can hear when a child breathes in. It sounds as though there is something caught in his airway. Stridor can be caused by a foreign object in the airway, severe croup, or an anaphylactic reaction that causes swelling and narrowing of the airway.

TOTAL PARENT BREATHING CHECKLIST©

THETOTALPARENT.com
Dr. Ron Kurzejka, M.D.
Call 920-PARENTS
(920-727-3687)

B — Breathing sounds (wheezing, congested, croupy "seal bark" cough, stridor=high-pitched inhalation)

R — Rate of breathing—more than fifty per minute—WARNING! (If age over four to six months)

E — Eye contact (focuses on you or looks away)

A — Abdominal breathing and appearance (pink or blue lips)

T — Temperature

H — Heavy breathing

I — Inner rib retractions

N — Nasal flaring

G — Grunting

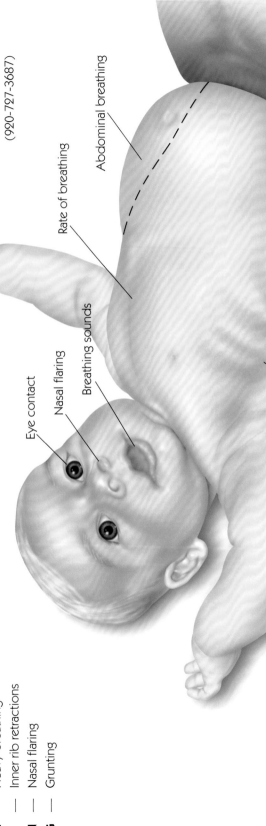

Abdominal breathing

Rate of breathing

Eye contact

Nasal flaring

Breathing sounds

Inner rib retractions

100.4°F (rectal) = Fever

38°C (rectal) = Fever

Age	Pounds	Kg	Normal Breathing Rate
Newborn	6–14	3–6 kg	30–50
6 month–1 yr	15–23	7–10 kg	30–40
2–4 yrs	24–35	12–16 kg	20–30
5–8 yrs	36–55	18–26 kg	14–20
8–12 yrs	55–110	26–50 kg	12–20
Over 12 yrs	>110	>50 kg	12–20

R—RATE OF BREATHING

You should count your child's breathing rate for a full sixty seconds. Keep in mind that one breath in and one breath out count as one breath. I watch the child's chest rise with each breath for a full minute, counting the number of times the child's chest rises during that time. The normal rate for children of different ages is in the table on page 114. It is important to know if your child's rate is higher than normal.

Count number of breaths per minute

E—EYE CONTACT AND EATING

Eye contact

A child who has trouble breathing also has trouble maintaining eye contact or focusing on other things. This is an important sign because it may indicate that the child is not getting enough oxygen. Children who are not getting enough oxygen become anxious. Infants express this with poor eye contact, irritability, and poor feeding. School-age children get anxious and wide-eyed with fear. They may also sit up straighter to try to get more air.

Eating

Children who are sick or having trouble breathing do not want to eat.

A—ABDOMINAL BREATHING AND APPEARANCE

Abdominal breathing

Abdominal breathing is a sign of deep breathing that causes the abdomen to move in an exaggerated up and down motion. This is due to the fact that when the child breathes deeply, the diaphragm moves lower and forces the abdomen to be pushed out. See the Breathing Checklist for a visual illustration of how this looks.

Appearance

What does the child's skin color look like? It is especially important to look at the lips. If a child's lips appear slightly dusky or bluish, that is a sign that she is not getting enough oxygen. The child's lips should be a normal pink color. However, this is difficult for some people to appreciate. I tell parents to compare the child's lips to those of their siblings. If they match, that's a good sign. If the lips look darker or duskier, that is a sign the child may not be getting enough oxygen.

T—TEMPERATURE AND TALKING

Temperature

If your child has a rectal temperature of 100.4°F or more, this means he has a fever and some type of infection. Mothers can usually tell very quickly whether the child's skin feels warmer than usual. In fact, a recent journal article on how accurate mothers were at detecting their child's temperatures was accurately titled "Mothers Are Thermometers."

But please keep in mind that feeling a child's skin is not a substitute for taking a temperature. Many times in the emergency room, I meet parents who have brought in their child who is two months or younger, and they have not taken the child's temperature at home. In many cases, they say they do not own a thermometer.

BUY A THERMOMETER! Please make sure to keep a digital rectal thermometer or a non-mercury rectal thermometer in your house at all times. Instructions for using a rectal thermometer can be found in chapter 2 on fever.

Talking

Older children experiencing significant shortness of breath can speak only in phrases or single words and are unable to speak in complete sentences. This is an important clue to use.

- Speaking in full sentences means mild shortness of breath
- Speaking in phrases means moderate shortness of breath
- Speaking in a few words means severe shortness of breath

H—HEAVY BREATHING

Look carefully to see if your child is having deep and rapid breathing. See if his chest is moving in and out deeper than normal. Also look for the abdominal breathing described above.

I—INNER RIB RETRACTIONS

A retraction or a pulling in of the muscles between the ribs is a sign your child is having difficulty breathing. This is illustrated in the photo below. When I examine

children in the emergency room, I ask the mom or dad to take the child's shirt off and put the child over a shoulder. In this way the child is usually quiet and comfortable, and I can carefully observe her breathing. (At home you might have your spouse hold your baby and perform your own examination.)

I then go through the breathing checklist to see which abnormal signs they have. I begin by counting the rate of breathing and looking at the ribs for inner rib retractions. If I see the rib muscles being pulled in with each breath, then I know that the child is having difficulty breathing.

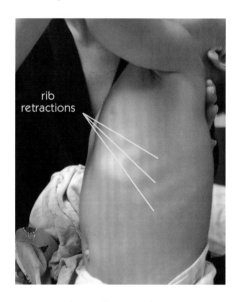

Inner rib retractions

N—NASAL FLARING

I then have the parent turn around with the child over his shoulder so I can look at the child's nostrils. I look to see if the nostrils dilate or become wider with each breath. This nasal flaring is another sign of labored breathing.

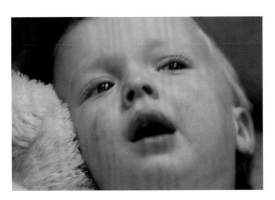

Nasal flaring

G—GRUNTING

Grunting occurs frequently in children with pneumonia because there is fluid in a portion of their lung. This is a very helpful clue in diagnosing pneumonia and sometimes congestive heart failure in children with congenital heart disease.

What are the most common causes of a cough and difficulty breathing in children?

1. The common cold—an upper respiratory tract infection
2. Bronchitis
3. Reactive airway disease
4. Bronchiolitis (viral illness)
5. Pneumonia
6. Croup
7. Asthma and allergies

What are the symptoms of the common cold?

The common cold is characterized by any or all of the following symptoms: cough, fever, runny nose, sore throat, sneezing, fever, and fatigue.

What should you do for children who have a cold?

The key elements of treating the common cold are:

1. Tylenol and ibuprofen for fever. (Tip: begin with Tylenol every four hours at the dose recommended on the bottle. Talk to your doctor about using a slightly higher dose if the fever is not controlled. If the fever remains relatively high, you may give ibuprofen every six hours in addition to the Tylenol. Ibuprofen should not be given, however, to children under the age of one or to children who are allergic to aspirin.)
2. Saline nose drops every four hours can be used for infants to keep their nostrils clear. Also suction their nostrils with a bulb syringe if they sound congested.
3. Children with the common cold do not need antibiotics, since colds are caused by viruses and not bacteria that would respond to antibiotics.

BRONCHITIS

Bronchitis is an inflammation of the large breathing tubes (bronchi) in the lungs. It is associated with cough and phlegm production. The chest x-ray looks normal. Most cases are caused by viruses and do not need antibiotics.

REACTIVE AIRWAY DISEASE

I consider reactive airway disease to be a general term for a variety of forms of airway disease that involves bronchoconstriction, more commonly known as wheezing. It includes asthma but is not limited to asthma.

Reactive airway disease is a condition in some children who have airways that are very sensitive to irritating factors such as cold viruses, smoke, allergenic substances, chemicals, etc. When these children get a cold, they frequently get short of breath and have some degree of wheezing. Their airways tend to constrict and cause wheezing when they are irritated by certain infections, dust particles, fumes, or allergic substances similar to asthmatics. However, they do not have asthma. It is a matter of degree. Asthmatics have more frequent episodes, and they may have wheezing episodes that are not associated with colds or other infections.

Children with various lung diseases, such as cystic fibrosis, also experience wheezing when exposed to various irritants and infections. They have a more severe type of reactive airway disease

BRONCHIOLITIS (RSV)

Bronchiolitis is a viral illness that occurs in children under the age of two, most often in infants between two and six months old. It usually occurs in the winter and spring, and about 75 percent of the time it is caused by RSV (respiratory syncytial virus). A rapid nasal swab can sometimes be performed in the emergency room or doctor's office to check for RSV. Children with severe cases or those under the age of six weeks may need to be admitted to the hospital. Some infants can even stop breathing from RSV bronchiolitis. (This is called apnea.)

Bronchiolitis is characterized by the following symptoms:
1. Difficulty breathing
2. Coughing
3. Wheezing
4. Inner rib retractions
5. Fast breathing rate (see normal rates on our chart on page 114)
6. Fever (in two out of every three children), which is typically about 100°–101°F rectally.
7. Runny nose
8. Congested lung sounds

What is the treatment for bronchiolitis?

The treatment is usually the same as that used for asthma—a breathing nebulizer or bronchodilator medicine, such as albuterol. This helps dilate the small airways in the lungs.

How do I know if I should bring my child in for possible bronchiolitis?

The key things to do are the following:
1. Evaluate your child's breathing using the Total Parent Breathing Checklist. If your child looks as though he is having a difficult time breathing, go to your doctor or emergency room immediately. (Remember, signs of labored breathing are poor eye contact, excessive fussiness, excessive sleepiness, nasal flaring, inner rib retractions, a fast breathing rate, and abdominal breathing.) Infants less than six weeks old with bronchiolitis frequently need to be hospitalized.
2. Check for any wheezing.
3. Check for exhaustion. Does your child appear to be tiring out from her breathing efforts?

4. Make sure your child is not getting dehydrated. Urinating five times over a twenty-four-hour period is a good sign they are not dehydrated. Less than four to five urines in twenty-four hours may be a sign of dehydration.

PNEUMONIA

Pneumonia is defined as an infection in part of the lung that shows up on a chest x-ray as a white area or an infiltrate. This is an area of infection that contains white blood cells, fluid, and antibodies. (See sample chest x-rays.)

What are the symptoms of pneumonia?
A child with pneumonia typically has one or more of the following:
1. Faster than normal breathing rate
2. Cough
3. Phlegm production (sometimes)
4. Fever 100.4°F rectal or higher (or over 99.6°F in children over the age of three)
5. Grunting
6. Pain in a particular part of the lung with breathing
7. Inner rib retractions
8. Nasal flaring

What are the causes of pneumonia?
Bacteria usually cause pneumonia in children. Some cases can be caused by viruses.

What is the usual treatment for pneumonia?
Children with bacterial pneumonia are treated with antibiotics. This may be done in a hospital or as an

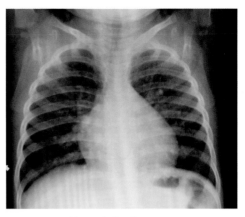

Normal chest x-ray

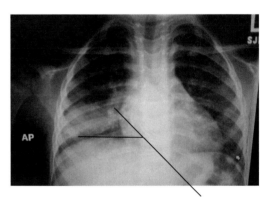

Pneumonia

Chest x-ray with pneumonia

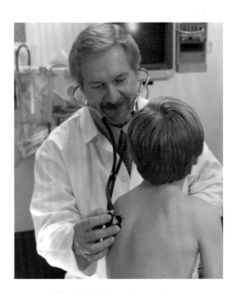

Physician listening to lungs for signs of pneumonia

outpatient, depending on the severity of the child's condition.

CROUP

Croup is a disease caused by a virus that usually occurs in children between the ages of one and three. The most prominent symptom is a cough that sounds like a barking seal. In the emergency room we call this a croupy cough. The cough and difficult breathing are due to the fact that the croup virus causes swelling in the upper airway. An x-ray of how the airway is narrowed is below.

Children with croup typically have a fever of up to 102°F. Their symptoms may gradually worsen over three to four days (especially at night) and then begin to get better on the fourth or fifth day.

Croup tends to occur during the winter and spring seasons. The symptoms frequently get better after the child is brought outside into cool air. Many of the children who are seen in the emergency room

are better, according to their parents, after they get to the ER. This is partially due to the fact that the cool, moist air they were exposed to on the way to the hospital helped relieve some of the swelling in their airways, enabling them to breathe better.

In some cases, croup can become very severe. Children with severe croup have significant trouble breathing. (Refer to the Total Parent Breathing Checklist for the signs of difficult breathing in your child.) Signs of difficulty in breathing include:

- A fast breathing rate. For example, a child who is two years old who is breathing over forty to fifty breaths per minute is breathing abnormally fast.
- Signs of inner rib retractions with each breath because the child is trying extra hard to breathe in while the rib cage is expanding.
- Nasal flaring (the child's nostrils enlarge every time he breathes in).

What is the treatment for croup?

Mild cases of croup can be treated at home with a cool mist humidifier. Children who have significant trouble breathing should be seen by a doctor or taken to an emergency room immediately.

The assessment of your child's breathing is based on your gut instincts, selective observation of the items noted in the breathing assessment tool, and your sense of your child's distress. If there is any doubt, call your doctor or bring

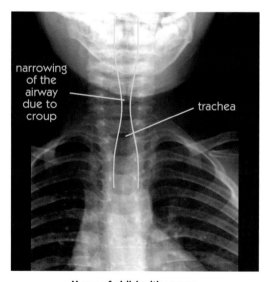

X-ray of child with croup

your child to the emergency room immediately.

Your physician will determine whether your child is well enough to be treated at home or needs to be admitted to the hospital. If you child is well enough to go home, the physician may recommend using a humidifier in the bedroom. The warm mist created by a warm shower in a closed bathroom is also effective.

However, if this does not help and your child's breathing problems get worse, he should be brought back to the emergency room immediately. In some cases, the doctor may give the child a steroid medicine to help reduce the inflammation in the airway caused by the croup virus.

Children who are admitted to the hospital will be kept under close observation for any worsening of their breathing. The physician will monitor their oxygen levels very closely. In some severe cases of croup, children need to have a special tube—an endotracheal tube—placed in their airways. They are then placed on a ventilator to help their breathing. This is necessary in cases where the child would otherwise become so exhausted from the work of breathing that he might stop breathing. Some children with severe croup can actually die if the narrowing of the airway becomes severe.

Finally, since croup is caused by a virus, it is not treated with antibiotics. However, your physician may decide to use antibiotics if there is a concern about a secondary bacterial infection.

ASTHMA

See chapter 23 for complete information on asthma.

ALLERGIC REACTIONS

See chapter 22 for more information on allergic reactions.

The signs are:
1. Hives (urticaria) either localized to one area or all over the body.

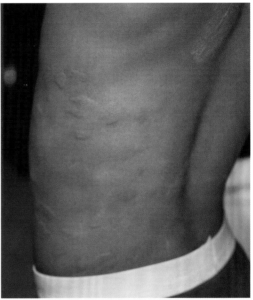

Hives

2. Itching
3. Tightness in the throat or a sensation of "my throat feels like it is closing up."
4. Shortness of breath
5. Wheezing in more severe cases
6. Stridorous—high pitched—breathing in severe cases (as though there is something caught in the windpipe or airway. This sound is most prominent when the child breathes in.)
7. Low blood pressure, and in severe cases, shock.

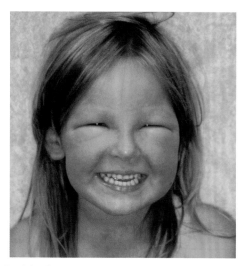

Facial edema (swelling) from allergic reaction

What is the treatment for allergic reactions?

1. Benadryl for itching
2. Steroids for swelling and inflammation
3. Epinephrine (adrenalin) for children in shock (an EpiPen is available by prescription and can be self-injected by children with life-threatening allergic reactions).

WHOOPING COUGH (PERTUSSIS)

Whooping cough, or pertussis, is a respiratory infection characterized by severe spasms of coughing, often followed by a sharp inhale of breath that makes a whoop sound. It is spread by sneezing or coughing on other people. Whooping cough is not as common as the other causes of coughing in children, but the number of cases of whooping cough has increased since the 1980s, especially among adolescents, ages ten to nineteen, and in infants five months old and younger.

Infants who are under the age of one tend to have more serious cases, more complications, and tend to develop pneumonia or convulsions. In some cases, whooping cough can be fatal. There have been approximately fifteen to twenty deaths from whooping cough reported to the Centers for Disease Control over the past several years. That is partly because infants younger than five months of age are too young to be completely protected by the pertussis vaccine.

What you need to know about whooping cough (pertussis)

The best way to protect children or young infants from whooping cough is to make sure they receive their first DTaP vaccine starting on time at the age of two months. They should receive further boosters of the DTaP vaccine at four and six months of age. The pertussis vaccine is also recommended at the age of fifteen to eighteen months and again between four and six years of age.

TOTAL PARENT POINTERS
DIFFICULT BREATHING AND COUGH

1. We use a special acronym—BREATHING—to assess a child who has trouble breathing.

   B—Breathing sounds—Does the child sound congested, wheezy, croupy (barking seal cough), or emit a high-pitched sound during inhalation?

   R—Respiratory rate—Is the child breathing faster than normal?

   E—Eye contact and eating (diminished appetite)

   A—Appearance and abdominal breathing
   - dusky or bluish lips indicates a lack of oxygen
   - belly moving up and down indicates a need to pull in more air.

   T—Temperature and talking
   - Is there a fever of 100.4°F rectal or more?
   - Is the child talking in full sentences (mild shortness of breath), phrases (moderate/severe shortness of breath), or words (severe shortness of breath)

   H—Heavy breathing
   I—Inner rib retractions
   N—Nasal flaring
   G—Grunting

2. What are the most common causes of **cough?**
   - The common cold—an upper respiratory tract infection
   - Bronchitis
   - Reactive airway disease
   - Bronchiolitis
   - Pneumonia
   - Croup
   - Asthma and allergies

3. The **common cold** consists of fever, cough, and a runny nose. Antibiotics are not needed since it is caused by a virus.

4. **Bronchiolitis** is a viral illness characterized by a slight fever, wheezing, and a cough, which usually occurs in children under the age of two.

5. **Croup** typically presents in a child between one to three years of age with a characteristic "barking seal" type of cough, a low-grade fever, and difficult breathing. Croup is also a viral illness. It is usually caused by RSV (respiratory syncytial virus).

6. **Pneumonia** consists of fever, cough, difficult breathing, and phlegm production. Severe cases require hospitalization. It is frequently caused by bacteria and requires antibiotics.

11

Cuts and Bruises

You already know the basic care involved when your child has an abrasion or superficial cut of the hands, feet, arms, or legs. Spray the wound with an antiseptic and numbing spray (if available) to relieve the pain and prevent infection. (Children will deal with the pain of cleaning much better if a numbing spray has been used first.) Wash the wound thoroughly to remove dirt and bacteria, pat the wound dry, and then apply an antibiotic ointment and a sterile bandage.

But what do you do if the cut is more serious?

CUTS (LACERATIONS)

One of the first questions parents have concerning cuts is how to decide which ones require suturing and which ones do not. This is a difficult question to answer because there are many different factors involved. However, a few general guidelines can be reviewed:

1. Within the first three to four hours of a gaping or deep cut to the face, an emergency physician, pediatrician, or family physician should evaluate the cut for the need for sutures.
2. Any lacerations of the hands, feet, or joints should be evaluated within the first three to four hours.
3. Puncture wounds of the hands or feet should be evaluated within the first three to four hours for thorough wound cleansing and possible antibiotic treatment.
4. Injuries to the scalp should be evaluated early to determine if there is any associated head injury, which may require a CT scan.
5. Any puncture wounds or cuts that may involve a foreign body such as broken glass, metallic objects, or wood splinters should be evaluated within the first three to four hours to allow the physician time to explore the wound for the presence of a foreign body.
6. All of the above are based on having a cut sutured (or stitched up) in the first six hours from the time of the injury.

7. Certain cuts, such as dog bite wounds to a hand or foot may not be sutured because this can increase the chances of an infection. The teeth of dogs and cats are covered with bacteria. When a bite wound injects these bacteria deep into a hand or foot, closing the cut with sutures can prevent the wound from draining and increase the risk of an infection. The poor blood flow to the tendons in the hand also increases the risk of infection.

The only exception to this are dog or cat bites to the face. These cuts are frequently sutured because the better cosmetic results outweigh the risk of infection.

What options does a parent have in terms of closing a wound besides sutures?

For most wounds, sutures or stitches are frequently the best choice. However, in many cases, we now have another way of closing a wound using a type of skin glue, which is similar to superglue, but designed for use on skin. This skin glue can close many wounds effectively, although it has limited use in

Boy with laceration above eye that was sutured

areas such as over a joint or where there is skin tension, which may pull the wound apart.

There are also skin staples that can be used on the scalp or other areas of the body, except the face. Skin staples can be completed within thirty to sixty seconds and produce comparable results to sutures in areas like the scalp, arms, and legs. Adhesive strips called Steri-Strips may be used to close other wounds. These are usually applied to small wounds. Prior to placing the strips, a nurse or physician will apply an adhesive to either side of the wound and then close the wound with these special small strips.

If my daughter has a laceration on her face, when should I request a plastic surgeon to close the wound?

In general, any board-certified emergency medicine specialist is qualified to close almost all facial lacerations. However, parents need to consider several factors in requesting a plastic surgeon. Any laceration that occurs parallel to the wrinkles of the face or skin lines will be less visible. This is simply based on the fact that they occur in the same direction as wrinkles on the face. For example, a horizontal laceration of the forehead will be less visible than a vertical laceration.

I tell parents not to worry about how the scar looks for the first few months. The body will smooth out the scar naturally. The final scar is what is left after about six to eight months.

Keep in mind that parents also have the option of seeing a plastic surgeon or dermatologist eight to twelve months down the road to determine if a scar can be made less visible. Dermabrasion is the process of removing the top layer of skin to smooth over scars or wrinkles. It is usually done by dermatologists or plastic surgeons.

TETANUS SHOTS

In general, a tetanus shot should be given to children if the wound is very dirty or contaminated and if the last shot was more than five years ago. However, clean wounds, such as those from a clean glass cup in a kitchen, require a tetanus shot only if more than ten years have elapsed.

How often should a child receive a tetanus shot for a cut or abrasion?

Typically, children receive tetanus shots at two, four, and six months, and again at four to six and fourteen to sixteen years of age. It is always a good idea to keep a copy of your child's immunizations with you. In the ER, we know that a seventeen-year-old with a cut probably received his last tetanus booster at age sixteen and therefore would not require another tetanus shot.

What about bruises? Should I be concerned and how do I handle them?

Bruises are usually harmless. They are caused by injured blood vessels that leak blood into the surrounding tissue. Bruises are very common among children, who often bump into things while they are playing and taking part in sports.

The only reason to be concerned is if bruises appear on your child's skin for no apparent reason. If it does disappear with two weeks, or if it becomes large after a minor injury, a bruise could be a sign of an infection or a blood disease, such as a lack of clotting elements in the blood or certain leukemias. Make an appointment with your doctor if you are concerned about excessive bruising or bruising without a known cause.

MEDICAL PROBLEMS THAT CAN CAUSE APPARENT BRUISES

Certain illnesses can create what look like ordinary bruises. Take a look at the next few photos. This child developed these discolored, raised areas that appear to be bruises all over his legs. No injuries or trauma caused these.

This child actually had a condition called HSP, or Henoch-Schönlein purpura. This is a disease that causes these raised bruises because an antibody is attacking the child's blood vessels. (This is called a vasculitis.) This can occur in any area of the body, such as under the skin, the intestines, the brain, and the kidneys. As a result, these children can develop apparent bruises (called purpura), bleeding in their intestines, kidney damage, and bleeding in the brain. It is usually treated with steroids.

HSP is called an autoimmune disease because the body's antibodies are attacking something within the body. (Antibodies are substances that attach to bacteria and viruses to help prevent or cure the infection.)

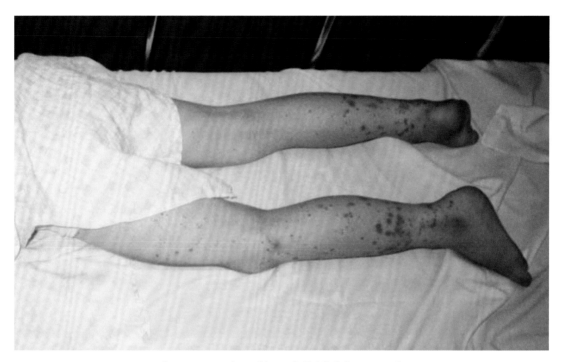

Purpura over legs (Henoch-Schönlein purpura)

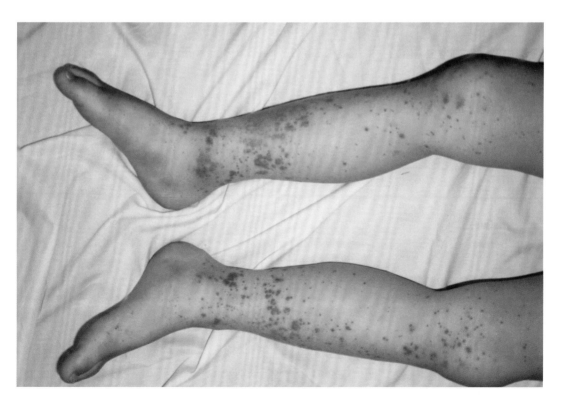

Henoch-Schönlein purpura

TOTAL PARENT POINTERS
CUTS AND BRUISES

1. Any gaping laceration of the face should be evaluated by an emergency physician within the first two to three hours.

2. **Puncture wounds of the foot,** especially those through a gym shoe, should be evaluated by your pediatrician, family doctor, or an emergency physician within the first few hours. A bacterial infection from the puncture wound can occur and lead to a serious infection. Your doctor may prescribe an antibiotic for a puncture wound of the foot.

3. **Puncture wounds of the hand** should also be seen by a physician within the first two to three hours for early treatment and possible antibiotic treatment.

4. Puncture wounds of any part of the body **that could involve a foreign body** should be treated immediately. In many cases an x-ray will reveal a foreign body, such as metal or glass. However, x-rays will not show the presence of other foreign bodies, such as those composed of wood, plastic, etc.

5. Any significant laceration to the face or elsewhere will result in a scar, regardless of how much experience the physician has in suturing those lacerations. However, the final result of a wound closed by sutures, skin adhesive, or Steri-Strips will typically show the final healed appearance in approximately six to eight months. Parents need to wait six to eight months for the skin to regenerate and show the final appearance of the healed laceration.

6. Bruises are usually harmless; the ruptured blood vessels beneath the skin heal on their own. **Call your doctor if your child has bruises that don't go away or that seem to appear without a preceding injury.**

12

Earaches and Nose and Throat Problems

Earaches and sore throats are so common in children that you may feel a sense of déjà vu when your little one has ear pain or a red and painful sore throat. It is usually the beginning of the common cold and will probably go away on its own. How, then, do you know when to get to a doctor?

Children with ear pain often have an external ear or a middle ear infection. External ear infections are also called swimmers ear. Middle ear infections are the more common and are often due to an infection inside the eardrum.

EXTERNAL EAR INFECTIONS

External ear infections occur in the outer cannel of the ear and tend to occur more during the summer months, thus the name swimmers ear. It can also be caused by over-enthusiastic cleaning of the ear with cotton swabs.

Signs of an external ear infection are:
1. Pain with pulling on the ear lobe
2. Earache

3. Fluid drainage from the ear canal in some cases
4. History of frequent swimming

What should I do for my child with ear pain until I can get to a doctor?

In general, the only home treatment for external ear infections is pain medication such as Tylenol or Motrin. Children with ear pain should be evaluated by a physician to determine if the infection is in the external ear canal or in the middle ear.

Do not put sweet oil or other oils in the ear. This can create serious problems because the oil will make it impossible for your doctor to see the eardrum the next day and properly diagnose the problem. It is also a nonsterile liquid that can cause complications, especially if your child has a hole in his eardrum from the infection and the oil gets into the middle ear space.

MIDDLE EAR INFECTIONS

Children with a middle ear infection have ear pain and often a fever due to a coexisting cold or upper respiratory tract infection. The infection usually begins because there is some blockage in the eustachian tube (the tube that connects the middle ear to the throat area). This tube acts as a relief valve to help equalize the pressure in the middle ear.

A good example of this is when you go up or down in an elevator in a tall building. You notice that you develop ear pain or pressure because your eardrum is bulging due to the change of atmospheric pressure when the elevator is traveling quickly up or down. We all know it helps to yawn or hold our nose and blow gently. When you do this, you are equalizing the pressure in your middle ear by opening your eustachian tube; you are relieving the pressure between your throat and your middle ear. When this tube becomes swollen and blocked due to a cold, children can develop an ear infection. The tube can also become blocked as a result of smoking in the house. The tube can also be kinked due to an abnormality from birth. Some children have a eustachian tube that kinks or blocks up too easily. It is like a drinking straw that has a kink in it when you bend it. The eustachian tube can be partially narrowed or kinked in some children at birth. Colds or other infections can cause it to block, and therefore it cannot relieve pressure in the middle ear.

HOME TREATMENT OF EAR INFECTIONS

In general, the only home treatment recommended is pain medicine such as Tylenol or Motrin.

When should I bring my child to a doctor for an earache?

You should see a doctor if your child has the following:

1. Severe ear pain
2. Ear pain and fever
3. History of recurring ear infections
4. Fluid drainage from the ear
5. Pain with pulling on the ear (a sign of external ear infection)

What is the usual treatment for middle ear infections?

Your physician will usually prescribe an antibiotic for a middle ear

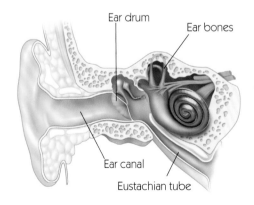

Middle ear and eustachian tube

infection. There are several different types of antibiotics, depending on whether your child is allergic to penicillin or not. Make sure that you treat your child for the number of days recommended by your physician. It is also important to have the child return for a follow-up visit to make sure that the infection is cleared up. It may take several weeks for the ear to look normal after an ear infection. In some cases, children can have partial hearing loss due to recurrent ear infections. Your doctor may also do a tympanogram test for follow-up. This is a test that measures how well the eardrum is moving with sound vibrations.

When does a child need ear tubes?

The criteria for putting in surgical ear tubes (PE tubes) change periodically. Check with your pediatrician, family doctor, or an ENT (ear, nose and throat) specialist for the most current recommendations.

NOSE PROBLEMS

The most common nose problems in children are:
1. Nosebleeds
2. Nasal fractures
3. Foreign bodies in the nose

NOSEBLEEDS

Nosebleeds are usually caused by the repetitive trauma of nose picking. A crust will start to form at the site of the irritation. Eventually this crust is picked off and the nosebleed occurs. Other causes are dry air, local infection, and sometimes inherited bleeding problems such as hemophilia A or B. Children with a history of bleeding problems may have a history of easy bruising.

What should I do for my child with a nosebleed?

The most important thing is to apply pressure to both sides of the nose to compress the bleeding vessels. Do not put pressure over the open end of the nose. This does not apply any pressure to the bleeding area. Applying pressure for at least twenty to thirty minutes usually stops most nose-bleeds. If the bleeding persists, bring your child to a doctor.

The doctor will sometimes use a cotton ball soaked in a medicine that constricts the blood vessels. There is also a gel that contains a clotting substance that can be placed inside the nose to stop the bleeding.

NASAL BONE FRACTURES

Nasal fractures usually occur as a result of trauma. It may be a sports injury, a fight with another child, a fall, or a motor vehicle accident.

How do I know if my child's swollen and bruised nose is fractured or not?

If the child's nose is deformed or pushed to one side, this is a reliable sign of a nasal fracture.

Other signs that are suggestive of a nasal fracture are:
1. A nosebleed with nasal swelling after the trauma
2. Breathing obstruction in one or both sides of the nose

3. Significant tenderness of the nose to touch
4. A direct impact blow to the nose, such as from a baseball or a fist

FOREIGN BODIES IN THE NOSE

Unfortunately, some children find ways of putting all sorts of different objects in their nose, such as beads, eraser tips, small toy pieces, corn kernels, tissue, and even candies.

How do I know if there is something in my child's nose?

You will find out about the object in the child's nose in one of several ways:

1. The child will tell you he put something in his nose. You will then look and usually see something in his nostril.
2. The younger child will complain of pain in his nose.
3. The child will have a foul odor coming from the nostril due to an object that has been there for a few days and has caused an infection.
4. There will be a persistent discharge from one or both sides of the nose.
5. The child will have a nosebleed.

If I see an object in my child's nose, what can I do at home to try to remove it?

If the object is fairly round, you can hold the good nostril closed and have the child blow air as hard as he can out the other nostril. After a few attempts, you might get lucky and the child will dislodge the foreign object. However, most of the time, the object is fairly well impacted and requires removal by a physician.

Here is a brief case of a young girl who had a foreign body in her nose. She told her mom that she put it there and mom was able to see something in the child's nostril. She then brought her to the ER where we examined her.

Take a look at the photo below and see if you can spot it.

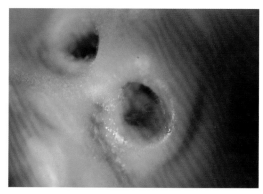

Child with foreign body in left nostril
(Corn kernel)

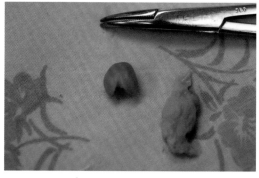

Corn kernel and tissue
removed from child's nostril

We removed the corn kernel first and then found some tissue paper that the child also inserted. We always check the other nostril to make sure no foreign bodies are there also. Fortunately, none were found in this case. The child went home on antibiotics and did fine.

SORE THROAT

What are the most common causes of a sore throat ?

Viruses cause most cases of pharyngitis or sore throat (around 70 percent). About 20 percent are caused by the strep bacteria and 10 percent by infectious mononucleosis.

What are the symptoms of a sore throat?

Most children with a sore throat will also have a fever and pain with swallowing. Patients with strep pharyngitis or a strep throat typically do not have a cough. Children with strep pharyngitis have an enlargement of the nodes under the corner of the jaw as illustrated in the photo below.

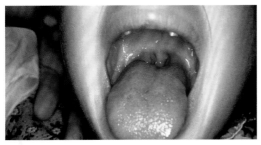

Note the redness of the pharynx and the strawberry-like tongue in a child with strep pharyngitis

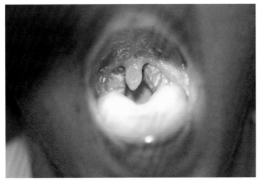

Exudative tonsillitis. This child had a sore throat, a 102°F oral temperature, and a positive test for strep throat. The child was placed on erythromycin since he was allergic to penicillin.

Children with strep throat are also at risk of contracting rheumatic fever.

In addition, a child with strep throat is at risk of developing scarlet fever. Symptoms of scarlet fever include a faint sandpaperlike rash over the entire body or peeling skin. The rash typically leaves a pallor or whiteness around the lips as seen in this photo.

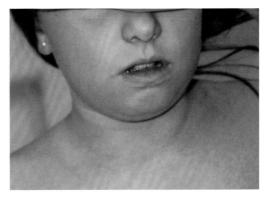

Pink rash with white area around mouth in scarlet fever

What is the best home treatment for sore throat?

The best home treatment includes pain medicine such as Tylenol and/or Motrin, cool things (that is, temperature-wise) to eat and drink, and lozenges or spray that have a numbing medicine to help relieve the pain.

If my child has a sore throat, when should he see a doctor?

Any child with a sore throat and any trouble breathing should be seen by a doctor immediately. Other children can be seen by your doctor in the next twenty-four to forty-eight hours if they do not look sick or have any trouble breathing.

RHEUMATIC FEVER

Rheumatic fever is a serious disease caused by the Streptococcus bacteria. Rheumatic fever can cause damage to the heart valves and inflammation of the heart (myocarditis) if left untreated. If your doctor is concerned that your child may have strep throat, she may prescribe antibiotics. The antibiotic used may be penicillin or some other antibiotic. Although the antibiotic only speeds up the resolution of a sore throat by a day or so, the main reason the antibiotics are prescribed is to prevent rheumatic fever from occurring.

The signs of rheumatic fever, which can occur weeks to months later, include:

1. Joint pain (arthritis)
2. Fever
3. Rash
4. Inflammation of the heart

MONONUCLEOSIS (INFECTIOUS MONO)

Children who have infectious mono (mononucleosis) usually have severe fatigue, sore throat, fever, and enlarged lymph nodes in the neck and sometimes a rash. This can be diagnosed based on a physical exam or by a blood test. The mono test, however, can be negative during the first week of the illness and may need to be repeated after a week or two. The fatigue from infectious mono can last one to three weeks.

Does mono cause any other complications?

1. Rash (in 10 percent of cases)
2. Fatigue

3. Enlargement of the spleen
4. Liver inflammation with elevated liver enzymes

Some children with infectious mono will have liver inflammation (called mono hepatitis) and elevated liver enzymes. The clue to liver inflammation may be pain in the right upper part of the abdomen (where the liver is located). See the diagram below. Another clue to liver inflammation is brownish or tea-colored urine.

Children who have infectious mono should not engage in any contact sports, such as soccer or football, because they can develop an enlarged spleen, which can be ruptured during a sporting activity if the child falls or is hit. The spleen

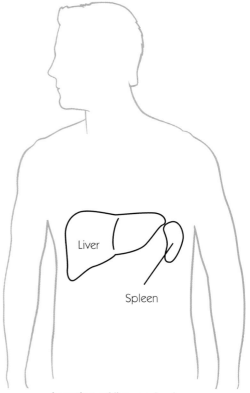

Location of liver and spleen

is in the left upper portion of the abdomen as seen in the diagram on page 134. A few children die each year in this country as a result of a ruptured spleen that occurs during contact sports.

EPIGLOTTITIS

Epiglottitis is a swelling of the epiglottis, the structure just above the vocal cords that is responsible for making sure that food enters the esophagus when we swallow (instead of entering the airway, or trachea, that goes to the lungs).

The symptoms of epiglottitis include sore throat, high fever, and painful swallowing. Children with moderate or severe infections also will have trouble breathing. Epiglottitis is illustrated in the diagram below.

Epiglottitis is usually caused by bacteria called H. influenza. Fortunately, we now have a vaccine against these bacteria: Hib (short for Hemophilus Influenzae type B) vaccine. Thanks to this vaccine, we are seeing very few children who have epiglottitis. However, we are now diagnosing epiglottitis in older children and adults.

Points to know about the symptoms and treatment of epiglottitis

1. Sore throat and increased pain with swallowing
2. Fever typically in the 103°–104°F range with rapid onset
3. The child prefers to sit upright with his head pushed forward because it is easier to breath in this position
4. Occasional drooling
5. A stridorous sound when the child breathes in
6. Shortness of breath in moderately severe cases
7. Epiglottitis can be a life-threatening airway emergency, which may require the child to be placed on a ventilator for breathing
8. Treated with antibiotics
9. Much less common today compared to ten years ago due to the Hib vaccine which protects children from one of the main bacteria that causes this infection (H. influenza bacteria)

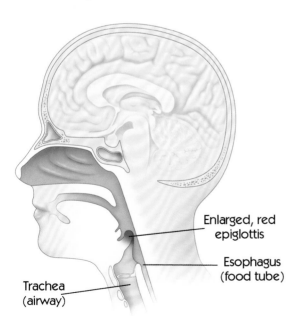

Enlarged, red epiglottis

Esophagus (food tube)

Trachea (airway)

Enlarged epiglottis due to epiglottitis

TOTAL PARENT POINTERS
EARACHES AND NOSE AND THROAT PROBLEMS

The following are key points that parents need to know.

1. **A fever is defined as:**
   a. **Rectal temperature of 100.4°F or more**
   b. Oral temperature of 99.5°F or more
   c. Axillary armpit temperature of 98.6°F or more

2. In infants under the age of two, a rectal temperature is the most accurate way of taking a temperature. Oral, eardrum, and armpit temperatures are unreliable in young children under the age of 2.

3. **Life threatening infections that occur in children include:**
   a. Meningitis
   b. Sepsis or an infection of the bloodstream
   c. Epiglottitis
   d. Severe pneumonia
   e. Severe croup

4. Symptoms of **infectious mononucleosis include:**
   a. Sore throat
   b. Occasionally a fever
   c. Fatigue
   d. Enlarged lymph nodes in the neck
   e. Rash in 10 percent of cases

5. Children with mono should not engage in contact sports for several weeks due to having an enlarged spleen, which can rupture and cause hemorrhage and death.

6. **Strep throat** is characterized by fever, sore throat, white patches on the tonsils, and enlarged lymph nodes below the corners of the jaw. Strep throat is treated with penicillin or other antibiotics to prevent the complication called Rheumatic Fever, which can damage the heart valves.

7. **Croup** is a disease caused by a virus and a cough that sounds like a "barking seal." Children with croup are usually in the one to three year age group and also have a low-grade temperature. Severe cases of croup may require hospitalization. A cool mist vaporizer and the cool air outside usually help croup symptoms improve.

8. **Pneumonia** is an infection in one or both lungs that causes a fever, cough, sputum production, shortness of breath, and rapid breathing. It is caused by viruses or bacteria. It is usually treated with antibiotics. In severe cases it may require hospitalization and IV antibiotics.

9. Know how to take a rectal temperature in young children. The preferred type of thermometer is a good digital rectal thermometer. Please remember that a fever is defined as a rectal temperature above 100.4°F rectally. Forehead fever strips and tympanic thermometers are not as accurate as a good rectal thermometer.

13

Eye Problems

Eye injuries are the second greatest cause of blindness in children under the age of twenty (after congenital problems). Approximately 150,000 children experience an eye injury each year in the United States. The most common eye injuries are:

- Corneal abrasions (a scratch of the cornea)
- Foreign bodies in the eye
- Bleeding in the white part of the eye (subconjunctival hemorrhage)
- Bleeding over the cornea of the eye (hyphema)
- Retinal detachment
- Chemical injuries to the eye
- Ultraviolet burns of the eye

EYE INJURIES

Some of the most serious eye injuries are due to projectiles, such as baseballs and rocks that hit the eye. These can result in abrasions to the cornea or more serious injuries, such as bleeding within the eye, eye lacerations, or retinal detachment.

How do you know if it is serious?

The most important thing for a parent to check for after an eye injury is how well the child can see. You can ask the child to identify two or three fingers held three to six feet in front of him. Younger children can be watched to see if they fixate on an object with the bad eye while a parent covers the good eye. Obviously, in cases of any significant eye trauma, the child should be brought in for a physician's evaluation.

FOREIGN BODIES IN THE EYE

The most common eye problem a parent may face is a foreign body or particle in the eye. These can usually be flushed out with a bottle of saline contact lens solution or, if that is not available, plain water.

Foreign bodies in the eye are a very common occurrence. They can be grains of sand, dirt, small pieces of metal, hairs, or any small objects imaginable.

Symptoms usually begin with a very sudden eye irritation. The child usually describes something suddenly going into her eye. She will immediately have increased pain with frequent blinking. There is usually increased tearing and irritation.

What you need to know about foreign bodies in the eye

Parents should carefully look at the eye and see if they can see any foreign body. The eye should then be irrigated with a saline solution such as those used for contact lenses.

In order to do this, have your child look down toward their feet while you apply a Q-tip to the outside of the upper lid. The bottom of the upper lid is pulled up so that the inside portion of the lid is facing outward. In many cases, a small particle or foreign body will be found sticking to the inside of the upper lid. This can also be repeated for the lower lid to check for foreign bodies

SECRET DOCTOR INFO: If the irritation persists, you may attempt to do a trick we use in the emergency room called lid eversion to help find a foreign body. (See photos below and facing.)

there as well. (Have the child look upward when everting the lower lid.) The foreign body can usually be removed by placing a drop of saline on a Q-tip and then removing the particle with the Q-tip.

Keep in mind that once a foreign body is removed, a physician will still need to check for any scratching of the cornea as a result of the foreign body. The physician normally does this by applying a drop of dye stain, called flourescein, in the eye and then looking at the eye with a black light. Any corneal

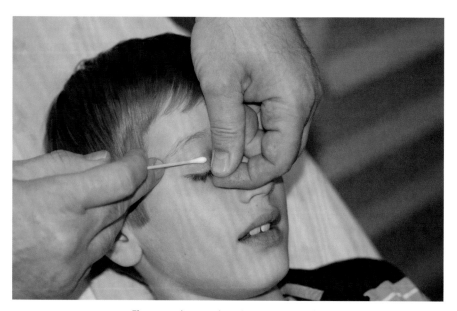

First step in everting the upper eyelid

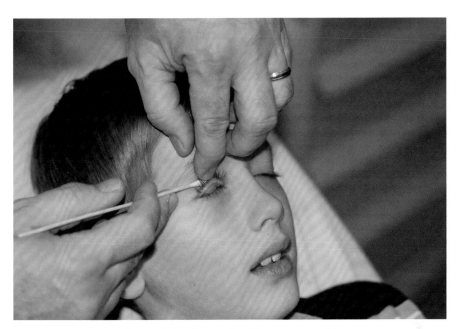

Second step in everting the upper eyelid

scratches (abrasions) appear bright orange under the black light. The corneal abrasion is usually treated with an antibiotic ointment or drops for several days. Your doctor may patch the eye closed in some cases. Corneal abrasions need to be followed up closely by your doctor or an ophthalmologist (eye specialist) because they can sometimes progress to a corneal ulcer, which can lead to permanent loss of vision.

If your child has an object in the eye that penetrates through the white part of the eye, resist the temptation to pull out the object. Your child should be brought in to the ER immediately. Keep the child comfortable and protect the eye as much as possible.

CORNEAL ABRASIONS

Corneal abrasions (or scratches of the cornea of the eye) can occur due to particles in the eye, scratches by a finger, a thrown object, or by contact lens irritation. In order to check for corneal abrasions, the physician will first put some numbing (anesthetic) drops in the child's eye to relieve the pain. This is usually a medication such as tetracaine. The physician will then put a drop of flourescein into the child's eye, the flourescein glows under a black light to show any scratches or abrasions.

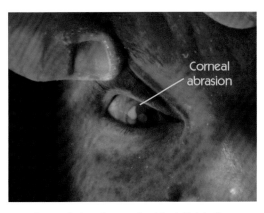

Corneal abrasion

Corneal abrasion under black light after flourescein staining

If an abrasion is detected, the physician will usually prescribe an antibiotic. In some cases, the physician may patch the eye for twenty-four hours, although eye patches are less commonly used nowadays. A child with a corneal abrasion will need to be rechecked within twenty-four to forty-eight hours to make sure the abrasion is healing well. The child may also be placed on a mild pain reliever.

SUBCONJUNCTIVAL HEMORRHAGE (BLEEDING IN THE WHITE PART OF THE EYE)

Subconjunctival hemorrhage is an area of redness or bleeding in the white part of the eye, the sclera.

This is frequently a spontaneous occurrence but may also occur after trauma. Symptoms include a patchy area of blood in the sclera. Some people develop these for no apparent reason. Often, friends or relatives may notice the blood before they do since it is painless.

In some cases of eye trauma, there may be some bleeding under the sclera. If the bleeding is a small amount and is limited to the white part of the eye, this is not a serious problem. However, a close inspection by a physician is necessary to make sure that there is no blood in the part of the eye over the iris and pupil. In addition, a doctor needs to look inside the eye with an ophthalmoscope to make sure there is no bleeding inside the eye and no detachment of the retina.

Simple subconjunctival hemorrhages usually clear up in one to two weeks.

Hyphema (blood in front of cornea)

HYPHEMA

A hyphema is bleeding in the front chamber of the eye under the cornea and over the iris.

This can be a serious problem because it can re-bleed in two to five days. This typically occurs when someone is hit in the eye by an object such as a baseball or fist. Bleeding inside the cornea occurs and can lead to a permanent staining of the cornea and impaired vision.

What you need to know about a hyphema

Any child who sustains trauma to the eye should have it immediately evaluated by a physician.

Patients with a hyphema need to sleep upright at an approximately forty-five-degree angle so that blood does not layer out horizontally and get absorbed throughout the cornea. They also need to be watched closely for a re-bleed, which can occur in two to five days. As with other eye injuries, a doctor will need to make sure that there are no other associated problems, such as retina detachment or blood within the posterior portion of the eye.

RETINAL DETACHMENT

Retinal detachment is a pulling away of the retina from the inside lining of the eyeball.

Retinal detachments are serious problems that can occur after trauma or sometimes spontaneously. Any child who receives trauma to the eye should be watched closely for any decrease in her vision over the next several days. In some cases, a retinal detachment may occur several days after the initial trauma.

A typical retinal detachment will be described by your child as looking as if a curtain is being pulled down over that part of one eye. It may impair some portion of the vision in that eye and that area will look dark. Any change in vision or decrease in vision should be evaluated by a physician.

Parents need to pay particular attention to young children who have eye injuries and to check their

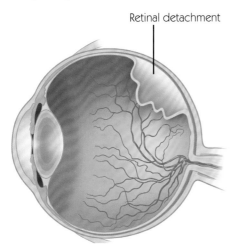

Retinal detachment

vision each day for the first two to three weeks after a significant eye trauma.

Treatment of retinal detachments

Retinal detachments are managed by ophthalmologists (eye specialists), who can sometimes reattach the retina to the back part of the eye with a special eye laser.

CHEMICAL BURNS OF THE EYE

Children may be splashed in the eye accidentally by some type of acid or alkali chemical. Examples of acids include hydrochloric acid or sulfuric acid. Examples of alkali are drain cleaners or oven cleaners. Between the two, alkali burns to the eye are much more serious. Alkali burns to the cornea cause the cornea to liquify and can lead to permanent scaring, impaired vision, or blindness.

What you need to know about alkali burns to the eye

The eye should immediately be flushed with normal tap water or with a contact lens saline solution, if available. The eye should be flushed with saline or water for at least five to ten minutes for an acid chemical burn and at least ten to fifteen minutes for an alkali burn. The child should be seen by a physician immediately. You should bring the chemical container to the emergency room or to your doctor's office so that the type of chemical and concentration can be identified.

RED SKIN AROUND THE EYE (PERIORBITAL CELLULITIS)

A child who develops redness around the eye may have a condition called periorbital cellulitis. This can become a serious condition if the infection extends to the area behind the eye. Any type of infection around the eye associated with a fever should be immediately evaluated.

What you need to know about periorbital cellulitis

Check your child's temperature. A temperature of 99.5°F oral or 100.4°F rectal or more is considered a fever. A child with fever and redness or cellulitis around the eye should be evaluated immediately by your physician to check for:

- Pain with movement of the eye
- An apparent pushing out of the eyeball
- Significant pain around the eye
- Loss of vision

Physician treatment of periorbital cellulitis

A physician will usually prescribe antibiotics and, depending on the severity of the infection, may admit the child to the hospital. Patients with very serious infections are in danger of losing part or all of their vision.

PINK EYE—WHAT IS IT?

Pink eye is a general term referring to a pink or reddish tint of the white part of the eye due to some irritation, infection, allergy, or trauma.

Pink eye has many causes, including the following:

- Bacterial infections of the eye (bacterial conjunctivitis)
- Viral conjunctivitis
- Eye trauma and corneal abrasions
- Allergic conjunctivitis
- Chemical irritation of the eye

What should you do for a child with pink eye?

Any child with a pink, irritated, or painful eye should be evaluated by a physician. If the child is old enough, try to determine if he has normal vision. This can be done by holding several fingers up while standing approximately ten to twenty feet away from the child. Have the child cover the good eye and see if he can identify how many fingers you are holding up.

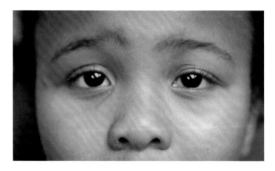

Child with pink eye

What are the signs of bacterial conjunctivitis?

Pink eye associated with pus on the eyelids suggests a bacterial infection. Bacterial infections can be treated with antibiotic drops obtained through your pediatrician or other physician.

Treatment of bacterial conjunctivitis

A child with bacterial conjunctivitis will receive antibiotic eye drops while

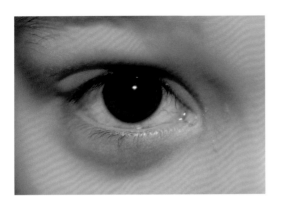

Conjunctivitis. Note redness of the white part of the eye and the collection of pus at the corner of the eye.

those with allergic conjunctivitis will receive an antihistamine eye drop. Children with allergic conjunctivitis will have itching and redness of the eye and sometimes have some mild swelling in the sclera.

The most common eye drops prescribed for children include:

- Sulfacetamide—This is a sulfa-containing eye drop, so children allergic to sulfa medication should not use this.
- Tobramycin—This eye drop does not contain sulfa.
- Erythromycin eye ointment
- Gentamycin
- Antihistamine eye drops—These are used for allergic reactions involving the eye.
- Pupil dilation drops—These are sometimes used to help relax the muscle inside the eye and to lessen the pain for certain eye problems.

Viral infections of the eye

A pink eye associated with a cough, cold, and a runny nose is usually due to a virus. Viral conjunctivitis does not require antibiotic eye drops because it is not caused by a bacterium.

One type of viral eye infection, herpes simplex, requires consultation by an eye specialist, called an ophthalmologist, because this can cause loss of vision.

ULTRAVIOLET BURNS OF THE EYE

Children can sustain ultraviolet burns of the eye from the following:

- Watching an eclipse
- Using tanning beds
- Watching a welder's torch
- Prolong glitter from snow
- Prolong reflective glitter from large bodies of water

Children with UV burns of the eyes will complain of tearing and pain in the eyes. There may be some redness around the colored part of the eye, the cornea, as well as the white part of the eye. The pain usually begins approximately twelve hours after the exposure.

These are usually treated with pain medications and eye drops. They usually heal in approximately twenty-four to forty-eight hours and result in no decrease or loss of vision.

LAZY EYE (AMBLYOPIA)

Amblyopia is a condition that occurs when one of the eyes develops weaker vision because the eyes are not lined up properly. For example, one eye may be turned more inward or more outward, which is known as strabismus. A lazy eye may also result when one eye is very nearsighted, farsighted, or astigmatic.

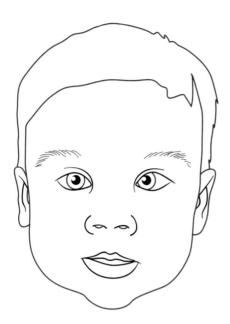

"Lazy eye" or Strabismus

What you need to know about children with a lazy eye

The treatment for lazy eye needs to begin before the age of seven and is usually by one of two methods:

- Patching the strong eye for several hours a day for a period of several weeks to months. The stronger eye needs to be patched anywhere from two to six hours per day so that the weaker eye can develop better vision through stimulating the connection to the brain.
- Use of eye drops that cause the pupil to dilate the stronger eye and make the child use the weaker eye more. With eye drops such as atropine (which causes the pupil to dilate in the stronger eye), the child's brain is forced to use the weaker eye more. This will make the eye-to-brain nerve connection stronger and improve the visual connection with the brain.

It is very difficult to treat a lazy eye or amblyopia past the age of nine.

TUMORS OF THE EYE (RETINOBLASTOMAS)

A whitish area inside a child's normally black pupil may indicate this tumor. When this occurs, the physician needs to evaluate the eye to determine if a tumor of the retina, called a retinoblastoma, is present. Unfortunately this is a very serious tumor or cancer of the eye, which requires evaluation and treatment by an ophthalmologist.

TOTAL PARENT POINTERS
EYE PROBLEMS

1. **Foreign bodies in the eye** can sometimes be flushed out with saline solution used by contact lens wearers.
2. **Trauma to the eye** can result in a **retinal detachment** several days later. The child will lose some vision in the eye or complain that it seems like "a dark curtain was pulled over my eye" on one side.
3. A **pink eye** can be caused by:
    a. Foreign particles in the eye
    b. Bacterial or viral infections
    c. Trauma
    d. Allergic reactions
    e. Chemical irritations

4. **Redness of the skin around the eye** is called **periorbital cellulitis.** It is usually associated with **a fever. It can progress to an infection behind the eye, which can be very serious.** See your child's doctor immediately if this is present.
5. If you notice a whitish area inside the black part (pupil) of the child's eye, this could be **a serious tumor called a retinoblastoma.** It needs immediate attention by an eye specialist (ophthalmologist).
6. **A child who has a lazy eye (strabismus) needs to have this treated before the age of seven.** Delaying treatment to the age of nine has a negative effect on the outcome.

14

Frostbite and Cold Injuries

It's the perfect winter scene. Your child is out in the snow, sledding or ice skating, energized and enthusiastic, having fun. Then she comes in with reddened cheeks and starts complaining of numb toes or fingers.

FROSTBITE

Frostbite is the most common cold-related emergency in children. Any child's skin can become frostbitten after exposure to cold weather for a significant period of time. The skin will appear swollen and red.

How should I treat frostbite?

If you suspect frostbite and your child is still outside, bring her into a warm environment. Do not rub the frostbitten area with snow. The area should be warmed as quickly as possible with warm water at a temperature of 104°–106° F. Change the water frequently to ensure that it stays near this temperature. The child may experience some pain, as the area is rewarmed. Tylenol or Motrin may be given for the pain.

Rewarming should continue for at least thirty minutes. It is very important that any frostbitten child avoid exposing that part of her body to the cold again for several weeks. Repeated episodes of frostbite can result in persistent pain, numbness, and sensitivity of the frostbitten area.

When should we see a doctor?

If you have any doubt whether your child's symptoms are improving with home care, get to an emergency room right away. Second- and third-degree frostbite are severe. Symptoms of second-degree frostbite include blisters. Second-degree frostbite can result in some loss of the skin.

Third-degree frostbite is characterized by firm, pale skin with little or no sensation. Third-degree frostbite can result in loss of fingers, toes, and the skin on various exposed parts of the body, such as the ears and nose.

TOTAL PARENT POINTERS
FROSTBITE AND COLD INJURIES

1. **Frostnip** is characterized by redness and pain on the ears, nose, etc. This is mild or first-degree frostbite.
2. The main treatment of **frostbite** is rewarming the area in water heated to 104°–106°F.
3. The extremity should not be exposed to the cold again for several weeks or longer.

4. Symptoms of **second-degree frostbite** include **blisters** and pain from the cold exposure.
5. The most serious form of frostbite is **third-degree frostbite.** Symptoms include **pale or white skin with little or no sensation.** This can result in loss of the skin and amputation of fingers and toes due to lack of blood flow.

15

Headaches

As adults, we all know how miserable a headache can be. It's no different for children. Sometimes headaches are due to a cold or virus and are relatively uneventful, but sometimes headaches are a symptom of a more serious condition that requires prompt diagnosis and treatment. Here's a primer on what you need to know.

What are some of the causes of headaches in children?

- Migraines
- Meningitis
- Subarachnoid brain hemorrhage (bleeding in the brain due to a ruptured aneurysm)
- Muscle tension
- Carbon monoxide poisoning
- Eye problems (nearsightedness and farsightedness)
- Brain tumors
- Sinus infections
- High-altitude headaches

What are some of the signs a headache may be caused by something serious?

- A headache associated with a fever (100.4°F rectal or 99.5°F oral), neck stiffness, lethargy or confusion, and irritation by bright lights (signs of meningitis)
- A headache associated with confusion, a change in behavior, or a significant change in alertness.
- A headache that awakens the child from sleep
- A headache that becomes worse with coughing, sneezing, straining, or lying down

If your child has any of these symptoms, go to your nearest emergency room immediately. At worst, these symptoms can indicate meningitis, a ruptured aneurysm, or a brain tumor.

MIGRAINE HEADACHE

A migraine headache typically begins with a throbbing pain on one side of the head, but it may occasionally occur on both sides of the head. The child may also experience nausea and vomiting. Bright lights and loud noises may bother the child. Children with a classic migraine will describe an aura that occurs before the headache. The aura is usually described as blurred vision, dark spots, twinkling lights, wavy lines, or a distorted perception of objects (the Alice in Wonderland syndrome). It may also be described as an unusual smell or sensation. Children have less chance of having an aura than adults.

Children who do not complain of an aura have a common migraine. Most children can have common migraines.

According to the International Headache Society, serious migraine sufferers have:

1. Five or more headache attacks per year.
2. Headaches that last four to seventy-two hours.
3. Headaches with at least two of the four characteristics listed below:
   a. One-sided headache
   b. Pulsating headache
   c. Moderate or severe pain
   d. Pain made worse by activity

Other symptoms include:

1. Nausea or vomiting
2. Discomfort caused by bright lights or loud noises

What types of triggers can lead to a migraine headache?

- Emotional stress
- Lack of sleep
- Cheeses (rich in tyramine)
- Smoked meats and salami (rich in nitrates)
- Foods that contain MSG (monosodium glutamate), such as Chinese and Mexican foods
- Caffeine products (chocolate, sodas, tea, coffee)
- Bright lights or loud noises

What are some treatments for migraine headaches?

Some of the nonmedication treatments include:

1. Relaxation therapy
2. Avoiding migraine-triggering medicines (certain inhalers and contraceptives)
3. Avoiding migraine-triggering foods
4. Adequate sleep each day

Additionally, several medicines are used to treat migraine headaches. You should discuss these with your doctor. In general, however, acetaminophen (Tylenol) and ibuprofen can be used for the pain. Other prescription medications that can be taken for nausea and vomiting include metoclopramide, Zofran, and promethazine. Other medications may be suggested for long-term treatment. These include some antidepressants as well as some specific anti-migraine medications. Keep in mind that most migraine headaches are relieved by sleep.

MENINGITIS

Physicians become concerned about the possibility of meningitis if the child has the following three symptoms:

- Fever
- Headache
- Stiff neck

Children with meningitis may also have a change in their mental status and may become very tired, lethargic, or confused. Meningitis is due to an infection in the spinal fluids surrounding the brain and spinal cord. This infection can be caused by a virus or bacteria. Either way, meningitis can become a potentially life-threatening problem and can lead to permanent brain damage.

Even though most patients with meningitis recover uneventfully, some may experience seizures, permanent hearing problems, intellectual problems, behavioral problems, retardation, blindness, or weakness on one side of the body.

It is critically important that infants under the age of twelve weeks who have a fever of 100.4°F rectal or more have an immediate evaluation by a pediatrician, a family doctor, or an emergency physician.

RUPTURED BRAIN ANEURYSM (SUBARACHNOID HEMORRHAGE)

The signs of a headache caused by a ruptured aneurysm include:

1. Sudden onset of "the worse headache I've ever had"
2. Confusion or a change in mental alertness or behavior
3. Vomiting
4. Trouble walking due to lack of balance or coordination
5. Blurred vision or double vision
6. Neck stiffness

MUSCLE TENSION HEADACHE

Muscle tension headaches are the most common headaches in children. These result from prolonged contraction of the muscles in the head or neck due to stress, tension, or lack of sleep. The pain is usually constant or squeezing. Children do not have vomiting, nausea, blurred vision, or any visual problems with this type of headache. A muscle tension headache is treated with a mild pain reliever such as Tylenol or ibuprofen.

CARBON MONOXIDE POISONING

Children with carbon monoxide poisoning often complain about a dull headache. The pain may be mild, moderate, or severe. The child may also be somewhat tired or sleepy.

Parents should be concerned about carbon monoxide poisoning during the winter months when the furnace is on and everyone in the family seems to have a headache on the same day. In some cases, the entire family can become overwhelmed with carbon monoxide and become unconscious before anyone realizes what is going on. Since carbon monoxide does not have an odor, it is difficult to detect. It is very important to have carbon monoxide detectors in your home in case your furnace malfunctions. Approximately twenty-four children die each year due to carbon monoxide poisoning.

If you have any suspicion that your furnace is not working right or everyone in the house seems to have a headache on a fall or winter day, call your local fire department to check your house for carbon monoxide. Most fire departments have carbon monoxide detectors that can measure the amount of carbon monoxide in the air.

What should I do if my child complains of a headache while I am using a paint stripper in the house?

Certain paint strippers have a chemical—methylene chloride—that can turn into carbon monoxide. (Be sure to check the ingredients in your paint stripper.) People who are exposed to this chemical can sustain carbon monoxide poisoning if they are not in a well-ventilated area. If you or your children develop a headache while using a paint stripper, go to the nearest emergency room. Testing the air, however, will not pick up carbon monoxide; the carbon monoxide is produced in your body when your body absorbs the methylene chloride.

HEADACHES FROM EYE PROBLEMS

If your child is having headaches, you can ask if he can see the blackboard at school clearly or if it seems blurry. If poor vision at school is an additional symptom to the headache, a vision test is a good idea. Children should have their vision checked on a regular basis.

The American Academy of Ophthalmology recommends that a child have his eyes tested beginning at age three and every year or two thereafter. Most schools do routine eye testing. Your child's school may alert you to a vision problem before your child complains.

BRAIN TUMORS

Headaches associated with brain tumors are characterized by:

- Headache is worse in the morning, better later in the day.
- Blurred vision or double vision

- Trouble walking
- Loss of some coordination of an arm or leg or one side of the body or face.
- Confusion or change in mental status or alertness

SINUS INFECTION HEADACHE

The headache caused by a sinus infection is worse over the sinus areas of the face and is associated with congestion, fever (occasionally), nasal drainage, and seasonal allergies.

HEADACHES FROM HIGH ALTITUDE

A child who travels from a lower altitude city (such as Chicago) to a higher altitude city (such as Denver), may develop high-altitude sickness. Generally, high-altitude sickness affects only mountain climbers. High-altitude headaches occur when the body tries to adjust to a higher altitude. Several problems can occur during the initial exposure to high altitude: headaches, nausea, and trouble breathing. Most children adjust to this in a day or two. If your child has a progressively worsening headache, trouble breathing, or confusion, take her to the nearest emergency room.

TOTAL PARENT POINTERS
HEADACHES

1. **Signs of serious headache include:**
   - **A headache associated with a fever** (100.4°F rectal or more—99.6°F oral or more), neck stiffness, and irritation by bright lights (signs of meningitis).
   - A headache with confusion, a change in behavior, or a significant change in alertness.
   - A headache that awakens the child from sleep.
   - A headache that becomes worse with coughing, sneezing, straining, or lying down.
2. **Migraine headaches (International headache society criteria)**
   a. Five or more headache attacks per year
   b. Headaches that last four to seventy-two hours
   c. Characteristics of the headache (must have two out of the four below)
      1. One-sided headache
      2. Pulsating headache
      3. Moderate or severe pain
      4. Pain made worse by activity
   d. Other symptoms:
      1. Nausea and/ or vomiting
      2. Discomfort caused by bright lights or loud noises
3. **Signs of headache due to meningitis are:**
   a. fever
   b. headache
   c. neck stiffness
   d. bright lights are bothersome (photophobia)
   e. change in mental status, such as confusion, lethargy, or irritability

4. **Sinus infection headache**—The headache caused by a sinus infection is worse over the sinus areas of the face and is associated with congestion, fever (occasionally), nasal drainage, and seasonal allergies.
5. **Carbon monoxide poisoning**—should be suspected if everyone in the family has a headache on a winter day while the furnace is running.
6. **Brain tumors**—Headaches associated with brain tumors are characterized by:
   a. Headache is worse in the morning, better later in the day.
   b. Blurred vision or double vision
   c. Trouble walking
   d. Loss of some coordination of an arm or leg or one side of the body or face.
   e. Confusion or change in mental status or alertness
7. **Ruptured brain aneurysm (subarachnoid hemorrhage)**
   a. Described as "the worst headache I ever had"
   b. Comes on suddenly and is severe at the onset.
   c. Sometimes accompanied by confusion, collapse, or coma
   d. May cause weakness in an arm or leg
   e. May have trouble speaking.
8. **Muscle tension headaches**—These headaches are described as bandlike or squeezing headaches. The child will not have other symptoms, such as fever, confusion, a cold, nausea, or vomiting.

16

Head Injuries

Approximately twenty-five thousand children die or are disabled each year by head injuries, with boys affected twice as often as girls. The most common cause of head injuries in children is a fall. However, the most severe head injuries are usually caused by car accidents.

The key to the prevention of head injuries includes:

- Wearing seat belts in cars, strollers, and grocery carts at all times
- Wearing a helmet at all times while riding bicycles, or engaging in sports such as football, horseback riding, hockey, and inline skating.

CONCUSSIONS

Any child with a head injury who blacks out or becomes unconscious for any period of time should be evaluated by a physician as soon as possible. A child who loses consciousness or has some alteration of his mental function has a concussion, which means he has blacked out or has amnesia, confusion, or some change in his mental status shortly after the head injury.

What are the main signs of head injury that indicate my child needs immediate help?

You should bring (or call an ambulance to bring) your child to an emergency room immediately if she has a head injury and any of the following:

- Blacking out or loss of consciousness for any period of time
- Vomiting
- Confusion
- Amnesia
- Inability to remember what happened before or after the injury
- Inability to walk normally
- Repeating the same question over and over ("What happened?")
- Strange behavior
- Excessive sleepiness
- A dilated pupil in one eye
- A headache after the injury
- Less than two years old
- Seizure

- Neck pain (be sure to have the child lie down, immobilize the neck to protect the spine, and call an ambulance)
- Tingling or numbness in the arms or legs (immobilize the neck and call an ambulance)
- Any weakness in an arm or leg

Any child with any of the symptoms noted above should be seen by a physician immediately. In particular, children age two or less are very difficult to evaluate, even by trained emergency medicine specialists. Many times a mother or father will notice very subtle changes in a child's behavior, which become a cause for concern. Physicians need to pay close attention to the mother's and father's intuitive sense about something being wrong with their child after a head injury.

PHYSICIAN'S EVALUATION OF HEAD INJURY

The physician will ask exactly how the head injury occurred. This should include an estimation of how far the child fell, if this was from an accidental fall. Other questions of interest to the physician include whether the child is acting normally. He will also ask:

- Did the child vomit?
- Is the child walking normally?
- Is the child excessively sleepy?
- Does the child act confused?
- Does the child have any neck pain?
- Does the child have any numbness, burning, or weakness in the arms?

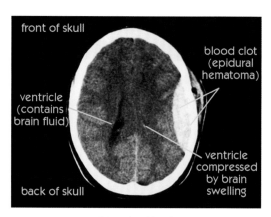

CT scan of brain

If the physician is concerned about the possibility of a significant head injury, she may order a CT scan. A CT scan is a special type of x-ray that takes a very detailed picture of the brain and the surrounding bones of the skull. A CT scan will determine if there is any bleeding within the brain or on top of the brain.

A blood clot in the brain is called a hematoma. If a hematoma is present, the physician will contact a neurosurgeon, and the child will be admitted to the hospital. If the blood clot is large and is causing compression of the brain, the child will be taken to surgery for removal

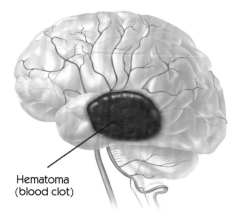

Epidural hematoma

Neurosurgery for an epidural hematoma shows the scalp flap and fracture of skull. Beneath this fracture on the side of the patient's head (at the temporal bone) is the blood clot, an epidural hematoma. This teenager was punched in the side of his head. When he was first seen in the ER, he was alert but unable to speak because the blood clot was pressing on the speech center of his brain. A few days after surgery his speech was normal.

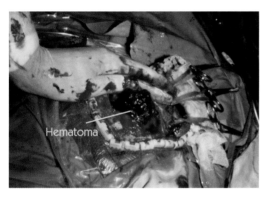

The neurosurgeon has removed a section of the skull bone to reveals the blood clot underneath.

The blood clot has been removed, and the thick tissue that covers the brain (called the dura) can be seen. The skull bone will be replaced and will heal over a few weeks.

of the blood clot. If the blood clot is small, the neurosurgeon may decide to keep the child in the hospital for observation and repeat the CT scan to see if the clot is getting smaller or larger.

What are some of the complications that can occur from a blood clot (hematoma) on a child's brain?

- Seizures
- Progressive brain swelling that can lead to confusion, weakness, paralysis, and even death
- Personality changes
- The child's breathing can slow down and even stop, which may require the child to be placed on a ventilator
- Permanent behavioral or intellectual changes

Every parent wants to know whether her child will have normal brain function after a head injury. The answer is that this depends on the severity of the injury. In most cases of mild concussions, the child will have no intellectual or personality changes. However, patients with severe head injuries may have a permanent decrease in their intelligence as well as permanent personality or behavioral changes. Children with head injuries may also have seizures for an indeterminate period of time.

NECK FRACTURES (CERVICAL SPINE)

Do neck fractures frequently occur with severe head injuries?

One of the key concerns about head injuries is that, if the child had a significant head injury and has neck pain associated with the head injury, the child may have a possible neck fracture or spine injury. The child should lie flat on the ground, and his neck should be immobilized. If the child is still seated in a car after a car accident, the neck should be held still by a parent or some other adult. Paramedics should be called so that the child can be placed on a special spine board with an immobilizing collar for transport to an emergency room. This must be done without moving the child's neck in case the patient has a cervical spine injury.

What are the signs of a cervical spine (neck) injury?

- Numbness, tingling, or stinging pain in the arms
- Weakness of one or both arms
- Weakness of both arms and legs
- Paralysis of the legs and arms

What are some of the high-risk injuries that can cause neck fractures and damage the cervical spine?

- Falling from a height greater than two times the child's height
- Pool or water diving accidents
- Motor vehicle accidents
- Horse riding accidents
- Any contact sports that can result in a significant trauma to a child's head, such as football, hockey, or rugby

TOTAL PARENT POINTERS
HEAD INJURIES

1. **Bring your children to the nearest emergency room if they have any of the symptoms associated with a head injury.**
   - Blacking out or loss of consciousness for any period of time
   - Vomiting
   - Confusion
   - Amnesia
   - Inability to remember what happened before or after the injury
   - Inability to walk normally
   - Repeating the same question over and over
   - Strange behavior
   - Excessive sleepiness
   - A dilated pupil in one eye
   - A headache
   - Is less than two years old
   - A seizure
   - Neck pain (be sure to have the child lie down, immobilize the neck, and call an ambulance)
   - A bruise of the scalp

2. Be aware that **neck fractures can also occur with head trauma.** If your child is complaining of neck pain, tell her to lie down, immobilize her neck with your hands, and call for an ambulance.

3. **Wearing a helmet** during sports activities **is one of the best ways to prevent head injuries.** Be a good role model to your children and make sure you wear one while bike riding or inline skating.

4. **Using seat belts** is one of the most effective ways to prevent head injuries and save your child's life.

5. **Tell your children never to dive head first into a river or lake** because it can be very shallow in that area.

6. Any child who blacks out or loses consciousness has had a concussion. Any child with a concussion should be seen by a physician immediately.

17

Heat-Related Illnesses

HEAT STROKE AND HEAT EXHAUSTION

The sun and heat can sneak up on children, who often don't think about resting and cooling their body temperature when they're having fun outdoors. Heat-related conditions are especially dangerous for infants since their internal thermostat hasn't fully developed. Here's what you need to know so that you and your family can enjoy the warm weather safely.

Who is most susceptible to heat-related conditions?

Infants under the age of one are most susceptible to heat-related emergencies. Tragically, several children die every year as a result of being left alone in a hot car. But heat-related conditions can affect any child who is exposed to warm temperatures—and that includes those exercising outside when it's hot and humid. Under such conditions a child can develop:

- Heat rash
- Heat cramps
- Heat exhaustion
- Heat stroke

HEAT RASH

Heat rash (also called prickly heat) is a red rash that occurs over the areas of the child's body normally covered by clothes. The rash is actually due to inflammation and swelling of the sweat glands. The rash usually goes away on its own within a few days. Move the child to a cool, shady spot and apply cool towels for immediate comfort.

HEAT CRAMPS

Heat cramps are more likely to occur in older children after they work out or exercise in hot weather. Severe pains or cramps develop in the larger muscles of the body, such as the thighs, back, and upper arms. Heat cramps can be treated by getting the child to a cool environment so he can rest and drink plenty of fluids. Salt tablets should never be given. Over-the-counter pain relievers, such as acetaminophen and ibuprofen, can be used.

HEAT EXHAUSTION

Heat exhaustion is a medical illness caused by being active in a hot environment. The symptoms of heat exhaustion are nausea, light-headedness, dizziness, weakness, fatigue, muscle aches, thirst, and sometimes vomiting and headache. A mild increase in body temperature, up to 100°–101°F, may also occur. Treatment for heat exhaustion includes moving the child to a cool environment to rest and having him drink fluids. Sometimes IV fluids may be needed.

People with heat exhaustion are not confused. A person who is confused and who also has a high temperature is experiencing heat stroke. Immediate medical attention should be sought.

HEAT STROKE

Heat stroke is a life-threatening medical emergency characterized by confusion, disorientation, high fever (103°–104°F), and sometimes seizures. If your child shows symptoms of heat stroke, call 911 for an ambulance and get the child to the nearest hospital emergency room immediately. While waiting for the ambulance, you can cool off your child by moving him to a cooler place, placing ice packs around his body, giving plenty of fluids orally if he is alert, spraying him with water, fanning him, or placing cool towels on him. The paramedics may administer IV fluids.

When are these emergencies likely to occur?

Heat cramps, heat exhaustion, and heat stroke usually occur in the first few weeks of summer. It takes an adult approximately three to four weeks to become accustomed to the warm weather. It normally takes children a few weeks longer. As a person's body becomes accustomed to the hot, humid temperatures, the body makes changes that promote sweating, and a more seamless control over body temperature naturally occurs.

How can I prevent heat-related emergencies in my child?

Children who are exercising in a hot and humid environment should drink several ounces of fluid every twenty to thirty minutes. You should be vigilant about pushing water, because a child's sense of thirst will not keep up with the amount of fluids that his body loses in the heat.

CHILDREN AND HEAT EXPOSURE

Children under the age of one should not be exposed to a hot and humid environment for a prolonged period of time. An infant's ability to control her body temperature is not yet well developed. Signs of a child becoming overheated include excessive sleepiness, excessive sweating, and decreased appetite. When in doubt, move your infant to a cool environment and take a rectal temperature. Any rectal temperature over 100.4°F is considered abnormal. If your child has a rectal temperature of 100.4°F or more, call your doctor for further advice.

Never leave a child in a car for even a few minutes on a 75°F day. The temperature in the car can rise dramatically, and children can die from heat stroke in less than an hour.

The best fluid for older children to drink is plain water. Salt tablets should never be given to children or adults to prevent or treat heat exhaustion.

TOTAL PARENT POINTERS
HEAT-RELATED ILLNESSES

1. **Heat cramps** occur in the larger muscles of the body, such as the thighs, back, and upper arms. The treatment is rest, plenty of fluids, and over-the-counter pain relievers, such as acetaminophen and ibuprofen.

2. The signs of **heat exhaustion** are:
   a. Fatigue
   b. Nausea and vomiting
   c. Lightheadedness and dizziness
   d. Thirst
   e. Muscle aches in thighs, back, and upper arms

3. The **treatment of heat exhaustion** is oral and sometimes IV fluids, rest, movement to a cool environment, checking for any fever, placement of wet, cool towels on the person to cool them off.

4. **Heat stroke is a serious medical emergency.** The signs of heat stroke are:
   a. Confusion, lethargy, agitation, or a change in mental status
   b. Marked temperature elevation
   c. Sometimes seizures

5. The **treatment of heat stroke** is:
   a. Put ice packs on the chest, groin, neck, armpits, head, and abdomen
   b. Put cool, wet towels on the child
   c. Move the child to a cool environment
   d. Give plenty of fluids orally if the child is alert and able to do so
   e. Call an ambulance
   f. Fan the child to increase the cooling effect
   g. Paramedics will give IV fluids

6. Never leave an infant or child in a car. The temperature in a car can increase dramatically, and infants can die of heat stroke within an hour.

18

Rashes and Skin Diseases

Sometimes it's the seemingly little things, like rashes or skin problems, that can be just as perplexing as the bigger conditions. This chapter addresses the most common rashes, skin and hair problems, and their causes and treatment.

HIVES

One of the most common rashes in children is hives, a rash usually caused by an allergic reaction to medications, strawberries, peanuts, tomatoes, bee and wasp stings, or seafood. Some cases, though, are caused by viruses or bacteria. Many cases have no known cause.

As seen in the photo to the right, hives are characterized by raised red blotches of skin, which are itchy. This is due to a substance called histamine, which the body releases during an allergic reaction. It makes sense that antihistamines, such as diphenhydramine (Benadryl), are used to treat allergic reactions.

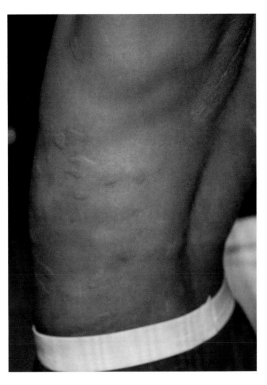

Hives on a child due to a bee sting

SECRET DOCTOR INFO: Did you know that medications such as Pepcid, which is used for stomach ulcers, also have antihistamine properties and are used to treat allergic reactions?

What are some of the most common causes of allergic reactions?

1. Drugs such as the penicillins, ibuprofen, and aspirin

2. Stinging insects—wasps, hornets, honeybees, yellow jackets, fire ants, and harvester ants
3. Peanuts, shellfish (lobster, crab, etc.), eggs, fish, tree nuts, certain fruits such as strawberries
4. Soaps, detergents, lotions
5. House dust mites, molds, pollens, and other inhaled dusts

What is the difference between a mild, moderate, and severe allergic reaction?

Mild allergic reactions occur on one part of the body and are not associated with any shortness of breath or wheezing. A moderate allergic reaction is characterized by hives over several areas of the body, some mild shortness of breath, and/or wheezing. Severe allergic reactions are also called anaphylactic reactions. These are characterized by hives; wheezing; shortness of breath; swelling of the face, lips, or eyelids; and shock (low blood pressure).

Severe cases can result in death. About five hundred to one thousand people (adults and children) die each year in the United States due to severe anaphylactic reactions.

What is the treatment for hives or allergic reactions?

Children that have hives without any shortness of breath can be treated with Benadryl four times a day as needed. Check the exact dosage against your child's weight. In some cases a doctor may prescribe a steroid pill or liquid.

KEY POINT ABOUT ALLERGIC REACTIONS

Any child with hives and symptoms of shortness of breath, wheezing, tightness in the throat, or a change in voice or hoarseness should be brought to an emergency room via ambulance as soon as possible. In general, the quicker the reaction starts, the more severe the reaction. Symptoms can start within minutes and up to four hours after the exposure.

Severe anaphylactic reactions may require injected medications (such as epinephrine) and steroids to treat a child who is in shock or has a narrowed and swollen airway. Children who have had severe reactions in the past may be prescribed an EpiPen, which enables the doctor to inject epinephrine into the child's thigh if she experiences a severe reaction to a bee sting, food allergy, etc.

Some patients may suffer a complete blockage of their airway due to swelling within the airway. In such cases physicians or paramedics place a tube in the airway (intubation) and attach the child to a ventilator. This is a life-saving procedure that emergency medicine specialists, anesthesiologists, doctors, and paramedics are trained to do.

What can you do to prepare for a severe reaction if you know your child has a severe allergy?

1. Have the child wear a medication alert bracelet noting his allergies.
2. If your child has a food allergy, read the ingredients on every

food product. If there is no list, do not let your child eat it.

3. Educate your child about what foods to avoid. Tell the parents of your child's friends about the allergy.

4. Teach your child to avoid stinging insects and their nests if they have an insect sting allergy. The most common biting insects in the United States are honeybees, hornets, bumblebees, yellow jackets, fire ants, and harvester ants.

5. Talk to you doctor about prescribing an EpiPen that can be self-injected for children with severe allergic reactions.

CONTACT DERMATITIS

Contact dermatitis is an allergic reaction due to a specific substance, such as secretions from poison ivy, poison oak, and poison sumac. Other things that can cause a contact dermatitis are metals (such as nickel, latex, rubber gloves) and certain chemicals found in tanned leather or dyed clothes.

Keep in mind those children who have been in contact with poison ivy or poison oak should remove their clothes and bathe as soon as possible.

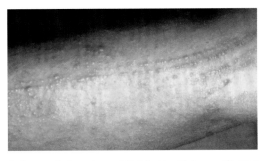

Poison oak (courtesy of Public Health Image Library)

What is the treatment for poison ivy or contact dermatitis?

The usual treatment consists of any combination of the following:

1. Benadryl
2. Steroids
3. Pepcid
4. Steroid creams or lotions
5. Oatmeal bath

ATOPIC DERMATITIS (ECZEMA)

This is a condition in which children have a scaly, red, itchy rash that can appear on the face, neck, armpits, behind the ears, and in the diaper area. This may begin in infancy with cradle cap, which is a crusted, scaly rash on an infant's scalp.

 SECRET DOCTOR INFO:
Parents should know the difference between a drug allergy and a side effect.

A child who develops hives, throat tightness, and wheezing after a shot of penicillin has an allergy to the medication. However, a child who has diarrhea after receiving an oral antibiotic for five days is having a side effect from the medication.

Parents tend to consider any kind of unusual reaction to a medication to be an allergy. Don't fall into this trap! Try to understand the difference between an allergy and a side effect. If your child is seriously ill with an infection, knowing her real allergies can be very important for doctors to pick the best antibiotic to treat her.

SECRET DOCTOR INFO: It is a myth that poison ivy "spreads" to different areas of the body over several days. In reality, different parts of the body respond at different times. For instance, the rash from poison ivy for the first day may begin on the legs but occur two days later on the chest and arms due to a delayed reaction. However, the rash is not continuing to spread once the plant chemical called "rhus" is washed off the body. The skin on the chest and arms is just taking longer to react. Other issues: may have to do some scrubbing to get the resin off the skin. It also gets under the nails with scratching and can be transferred from body area to body area that way.

The rash can be very mild with only dried skin or it can be severe with cracks in the skin. This is sometimes called the itch that rashes, instead of the rash that itches.

Atopic dermatitis

What's the treatment for atopic dermatitis?

The main treatment is the relief of skin dryness, inflammation, and itching. The child should limit baths to avoid dryness, and topical moisturizers can be used. Episodes of inflammation can be treated with a steroid cream. Benadryl can be used four times a day for itching.

Cradle cap can be treated with various shampoos that your doctor can recommend. Some pediatricians suggest using mineral oil overnight to remove the scales.

BACTERIAL INFECTIONS OF THE SKIN

Bacterial infections of the skin include:
1. Cellulitis
2. Methicillin-resistant Staphylococcus aureus (MRSA)
3. Acne
4. Imetigo
5. Scarlet fever

CELLULITIS

Cellulitis is a superficial skin infection that makes the skin appear red and inflamed. In children, cellulitis is sometimes accompanied by a fever. Cellulitis is usually caused by a staphylococcus or streptococcus bacteria. Antibiotics are prescribed to treat skin cellulitis.

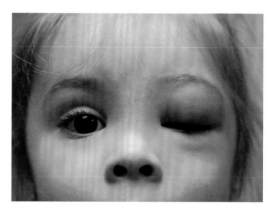

Cellulitis of the eyelid (bacterial skin infection)

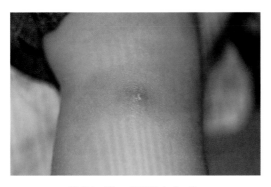

**Child with a MRSA infection
on the leg, called cellulitis**

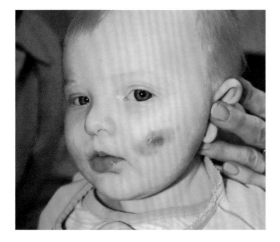

Child with a MRSA infection on a cheek

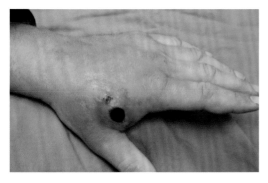

Child with a MRSA infection on the hand

MRSA (METHICILLIN-RESISTANT STAPHYLOCOCCUS AUREUS)

MRSA is an abbreviation for a particular bacterium called methicillin-resistant Staphylococcus aureus. This is important because

we are seeing a significant increase in the number of children and adults who have MRSA skin infections.

The typical appearance of MRSA skin infection is seen in the photo immediately to the left. Parents usually believe their child has a spider bite, but no one saw the spider.

MRSA infections can begin as a small red, raised area as in the photo. This can progress to a large boil or abscess. I have seen a number of children with these small abscesses on different parts of their body: the face, chest, abdomen, buttocks, legs, or arms. In addition to significant redness or an abscess, a fever may also develop. In severe cases the infection can spread into the bloodstream and cause an even more severe infection called sepsis.

Infant with MRSA infection of the scrotum and inner thigh. This child also had a fever and an abscess (pus collection).

What is the treatment for MRSA infections?

The MSRA bacterium is resistant to a large number of antibiotics. It is therefore important for doctors to identify MSRA quickly because only a small number of specific antibiotics (such as clindamycin or a sulfa antibiotic) will kill this bacterium.

ACNE

Acne is a skin condition known to almost all teenagers. Acne in teenagers is due to the increased activity of the sebaceous glands, which is caused by increased hormone levels at puberty. In young teens, the glands produce an oil (called sebum) faster, and the glands tend to block. This results in whiteheads and blackheads.

What is the best treatment for acne?

1. Over-the-counter benzoyl peroxide medications are reasonably effective.
2. Some cosmetics make acne worse. Isopropyl myristate can even stimulate acne to occur.
3. Sunlight can be beneficial by drying the acne.
4. Topical lotions containing antibiotics can be helpful.
5. Vitamin A cream or liquids can be used for severe cases.

IMPETIGO

Impetigo is a bacterial infection that causes crusted yellow, scaly, red lesions around the mouth and other areas of the body. The impetigo crust has a honey-colored appearance.

Some cases of impetigo are called bullous impetigo because the rash becomes a fluid-filled skin blister (bulla).

What is the treatment for impetigo?

Antibiotics are used to treat impetigo.

SCARLET FEVER

Scarlet fever is one of the most serious diseases that can be caused by the strep bacteria, and it results in a diffuse, sandpapery rash of the entire body. Scarlet fever frequently begins with a fever and sometimes with a sore throat or impetigo. It is caused by the same bacteria that causes strep throat and impetigo.

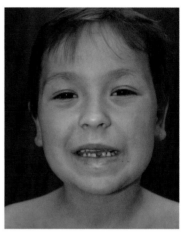

Scarlet fever showing red rash but white pallor around mouth

What are the main signs to look for in scarlet fever?

1. Diffuse, sandpapery, red-tinted rash of the entire body with area of no redness around the mouth. Instead, the mouth has a slight pallor around it (see photo above).
2. Fever may begin twelve to twenty-four hours before the rash.
3. The child also may have a sore or red throat.

What is the treatment for scarlet fever?

Antibiotics such as erythromycin or penicillin are used to treat scarlet fever.

Does scarlet fever have any complications?

Scarlet fever has the same complications as strep throat. In the most serious cases, a child may develop rheumatic heart disease (such as heart valve problems) or a kidney problem called AGN (acute glomeru-lonephritis). These may occur if the child is not treated appropriately with antibiotics.

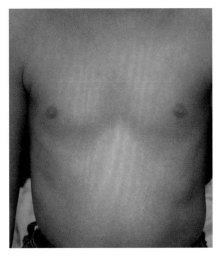

Scarlet fever rash of the torso showing the diffuse red rash. The rash has a sandpaperlike texture.

FUNGAL INFECTIONS OF THE SKIN

Fungal infections of the skin seen in the ER include:

1. Ringworm
2. Fungal infections of the scalp
3. Athlete's foot
4. Fungal infection of the groin, jock itch

RINGWORM (FUNGUS)

Ringworm is a fungal infection that is transmitted by contact or by con-taminated surfaces, such as gym floors. A fungus is a parasite that requires a living body to survive. Fungal infections can last for years if left untreated. A typical ringworm infection looks like a round, slightly raised, and itchy lesion, which can

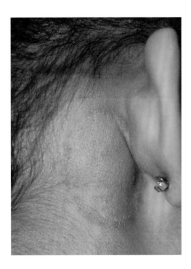

Ringworm

range in size from one-half inch to several inches in diameter.

Small ringworm lesions can be treated with an antifungal cream that can be bought over the coun-ter (such as tolnaftate, miconazole, and clotrimazole). Small areas of ringworm can be treated by apply-ing the cream two times a day for approximately three weeks. Ideally the cream should be applied for at least two weeks, even after the rash and itching clears up. However, larger rashes require an oral antifungal medication in addi-tion to an antifungal cream.

FUNGAL RASHES OF THE SCALP

A fungal infection of the scalp is called tinea capitis. The rash typically looks red and scaly with a clear central area. The bumpy areas (which can be seen in some cases) are referred to as kerion, and they are an inflammatory reaction to the fungus. This may be some-what confusing because it appears to look like small infected lumps in the scalp area. These small lumps under the skin may sometimes become infected by bacteria. If a secondary infection occurs, an antibiotic will be needed in addition to an antifungal medication.

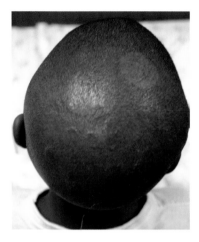

Tinea capitis is detected by the round areas of ringworm (fungal infection) on the scalp.

HEAD LICE

Head lice are a common occurrence in school-age children. Lice are very small, insect-type parasites that live on the scalp. The lay their eggs (nits) on the hair shafts in what look like small whitish crusts. The idea that kids who are not clean get lice is not true. Lice can occur on any child.

What are the symptoms of head lice?

The most obvious symptom is an itchy scalp. If you closely examine the hair shafts you may see a few white crusts attached to them.

What is the treatment for head lice?

Head lice are effectively treated with an anti-lice shampoo. After using the shampoo, use a fine-tooth comb to remove any nits from your child's hair. You should also wash your combs, headwear, and brushes in the shampoo to kill any nits. Bedsheets and pillowcases should also be washed in hot water.

SCABIES

Scabies are a parasite called mites that burrow and lay their eggs under the skin. It can be very itchy. Scabies are very contagious and are passed from one child to the next by physical contact.

The primary symptom of scabies is itching. The scabies rash looks like lines of raised burrows or red tracks. It frequently occurs between the fingers but can occur anywhere on the body.

The treatment is with an anti-scabies lotion that is applied from the neck down before bedtime. It is then washed off about eight to twelve hours later. All bedsheets and recent clothing should be washed in hot water.

ATHLETE'S FOOT

Athlete's foot is a fungal infection of the feet characterized by broken scaly skin between the toes and on the feet. This is frequently picked up by adolescents in the locker rooms of gyms, health clubs, pool facilities, etc. It should be treated aggressively with antifungal creams until there is a complete clearing of the rash. If left untreated, this rash may progress to a rash of the toenails, which can be extremely difficult to treat. In addition, the medication used to treat fungal infections of the nails has several significant side effects.

Medications previously described for the treatment of fungal rashes (tolnaftate, miconazole, and clotrimazole) should be used two times a day for athlete's foot. It should be used for two weeks after the rash is gone to make sure that the fungus is cleared up.

VIRAL RASHES

Chicken Pox

Chicken pox is an infection caused by a virus called varicella zoster. The incubation period for chicken pox is two to three weeks. The virus is spread from child to child by coughing as well as by direct contact. As you know, children receive a vaccine for chicken pox but some children can still get chicken pox. It can even occur in some children more than once.

See the photos of the chicken pox rash on the next page.

As you can see, the rash consists of three types of lesions. Characteristic of the chicken pox rash is that you can see three different crops of the rash in different stages of development. The first-stage rash begins on the torso with small, red, raised bumps. The second stage occurs when the bumps appear to contain a clear fluid surrounded by an area of redness. This is referred to as having the appearance of a dewdrop on a rose petal. The third stage of the rash is when the fluid-filled vesicle breaks open and forms a dried crust on top. It is generally believed that when the vesicles or lesions have become dried and crusted that the child is no longer infectious. This is

the only rash in which you can see all three stages present at the same time.

Chicken pox is also one of the few rashes that occur on a child's palms and soles. The other rashes include:
1. Rocky Mountain spotted fever
2. Hand, foot, and mouth disease
3. Syphilis

What are the complications of chicken pox?

Some children, and especially teenagers, can develop complications such as pneumonia, a brain infection called encephalitis, or a skin infection called cellulitis.

What is the treatment for chicken pox?

The main treatment is to keep the child in isolation from other children for at least one week or until all of the lesions have crusted over. Benadryl can be used for the itching. Patients with a severe infection who have a problem with their immunity can be treated with certain IV antiviral medications.

Children who are known to have a problem with their immunity can be given a shot of varicella immunoglobulin within forty-eight hours of known exposure to the chicken pox virus.

HERPES ZOSTER

Herpes zoster is a skin infection from the chicken pox virus that spreads along the skin on one side of the body, commonly in the mid-torso area. It's often referred to as shingles.

Shingles occurs on only one side of the body because the virus

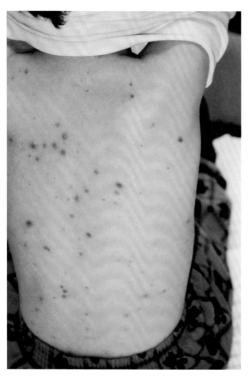

Note that there are lesions in all three stages of development: small red papules, fluid-filled lesions, and crusted, dried lesions. The presence of all three stages is characteristic of chicken pox.

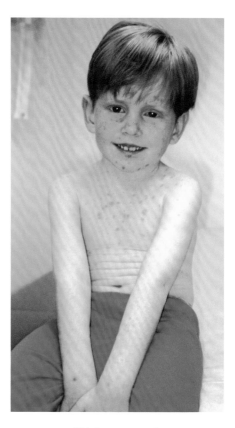

Chicken pox rash

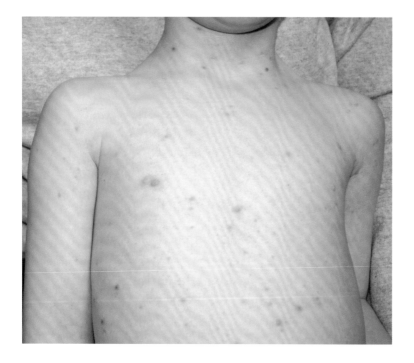

Chicken pox rash

remains dormant in the nerve roots near the spinal cord. For some reason, the virus reactivates later in life and causes shingles. In many cases, the pain along the area of the rash will precede the rash itself. The rash can last as long as two to four weeks and can be contagious from skin-to-skin contact.

What is the treatment for herpes zoster (shingles)?

The main treatment is to use antiviral medications and avoid skin-to-skin contact. Pain medicines are used for pain control.

COLD SORES (APTHOUS ULCERS)

Cold sores are caused by a virus called herpes simplex. Usually herpes simplex virus type 1 causes infections around the mouth. Herpes simplex type 2 causes infections in the genital area.

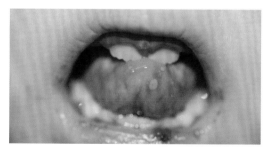

Cold sore of the inner lip due to a virus such as herpes simplex type 1

Cold sore (apthous ulcer) of tongue and lips

How is herpes simplex type 1 spread?

Herpes simplex type 1 can be spread by direct contact or through infected towels, spoons, glasses, etc. The incubation period is from one day to four weeks.

Signs and symptoms

Cold sores tend to occur in children under the age of five. Common symptoms include:
1. Painful sores on the tongue, mouth, and lips
2. High fever

HERPES SIMPLEX TYPE 2 IN PREGNANT WOMEN

A pregnant woman with herpes simplex type 2 needs to be aware that she can pass this virus to her child during delivery. This also can occur when a pregnant woman has an active cold sore around her mouth due to the herpes virus. Children who become infected with the herpes virus during delivery can develop a severe illness at any time within the first six weeks of life. These infections in infants can be a simple skin infection or a severe brain infection called encephalitis. It is therefore important for pregnant women to talk to their obstetrician about any past history of herpes genital infections or recurrent cold sores.

HAND, FOOT, AND MOUTH DISEASE

Hand, foot, and mouth disease is caused by a virus that usually occurs in summer and fall. It is characterized by a rash affecting the hands, feet, and mouth. The virus can also cause sores on the soft palate of the mouth as well as the tongue and gums. These sores usually last three to six days.

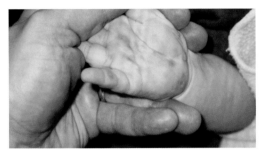

Hand, foot, and mouth disease lesions can be seen on the palm. This is one of the few diseases that causes a rash on palms or soles.

HERPANGINA

Painful cold sores or ulcers that occur in the back of the throat, tonsils, or soft palate are typical of herpangina, which is caused by a virus and can be identified by these symptoms:

1. Small sores or ulcers with a small halo of redness on the tonsils and soft palate
2. An unwillingness to eat due to throat pain
3. Herpangina
4. Fever
5. Fussiness

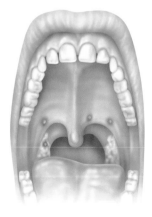

Viral sores in a mouth are characteristic of herpangina

What is the treatment for herpangina?

This illness is usually self-limited, meaning that the main treatment is pain medication, such as Tylenol, every four hours and cool foods, such as Popsicles, and cool liquids to help relieve the pain.

FIFTH DISEASE (ERYTHEMA INFECTIOSUM)

Fifth disease is caused by a virus called Parvovirus B19. Fifth disease usually occurs in school-age children during the spring and winter and is spread by other children's sneezing and coughing.

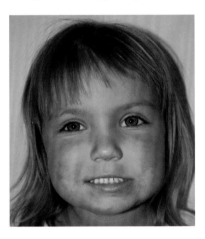

Slapped-cheek appearance of fifth disease

What are the symptoms of fifth disease?

The symptoms of fifth disease include a red "slapped cheek" appearance (see the photo above). It is called fifth disease because it was the fifth viral disease discovered after measles, mumps, rubella, etc.

This red rash on the face is the first thing noticed by parents. It is usually associated with a low-grade fever. The cheek rash slowly disappears as the child develops a lacy rash on the torso and extremities. The rash may change from day to day, but it usually has the lacy appearance as noted in the photo below.

Notice the characteristic slapped cheek appearance of fifth disease

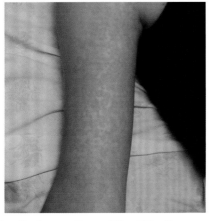

Notice the lacy pattern of the fifth-disease rash

What is the treatment for fifth disease?
The main treatment is Tylenol for any fever. But more important, keep the child away from pregnant women since this virus may cause serious complications in women who contract this virus. Fortunately, about 50 percent of pregnant women are immune to this virus, and their baby will not be affected. However, in some cases this virus can cause the unborn child to develop severe anemia (lack of red blood cells). A miscarriage can also occur. This is more common when infection occurs during the first half of pregnancy. Infection with this virus does not cause birth defects or mental retardation.

ROSEOLA
Roseola is a virus that causes a rash and high fever. A child with roseola usually has a high fever of 103°–104°F but otherwise appears to be very happy and well. Most cases occur in the spring and early fall. The incubation period is approximately five to fifteen days, and roseola usually occurs in children between the ages of six months and two years. The other clue to roseola is that fever comes on suddenly, without other warning symptoms. Shortly after the fever passes the rash will occur. Usually the rash goes away within forty-eight hours. One key thing to remember is that children who suddenly develop this high fever can have a febrile seizure (see more about seizures in chapter 19).

What is the treatment for roseola?
There is no specific treatment other than treating the fever with Tylenol. Motrin may also be used in patients over the age of twelve months. There are no major complications from roseola.

RUBELLA (GERMAN MEASLES)
Rubella, or German measles, is caused by a virus with an incubation period of fourteen to twenty-three days. The importance of rubella is that it can cause fetal malformations if a mother is

infected during the first or second trimester of pregnancy. This is one of the main reasons that children are given the MMR vaccine, which provides immunity against measles, mumps, and rubella. (Only twenty cases were reported in 1983.)

Some of the complications that the infant may experience if the mother is infected during the first twenty weeks of pregnancy include:

1. Heart defects
2. Brain defects
3. Eye defects
4. Hearing loss

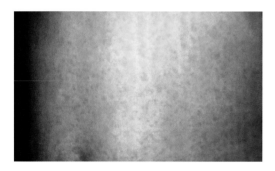

Rubella

What are the signs and symptoms of rubella in older children?

Children with rubella have the following signs and symptoms:

1. Slight fever
2. Enlarged lymph nodes, especially behind the ear and on the lower back of the head
3. A mild diffuse red rash
4. Occasional excessive fussiness

RUBEOLA (MEASLES)

Rubeola causes a rash approximately two weeks after the initial infection. The rubeola rash begins at the hairline and behind the ears, then spreads from the upper body to the lower body over approximately three days. The rash consists of several large patches of redness that eventually looks like one large rash.

Other signs and symptoms of rubeola include:

1. High fever
2. Cough
3. Nasal congestion
4. Pink eyes

Since the introduction of the MMR vaccine—which provides protection against measles (rubeola), mumps, and rubella—there have been very few reported cases of rubeola.

Any child diagnosed with rubeola should be documented and referred to the local health department.

PITYRIASIS ROSEA

Pityriasis rosea is a rash occuring in teenagers as well as adults. The rash consists of small oval or cigar-shaped scaly lesions that break out on the child's back in a Christmas tree pattern. This rash is usually

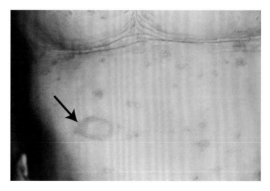

Herald patch in child with Pityriasis Rosea
(photo courtesy of the Public Health Image Library)

preceded by what is called a herald patch, a small lesion, about one inch in size on the trunk or on the extremities.

The cause of pityriasis rosea is not known. The rash may take several weeks to disappear. Some patients experience mild itching.

What is the treatment for pityriasis rosea?

The main treatment is to provide relief from any itching. The rash will usually disappear on its own. Exposure to sunlight may make the rash disappear more quickly.

DIAPER RASH

Diaper rash is one of the most common infant rashes. It is caused by a fungus called candida albicans. However, a bright red rash around the anus is usually caused by bacteria called strep. Diaper rash can be treated with a topical cream prescribed by a pediatrician, for example, clotrimazole, miconazole, or nystatin. If the rash appears to be a bacterial infection, a doctor will prescribe an antibiotic. One of the most important things you need to do for prevention and treatment is to keep the child's diaper area as dry as possible. Change the diaper as soon as it gets wet.

HENOCH-SCHÖNLEIN PURPURA

Henoch-Schönlein purpura (HSP) is a disease in which the child experiences inflammation in certain blood vessels and often accompanying arthritislike conditions. It is called an immune complex disease because

the body is forming antibodies that actually attack the blood vessels. The inflammation of the blood vessels causes different symptoms in different parts of the body, such as:

1. Joint pains (arthritis)—occurs in 80 percent of children
2. Rash
3. Blood in the urine due to kidney disease
4. Seizures
5. Abdominal pain

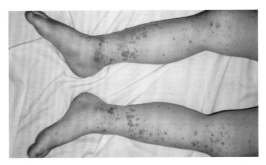

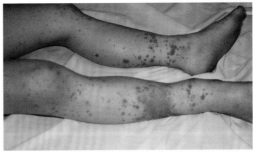

Henoch-Schönlein purpura

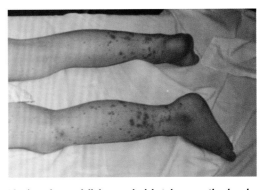

Notice the reddish purple blotches on the backs of the legs. These are called purpura.

The HSP rash begins as a simple allergy rash consisting of hives. Then it changes into large, raised, reddish purple blotches mainly on the back of the legs and the buttocks.

What are the main complications of HSP?
1. Kidney damage (nephrotic syndrome)
2. Seizures
3. Bleeding in the brain, which can cause seizures or brain impairment

What is the treatment for HSP?
The treatment is pain control for the arthritis. The other main issue is to carefully watch for any decrease in kidney function.

KAWASAKI DISEASE

Kawasaki disease is a rare illiness that typically occurs in a child under five years of age with a fever for more than five to twelve days (with no known source), severe pink eyes, red lips, and a rash of the trunk, palms, and soles.

The most serious complication of the disease is an inflammation (vasculitis) of the small and medium arteries in the body, especially the coronary arteries. This inflammation can result in weakening, bulging, and rupture of a coronary artery, which can cause a reduction of the blood flow to the heart, a heart attack, and sometimes death. (The death rate is less than one out of one hundred children.) Fortunately, most children with this disease recover without any serious problems.

Kawasaki disease affects boys more than girls. It can affect any child but tends to be more common in Japanese and Korean children. About three thousand cases are diagnosed in the United States each year.

What are the main signs and symptoms of Kawasaki disease?
- Fever lasting from five to twelve days (with no other cause) that is unresponsive to Tylenol.
- Severe pink eyes without pus drainage.
- Under five years of age.
- Lips may appear bright red with cracking and peeling.
- Strawberry tongue.
- Sore throat with redness in the back of the throat (pharyngitis).
- A skin rash may look like the scarlet fever or measles rash. The rash is primarily on the trunk, diaper area, hands, and feet.
- Swelling of the hands, fingers, feet, and toes.
- Redness of the palms and the soles.
- Scaling or peeling of the skin during the second week—especially the tips of the fingers, toes, and the diaper area.
- Swelling of the lymph nodes in the front sides of the neck.
- Other symptoms may include abdominal pain, joint pains, and diarrhea.
- Blood tests show a very high platelet count in the second week of illness.

What causes Kawasaki disease?

It is unclear what causes Kawasaki disease. It may be caused by an infectious process or an immune response to an infection.

What is the treatment for Kawasaki disease?

1. IV administration of gamma globulin, an antibody.
2. Aspirin. Before giving aspirin, your physician will make sure there are no signs of chicken pox. Aspirin can lead to Reye's syndrome, a serious complication of chicken pox and other viral illnesses associated with aspirin use.

3. Close observation for any signs of heart problems, such as coronary aneurysms (a bulging in an artery of the heart), abnormal heart rhythms, inflammation of the heart (myocarditis), and aneurysms in other parts of the body.

TOTAL PARENT POINTERS
RASHES AND SKIN DISEASES

1. The **most common causes of allergic reactions** are:
   - Drugs such as aspirin, ibuprofen, and penicillin
   - Stinging insects (fire ants, harvester ants, hornets, honeybees, wasps, and yellow jackets)
   - Eggs, fish, peanuts, shellfish (lobster, crab, etc.), tree nuts, and certain fruits such as strawberries
   - Detergents, lotions, soaps
   - House dust mites, molds, pollens, and other inhaled dusts

2. Severe allergic reactions are characterized by **hives, shortness of breath**, and **wheezing**. Call an ambulance if these symptoms occur.

3. Know the difference between a **drug allergy** and a **drug side effect**. A drug allergy cause hives, wheezing, or itching. A side effect is nausea or vomiting.

4. **Contact dermatitis** is an allergic reaction due to a specific substance such as secretions from poison ivy, poison oak, and poison sumac. Other causes include latex, metals such as nickel, rubber gloves, and certain chemicals found in tanned leather or dyed clothes.

5. **Eczema** (atopic dermatitis) appears as a rash on children's cheeks, the backs of their legs, the elbow flexion area, and the posterior or knee flexion area.

6. **Methicillin-resistant Staphylococcus aureus** (MRSA) infections of the skin often look like a spider bite. These bacteria are resistant to multiple antibiotics. The infection can gradually spread to cause a skin infection called cellulitis, which can be severe and can also cause a fever and skin abscesses.

7. **Acne** in teenagers is due to increased activity of the sebaceous glands, which is caused by increased hormone levels at puberty. In young teens, the glands produce sebum (an oil) faster and tend to get blocked up. This results in whiteheads and blackheads on the skin.

8. **Scarlet fever** is a rash caused by the streptococcus bacteria that also causes strep throat. It results in a diffuse, sandpapery rash of the entire body. Scarlet fever frequently begins with a fever but sometimes initiates with a sore throat or impetigo. It should be treated with an antibiotic to prevent the complications of rheumatic fever or acute glomerulonephritis (AGN).

9. **Ringworm** is a fungal infection that is transmitted to other children by skin-to-skin contact or by contaminated surfaces such as gym floors.

10. **Chicken pox** is an infection caused by a virus called varicella zoster. The incubation period for chicken pox is two to three weeks. Three types of lesions characterize the rash: small lesions that look like a dewdrop on a rose petal, small fluid-filled vesicles, and crusted lesions. It is one of the few rashes that can be seen on the palms and soles.

11. **Herpes zoster** is a skin infection from the chicken pox virus that spreads along the skin on one side of the body, commonly in the midtorso area. It is often referred to as shingles. It follows the course on one of the nerves that extends across one side of the body.

12. **Hand, foot, and mouth syndrome** is an illness caused by a virus that usually occurs in summer and fall. It is

TOTAL PARENT POINTERS
RASHES AND SKIN DISEASES

characterized by affecting the hands, feet, and mouth. The virus can also cause sores on the soft palate of the mouth, tongue, and gums.

13. **Herpangina** causes painful cold sores or ulcers in the back of the throat, tonsils, or soft palate.

14. **Fifth disease** has a characteristic rash that has a slapped-cheek appearance. Children with fifth disease should be kept away from pregnant women because it can cause miscarriage or stop red blood cell production in the developing infant.

15. **Roseola** is a viral illness that causes a sudden, high fever (103–104°F) in a six to twenty-four-month-old child who looks happy and playful. The rash usually begins three to four days after the fever. Be aware that this sudden high fever can cause a febrile seizure.

16. **Rubella** (German measles) is a mild viral illness that is very uncommon in the United States due to the MMR (measles-mumps-rubella) vaccine introduced in 1969. Rubella is characterized by a mild diffuse rash, slight fever, enlarged lymph nodes in the neck, and sometimes joint pain. Complications of a rubella infection in children whose mothers are infected during the first six months can include: mental retardation, hearing loss, and heart defects.

17. **Rubeola** (measles) is also very uncommon in the United States due to the 1969 MMR vaccine. Signs of rubeola are high fever, a rash that spreads from the hairline and behind the ears to the rest of the body, pink eyes, and nasal congestion.

18. **Pityriasis rosea** has a characteristic rash consisting of small oval or cigar-shaped scaly lesions that break out on a child's back in a Christmas tree pattern. This rash is usually preceded by what is called a herald patch.

19. **Diaper rash** in infants can be caused by a fungus or a bacterium. Your doctor may prescribe an antifungal cream or an antibiotic. It is important to change diapers frequently to keep the area dry.

20. **Henoch-Schönlein purpura** (HSP) begins as a simple allergic-type rash consisting of hives but then changes into large, raised, reddish-purple blotches of rash mainly on the back of the legs and buttocks.

21. **Kawasaki disease** is a rare illness that typically occurs in children under five years of age with a fever for five to twelve days (with no known source), severe pink eyes, red lips, and a rash of the trunk, palms, and soles.

19

Seizures

A seizure in a child is probably one of the scariest things a parent can witness. A seizure is caused by a sudden episode of uncontrolled electrical activity in the brain. Some seizures may be preceded by an aura. An aura is a sensation, a smell, a visual problem, or some other physical symptom that is a warning sign that a seizure is about to occur. There are many types of auras. However, each person usually experiences only one type of aura.

A seizure can result in a jerking of the entire body (grand mal seizure), a focal seizure of an arm or leg (partial seizure), or a simple episode of staring into space (petit mal seizure).

After a seizure, the child will usually sleep or remain groggy for several minutes to an hour or so. This is called a postictal state (ictal means seizure).

Some clues to look for to determine if a child has had a seizure include:

1. Losing control of their urine or bowels
2. Bite marks on their tongue as a result of a grand mal seizure

3. Confusion, sleepiness, or grogginess after the seizure
4. A family history of epilepsy

What are the two main types of seizures?

1. Generalized seizures (grand mal seizure, for example)
2. Partial (focal) seizures (a partial seizure may involve only an arm or leg, but some partial seizures may involve a specific body movement such as repetitive body gestures or repetitive chewing movements)

What are the most common causes of seizures?

- High fever (febrile seizure)
- Infections such as meningitis
- Head trauma (example: shaken baby syndrome that causes bleeding or blood clots in the brain)
- Drugs and toxins (iron overdose, lead poisoning, antidepressant medications, cocaine, stimulants)
- Failure to take antiseizure medicines
- Epilepsy

- Low blood sugar
- Low blood sodium (hyponatremia)
- Brain tumors
- Inherited nervous system problems

FEBRILE SEIZURE

A febrile seizure occurs as a result of a fever, usually at the beginning of a viral infection, such as a cold, stomach flu, or roseola. Sometimes a febrile seizure can be caused by meningitis, which is an infection of the spinal fluid around the brain.

Most febrile seizures occur between the ages of six months and five years. Approximately one out of three children who have a febrile seizure will have a second seizure.

What should I do if my child has a febrile seizure?

The initial step is to make sure that the child is getting enough oxygen and not injuring himself. Look at his lips and mouth to make sure they are not turning blue. If the child's lips become dusky blue, open the airway (see the diagrams above) and give mouth-to-mouth ventilation if necessary. Most febrile seizures stop on their own within a few minutes. Also, try to protect the child's head from hitting any hard surface.

Can my child swallow his tongue and choke if he has a seizure?

The notion of a child's swallowing his tongue is not quite accurate. The child can have trouble breathing because his tongue has fallen back and obstructed the airway. The key thing to be aware of is to

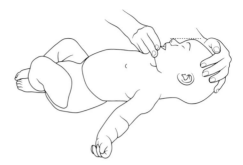

**Opening the airway of infant
(age less than twelve months)**

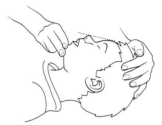

**Opening the airway of child
(one to eight years old)**

keep his head in a position that is not bent back too much or bent forward but is in the middle, as noted in diagram above. If the child is having trouble breathing, lift his chin slightly to open the airway. This will enable the child to breathe easier by pulling the tongue forward and thereby opening the airway.

Should I call an ambulance if my child has a seizure?

In general, a physician should evaluate a child after a suspected seizure as soon as possible. If the seizure occurs at home, call 911 (or your local emergency number) for an ambulance and transport the child to the nearest emergency room. EMTs and paramedics are trained to provide rescue breathing if the child needs assistance. EMTs and paramedics can also provide the child with supplemental oxygen.

Tonic phase of a grand mal seizure. Grand mal seizures frequently begin with an extremely stiff phase with very high muscle tone.

Clonic phase of seizure rapidly follows the tonic phase and is characterized by severe jerking movements of the arms and legs.

What is a complex febrile seizure?

A complex febrile seizure is defined as:

1. A seizure that lasts longer than fifteen minutes
2. A seizure that occurs in only one part of the body
3. A seizure that reoccurs within twenty-four hours

Can my child suffer permanent brain damage as a result of a simple febrile seizure?

There is no evidence that children with simple febrile seizures suffer any decrease in their intellectual performance. This assumes that the seizure lasts less than fifteen minutes and the child did not lack oxygen during the episode.

Only one out of one hundred children with febrile seizures will develop epilepsy (1 percent). The rate of epilepsy for other children who don't experience seizures is one out of two hundred or 0.5 percent.

What can I do to prevent further febrile seizures if my child has already had one?

Be alert to any signs of fever or infection. Febrile seizures usually occur at the beginning of an infection, just before you may realize your child has a fever. If your child's behavior changes or you see signs of infection such as a cough, runny nose, vomiting, or diarrhea, make sure you take the child's temperature. Acetaminophen can be given every four hours for children with fever. Ibuprofen can be given every six hours for children who are twelve months or older.

Antiseizure medications may sometimes be prescribed for certain children with recurrent febrile seizures.

GRAND MAL SEIZURE

A grand mal seizure involves a tense jerking of both arms and legs and lasts anywhere from seconds to minutes. The seizure may have both a tonic phase and a clonic phase. The tonic phase occurs when the muscles get very tense and stiff. The clonic phase is when the severe jerking movements occur.

Most febrile seizures are grand mal type seizures. Some types of epilepsy cause grand mal seizures.

PETIT MAL SEIZURE

A petit mal seizure occurs when a child stares off into space and seems to be unaware of what is going on around him. A petit mal seizure is also called an absence seizure because the child appears to be absent or detached from her surroundings. Sometimes a petit mal seizure can be mistaken for ordinary daydreaming.

EPILEPSY

Epilepsy is diagnosed when a child has two seizures with no specific provoking factor, such as a fever.

How is epilepsy further diagnosed?

1. A brain wave test called an electroencephalogram (EEG) can diagnose some cases of epilepsy.
2. Observing a child during the seizure can also be diagnostic.

How is epilepsy treated?

Your doctor may decide to prescribe one or more antiseizure medications. These are also called anticonvulsants. The prescribed medication will be based on the type of seizure disorder your child has.

Keep in mind that one of the most common reasons for children to come to the ER with a seizure is due to their not taking their medications on a routine basis. If a child misses one or more doses of the seizure medication, the level of the medication in her bloodstream will drop. If it drops below a certain level (called the therapeutic level), this can result in a seizure.

Blood levels of some seizure-prevention drugs can be measured with blood tests. Others cannot be routinely measured. For those drugs that cannot be measured by blood tests, your doctor will prescribe a dose of the seizure medication based on your child's weight and how well it controls the seizures.

OTHER CAUSES OF SEIZURES

1. Low blood sugar—This can occur in infants who have stomach flu (vomiting and diarrhea) who are given mainly water to drink. This causes the sugar or glucose level in the blood to fall, and that can result in seizures.
2. Low sodium in the blood—Just as above, an infant who is given only water may develop a low salt or sodium level in the blood. If the sodium level falls too low, the child may have a seizure.
3. Head trauma—Injuries to the head and brain can cause seizures by irritating a certain area of the brain by bruising or bleeding in the brain.
4. Nervous system diseases—Certain diseases of the brain can cause seizures. These include epilepsy, brain tumors, lack of oxygen during delivery, and certain genetic diseases such as phenylketonuria (PKU). (All newborns are tested for this disease before they go home from the hospital.)

TOTAL PARENT POINTERS
SEIZURES

1. A **seizure** is caused by a sudden episode of uncontrolled electrical activity in the brain. A seizure can result in a jerking of the entire body **(grand mal seizure), a focal seizure** of just an arm or leg (partial seizure), or a simple episode of staring into space **(petit mal seizure).**

2. The **most common causes of seizures:**
   - High fever (febrile seizure)
   - Infections such as meningitis
   - Head trauma (example: shaken baby syndrome that causes bleeding or clots in the brain)
   - Drugs and toxins (iron overdose, lead poisoning, antidepressant medications, cocaine, stimulants)
   - Failure to take antiseizure medicines
   - Epilepsy
   - Low blood sugar
   - Low blood sodium (hyponatremia)
   - Brain tumors
   - Inherited nervous system problems

3. Any child with a new onset seizure should have her head protected from injury and an ambulance should be called. Learn how to open the child's airway if she is turning blue. Review the Total Parent Breathing Checklist on page 114 to learn how to assess a child's breathing after a seizure.

4. **Febrile seizures (due to a high fever) are usually caused by a virus.** However, any first seizure needs a thorough evaluation by a physician. The younger the infant or child, the greater the concern. One of the most important diagnoses to rule out is meningitis. Meningitis is a bacterial or viral infection of the fluid around the brain. Severe cases of meningitis can cause permanent loss of intellectual function, hearing loss, or seizures.

5. An **absence seizure** (petit mal seizure) looks like the child is staring off into space and is unaware of what is going on. This may result in poor school performance if undiagnosed.

20

Tooth Problems and Injuries

The most important aspects of dental care for children include:
1. Brushing three times a day and after snacks whenever possible.
2. Seeing a dentist twice a year for checkups and for a complete cleaning by a dental hygienist.
3. Flossing daily to remove food particles from between teeth that the toothbrush can't get to.
4. Avoiding excessive intake of candy and sugary sodas.
5. If your house uses a well for drinking water, check with your doctor to see if your child should take a fluoride supplement in his vitamin. Ask about using a fluoride rinse.

How many teeth do children have compared to adults?

There are twenty baby teeth (deciduous teeth) in a child. These usually begin erupting with the lower bottom incisors. They are usually erupted by the age of three. Permanent teeth begin to erupt at about five or six years of age. Adults have thirty-two teeth.

What are the key points I need to know about injuries to the teeth?

1. Any child who has had trauma to the face and has had a permanent tooth knocked out must have that tooth replaced within the first thirty to sixty minutes in order for the tooth to have a reasonable chance for survival.

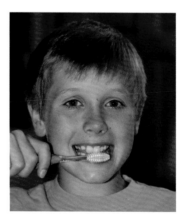

2. Baby teeth that are knocked loose or avulsed from the socket do not need to be replaced or treated aggressively.
3. If a permanent tooth has been knocked out and cannot be replaced into its socket, it

should be held in the mouth to keep it moist. If it cannot be held in the child's mouth because the child is too young, it should be placed in a cup of milk or salt water.

Fractured teeth or teeth that have been knocked out comprise the dental injuries most encountered by parents. A fracture of a baby tooth does not require immediate treatment by your dentist. However, there should be an evaluation by your dentist or your doctor to look for any fractures of the bone around the teeth or the jaw. In addition, children with dental injuries are often placed on an antibiotic, such as penicillin, erythromycin, or an equivalent antibiotic.

What kind of dental injuries require immediate evaluation by a dentist or oral surgeon?

1. A completely avulsed (knocked out) adult tooth
2. A fracture of a tooth that goes through the innermost part of the tooth, called the pulp (the diagram illustrates the enamel, the dentin, and the pulp)
3. Any significantly loose or displaced adult tooth that requires dental bracing for support

TOOTH BRUSHING

Many parents don't completely appreciate the importance of tooth brushing for their children. Children need to be taught at a young age how important it is to brush their teeth properly and

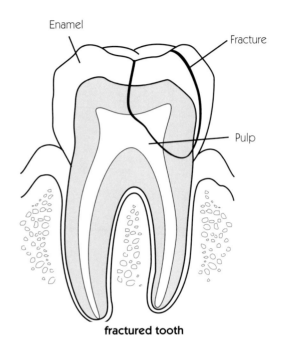

fractured tooth

thoroughly. One of the key reasons for this, obviously, is to preserve the teeth. However, another significant reason is because a healthy smile is also important for the child's future success in life. Having a pleasant smile will promote a child's interpersonal relationships and overall self-image.

Proper brushing involves holding the brush at an angle in order to get inside the crevice between the gum and the tooth. The brush should then be gently rotated in small circles in that area of the gum for approximately ten to twenty seconds. The brush should be moved to another section of two or three teeth, and the same process applied across the upper teeth. The same process should then be applied to the lower teeth to help clear the crevice between the gums and the teeth of any bacteria or calculus. Frequently, there is too much focus on brushing the white part of the teeth and not enough emphasis on cleaning inside the gum crevices.

The photo below shows what can happen to the teeth of children who have poor dental hygiene.

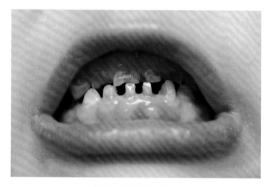

Poor dental care

FLOSSING

Flossing is the second important element of proper dental hygiene. Flossing should be done after brushing at least once a day. Since it is difficult for young children to use string floss, several companies have come out with flossing tools on plastic handles. The floss is placed on a type of Y-shaped handle that is easy for young children to use. Parents should teach their children to make brushing and flossing a game. Offer generous praise and awards for doing it properly. Tell your baby-sitters how important this is and make sure they watch the children brush their teeth before bed.

TOTAL PARENT POINTERS
TOOTH PROBLEMS AND INJURIES

1. Teach your children how to brush their teeth properly.
2. If an adult tooth is knocked out of its socket during an injury, rinse it off and **put it back into its socket as soon as possible.** If that cannot be done, have the child hold the tooth in their mouth or put it in a glass of water or milk and bring the child immediately to your dentist or the local emergency room.
3. **Ask your doctor about fluoride if your house has well water** instead of water from a water company.
4. **Children need to brush three times a day and after snacks** whenever possible. Keep toothbrushes and toothpaste in the car if possible.
5. **Help children floss their teeth daily.**

Childhood Diseases and Disorders

21

Attention Deficit Hyperactivity Disorder (ADHD)

Attention deficit hyperactive disorder (ADHD) affects 3 to 5 percent of children, but the incidence of the disorder may be higher, possibly up to 8 percent, according to recent research.* There is no laboratory test or brain scan that can definitely confirm a diagnosis of ADHD; rather the diagnosis is based on a behavioral assessment by a physician, psychiatrist, or psychologist, as well as behavioral rating scores given by teachers and parents.

There is some question whether ADHD may be related to environmental factors that the mother may have been exposed to during her pregnancy. There also is some concern as to whether alcohol or tobacco use during pregnancy may have some affect as well.

ADHD is characterized by:
- Significant and chronic inattention
- Hyperactivity
- Impulsivity

Researchers place ADHD children in one of three types based on which of the three symptoms predominate:

1. **Inattentive type**—These children seem to be unfocused and daydreaming. They have trouble following directions and frequently do not finish tasks. They are easily distracted. They become bored with a task after only a few minutes. It should be noted that there are many underachieving children who have this pattern but for whom the cause is not ADHD, which is why a careful diagnosis is so important.

2. **Hyperactive type**—These children seem to be constantly in motion. They have trouble sitting still; they squirm and fidget a lot. They talk incessantly and feel a need to be constantly busy.

3. **Impulsive type**—These children say things without thinking.

They act without regard to the consequences of their actions. They will blurt out inappropriate comments at times.

ADHD is frequently identified when a child is in school. The disorder is usually first noticed when he is having trouble with his schoolwork. Children with ADHD have trouble with the following:

1. The child cannot focus on one area or task, such as homework. She will frequently move from one task to another without completing any of them.
2. The child has trouble listening to and understanding directions. She has difficulty following a sequential order of directions.
3. The child is impulsive. He will sometimes blurt out things without thinking. He will say things that may hurt other people's feelings or that he will regret.
4. The child will tend to fidget. He seems to be in constant motion.
5. She has trouble taking turns with other children.
6. He may have trouble waiting in line.

The inattentive form of ADHD is sometimes more difficult to diagnose. Since these children are not always hyperactive or impulsive, they can be easily misdiagnosed as having a learning disability. It is, therefore, important to have these children thoroughly evaluated.

Any parent who suspects that her child may have ADHD or a learning disability should know that the school is required by state law to schedule an evaluation to determine if a learning disability or behavioral disorder exists. Educational evaluations usually consist of:

1. Interviews and behavioral scores by current and former teachers
2. Clinical evaluation by a child psychiatrist, child psychologist, and/or behavioral therapist (often involving testing as well as interviewing)
3. Evaluation by a learning disability specialist

Should the school refuse to provide this evaluation, the parent should contact the local Parent Teacher Association or the principal. If this is unsuccessful, she should contact the local school board. You can also contact the National Dissemination Center for Children with Disabilities at www.nichcy.org/states.htm. The center will direct you to the right contact person to have your child evaluated. It is important to make sure that the child does not have some other medical problem or psychological problem that may resemble symptoms of ADHD. Other medical or psychological problems that can mimic ADHD include:

1. Significant psychological stress in the family from loss of a parent, death of a sibling, divorce, or loss of a parent's job
2. A learning disability
3. Depression
4. Severe anxiety disorder
5. Undiagnosed hearing problems

6. Certain types of seizure disorders, such as petit mal seizures

7. Some types of motivated underachievement problems (which can mimic the inattentive type)

What causes ADHD?

No one really knows what causes ADHD, but many in the field conclude that there is a strong genetic component. If there is a family history of ADHD, there is a 25 percent chance that another child in the family may have ADHD. In addition, if a twin has ADHD there is a strong correlation that the other twin may have the disorder as well.

What medications can be used to treat ADHD?

The preferred treatment of ADHD is a combination of medications and behavioral therapy. The most common prescribed medications include stimulants or amphetamine-like drugs, such as methylphenidate (Ritalin). Although these drugs act as stimulants for most people, they help ADHD patients to slow down, to focus, and to pay attention. The stimulant drugs seem to work primarily on the brain transmitter called dopamine.

Some of the newer drugs can be given once a day. It is usually easier for children to take the medication once in the morning.

Some of the newer medications such as Strattera (Atomoxetine) apparently work on the transmitter chemical norepinephrine in the brain that helps the brain's neurons communicate with each other.

The side effects of ADHD drugs can include:
- Lack of appetite
- Nausea
- Insomnia
- Headache
- Stomach pains
- Increased irritability

BEHAVIORAL THERAPY TO TREAT ADHD

Children with ADHD benefit the most when medications are used in conjunction with behavioral therapy. There are several types of behavioral therapies. The child may be involved with one or more of these modalities. These include:

1. Psychotherapy: This is based on the traditional psychological approach of helping children accept themselves for who they are, resolve their interpersonal relationship issues with others (particularly their parents), and related issues.

2. Behavioral therapy: This is based on providing rewards for appropriate behaviors, organizing the child's schedules to optimize completing their tasks, and teaching them how to respond in different situations.

3. Social skills training: A trainer helps the child to develop the interpersonal skills needed to deal with specific social situations. The therapist teaches the child how to respond in different social situations. This may involve

teaching the child how to read the facial expressions of others so they can interact more appropriately.

Where can I find out more about ADHD and other resources for my child?

The National Resource Center is sponsored by the Centers for Disease Control and has both a Web site (www.help4adhd.org) and a call center (1-800-233-4050).

The earlier you identify the condition and begin therapy, the better your child's chance of reaching her full potential.

NOTES

* A. S. Rowland, C. A. Lesesne, and A. J. Abramowitz. "The Epidemiology of Attention-Deficit/Hyperactivity Disorder (ADHD): A Public Health View," *Mental Retardation and Developmental Disability Research Reviews* 8, no. 3 (2002): 162–70.

TOTAL PARENT POINTERS
ATTENTION DEFICIT HYPERACTIVITY DISORDER (ADHD)

1. **ADHD** is characterized by hyperactivity, impulsivity, and inattention.
2. **About 3 to 5 percent of children have ADHD.** Research suggests that number may actually be higher.
3. **Children with ADHD may have several of the following behaviors:**
   a. The child will frequently move from one task to another without completing any of them.
   b. The child will have trouble listening to and understanding directions.
   c. The child will be impulsive. The child will sometimes blurt out things without thinking.
   d. They will have trouble following a sequential order of directions.
   e. The child will tend to fidget and feel very restless.
   f. They have trouble taking turns with other children.
   g. They may have trouble waiting in line.
   h. The child will also have trouble with homework because of her lack of attention
4. Treatment of ADHD includes medication and behavioral modification techniques.

22

Allergies and Allergic Reactions

Your child's allergic reaction to a bug bite can be as nonthreatening as a single raised hive or bump or as serious as severe breathing trouble and death (anaphylactic shock). The thing to remember is that it's important to watch your child closely and get help if he has difficult (or stridorous) breathing, wheezing, severe hives or facial swelling, hoarseness, or trouble speaking due to swelling of the airway.

How can I tell if an allergic reaction is serious?

A severe allergic reaction usually occurs within the first one to two hours after taking a medication,

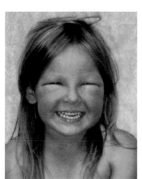

Allergic reaction to beesting

Allergic reaction to beesting—side view

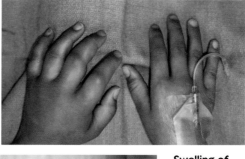

Swelling of hand due to beesting

Hive in girl with beesting

getting an insect bite, or eating an allergy-triggering food. The typical reaction includes generalized itching, hives, and tightness in the chest. Some children may develop swelling of the face, mouth, and eyelids.

Another warning sign is a stridorous sound (the noise caused by a partial obstruction) when the child breathes in. This indicates that the airway is becoming swollen and that immediate emergency treatment is needed. Other signs to look for include wheezing or feeling dizzy and lightheaded, which could indicate low blood pressure. These symptoms indicate a medical emergency; your child should be seen by a doctor immediately.

Treatment by paramedics and emergency physicians may include an IV, epinephrine, steroids, Benadryl (diphenhydramine), and other medications to assist breathing and improve blood pressure.

Some children with allergic reactions may only have swelling of their lips, as noted in the photo below.

However, any allergic reactions that involve facial swelling should be evaluated by a physician. Some cases can progress to severe trouble breathing and anaphylactic shock.

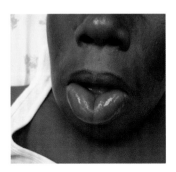

Lip swelling due to an allergic reaction

What causes allergic reactions?

The most common causes of allergic reaction in children are:

- Drugs—penicillin and other antibiotics, aspirin, ibuprofen
- Food and food additives—peanuts, milk, eggs, shellfish, wheat, soybeans, monosodium glutamate (MSG), nitrates and nitrites, and tartrazine dyes
- Insect bites—honeybees, wasps, yellow jackets, hornets, and fire ants
- Dyes used for x-ray procedures

What are the symptoms of allergic reactions?

Many allergic reactions cause a small area of hives. As long as there is no trouble breathing within the first few hours, this is usually not a serious reaction. Any child who has trouble breathing associated with an allergic reaction requires immediate emergency attention.

Can I treat an allergic reaction at home?

Mild allergic reactions can be treated with Benadryl liquid or Benadryl capsules. The dose of Benadryl (diphenhydramine) is usually one teaspoon (12.5 mg) four times a day for a twenty-five- to thirty-five-pound child. Benadryl will help decrease the itching and help minimize the hives.

How common are allergic drug reactions?

Penicillin is the most common drug to cause allergic reactions. Approximately three hundred patients die every year from allergic

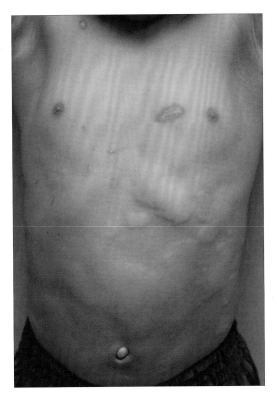

Hives (urticaria) on chest

reactions to penicillin. Interestingly, of the patients who have a reaction to penicillin, only 25 percent have had a previous allergic reaction to penicillin.

How serious are insect bite allergies?

Approximately one hundred people die each year from insect bite or sting allergies. Insect bite allergies are the second most common cause of death due to allergic reactions. If your child has had an allergic reaction in the past, you should carry a self-administered injector such as the EpiPen or the Ana-Kit. This consists of an injection of a dose of epinephrine, which can be given in the thigh if the child has been bit or stung and senses that an allergic reaction may be occurring.

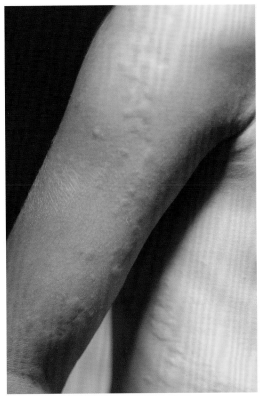

Hives on side and arm

ALLERGIES AND ALLERGIC REACTIONS

1. **Peanuts, penicillin-type antibiotics, insect bites/stings, aspirin, food dyes, shellfish, tartrazine dyes, milk, eggs, and x-ray dyes are some of the most common causes of allergic reactions.**

2. Any child who has **difficult breathing, wheezing, hoarseness, severe hives, tongue swelling, stridor, or facial swelling** should be seen by a doctor immediately. Several hundred people in the United States die each year from allergic reactions.

3. **Hives** are raised red areas on the skin due to the release of histamine from the allergic reaction.

4. Drugs such as steroids, diphendydramine (Benadryl), and even Pepcid are useful for treating allergic reactions. (Pepcid and similar acid-blocking stomach medicines are useful because they block the release of histamine.)

23

Asthma

Asthma is a serious but usually manageable disease that causes the airways of the lungs to constrict, resulting in shortness of breath, coughing, and wheezing. It affects six out of every one hundred children. It is also the third-leading cause of hospitalizations in children under the age of fifteen.

Amazingly, the number of children with asthma doubled from 1980 to 1995, and the death rate from asthma also increased during that time period. Fortunately, these rates have stabilized over the last few years.

What are the symptoms of asthma?

Wheezing, shortness of breath, and coughing, which occur on an intermittent basis. Children with asthma may have completely normal breathing periods between attacks of asthma, or they may have some persistent symptoms between attacks.

What causes asthma?

The airways in the lungs of children with asthma are very sensitive to certain substances called asthma triggers. When their airways are exposed to these allergenic or

Boy with asthma being treated with nebulizer mask

Boy with a smile after his asthma attack is controlled

irritating particles, they can become inflamed, bringing on an asthma attack. This causes the smooth muscle around the small airways in the lungs to tighten and narrow the airways, making breathing more difficult and causing wheezing.

What are the most common asthma triggers?

- Cigarette smoke
- Air pollution
- Animal hair or dander
- Dust mites
- Pollen
- Cockroaches
- Molds
- Sulfites in foods, such as dried fruits and wine
- Infections
- Aspirin and other medicines, such as ibuprofen
- Changes in weather or cold air
- Strong odors
- Active exercise

Which children have the highest risk for asthma?

Any child can develop asthma. However, children who tend to

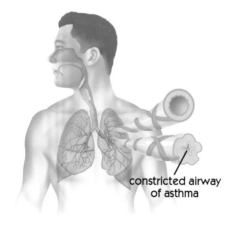

constricted airway of asthma

Lung airways

be at a greater-than-average risk include:

- Children who live in the inner cities
- Children who have a parent who has or had a history of allergies
- Children who have nasal polyps
- Children who have allergies to medications (such as aspirin and ibuprofen)
- Minorities

What is the difference between asthma and reactive airway disease?

The diagnosis of asthma should generally not be made in children under the age of two. This is because children under the age of two with wheezing usually have a viral cold with a fever and their reactive airways cause them to wheeze. This simply means that the small airways in the child's lungs are unusually sensitive to certain irritants, such as cold viruses or pollen. Usually, children who have reactive airway disease have a cold and a fever.

But if a child is wheezing and does not have a fever or cold symptoms, the diagnosis can lean more confidently toward asthma. Your physician will want to know if the child has had wheezing without a fever or a cold on several different occasions before diagnosing asthma.

The diagnosis of asthma in a child who is over the age of two is clearer when the child has no fever yet presents the three classic symptoms: wheezing, coughing, and shortness of breath.

If the diagnosis is questionable, your physician may order

a spirometer breathing test to measure how quickly your child can blow air into a tube that is connected to a special machine. If your child cannot blow air out of his lungs quickly enough, that means there is some type of airway obstruction that can be attributed to asthma.

After a diagnosis of asthma is established, your doctor will determine the level of severity. There are four such levels:

Level 1: Mild Intermittent Asthma—Having asthma symptoms twice a week or less. Between episodes, the child has no symptoms, and his lungs function normally. The symptoms may bother the child at night up to two times per month.

Level 2: Mild Persistent Asthma—Having asthma symptoms more than twice a week but not more than once a day. A mild persistent asthma attack may affect your child's participation or performance in normal activities. The child is bothered by asthma symptoms at night more than two times a month.

Level 3: Moderate Persistent Asthma—Having asthma symptoms every day. Asthma symptoms affect the child's daily activity. In addition, nighttime symptoms bother him more than once a week.

Level 4: Severe Persistent Asthma—Having symptoms that limit the child's activity on most days of the week. In addition, nighttime symptoms occur more often than not.

Child with nebulizer with a mask receiving a short-term medicine to dilate the airways in the lungs. This is called a bronchodilator medicine. Examples include albuterol and Xopenex.

Child using a nebulizer with a mouthpiece

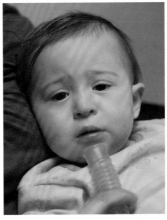

Infant receiving nebulized medication by blow-by inhalation

What medicines are prescribed for asthma?

Parents and children who have asthma need to be aware of the different kinds of medications that are used to treat asthma. There are two broad categories: quick-relief medications and long-term control medications.

Quick-relief medications include short-acting inhalers called bronchodilators. These inhaler medicines (albuterol, for example) dilate the airways in the lungs by relaxing the muscles around them. When a mild attack occurs, quick-relief medicines can be used up to four times a day to control asthma symptoms. They can be used before exercise for exercise-induced asthma as well. They are given via a handheld inhaler or a nebulizer machine at home. The nebulizer creates an aerosol solution that can be inhaled into the lungs.

Long-term control medications provide more lasting relief. They include inhaled steroid sprays or long-acting bronchodilator inhalers. Steroids can be given as a pill or in liquid form. There are other long-term medicines your doctor may discuss with you.

Asthma alert tool—peak flow meter

Many doctors suggest parents of children who experience asthma attacks should use a peak flow meter—a portable, handheld device that can help monitor the severity of their child's asthma. Peak flow meters measure the amount of air the child can push out of her lungs. By knowing what the child's normal

Child using a blow-by nebulizer

Child using peak flow meter. The child should blow into the meter as hard as he can three times. The highest reading is his current peak flow. Read on how to find out your child's red, yellow, and green zone peak flow readings.

capacity is—her personal best—parents (and older children capable of monitoring themselves) can use the peak flow meter to detect when their breathing is getting worse.

Patient case no. 1: Tammy's asthma attack put her in the yellow zone

Tammy is a twelve-year-old with asthma who was brought to the emergency room by her parents because she was experiencing increasing shortness of breath.

Tammy had already been diagnosed with asthma and had an asthma management plan from her doctor. She knew how to use an inhaler and a peak flow meter correctly.

Tammy said that she had been experiencing wheezing, coughing, and shortness of breath for two days. She was using her inhaler more than usual. In fact, even though she was using it about every four hours, her symptoms continued to worsen.

Tammy had been checking her peak flows with her handheld flow meter over the past few days. The day before, her peak flow decreased from her personal best of 320 liters per minute to 240 liters per minute. She was officially in her caution or yellow zone.

- The **green zone** is above 80 percent of the best peak flow reading. Tammy's green zone is above 256 (or 80 percent of 320).
- The **yellow zone** is between 50 to 80 percent of the child's personal best peak flow reading. Tammy's yellow zone is between 160 and 256.
- The **red zone** is below 160 liters per minute. Tammy's red zone is 50 percent below her personal best peak flow rate of 320.

Based on her **asthma management plan**, Tammy and her parents knew which readings on her peak flow meter represented the yellow or caution zone and which indicated the red or danger zone.

I noticed that her shortness of breath was forcing her to use words and phrases rather than sentences. It was causing her to sit up and lean forward on the side of the bed in order to use the accessory muscles in her neck to breathe. (These muscles help you to pull your chest up and enable you to take a deeper breath.) Fortunately, she was not feeling tired or sleepy.

When I listened to her lungs, I was glad to hear that she had very loud wheezing. Loud wheezing is much better than quiet wheezing.

When a patient has difficulty breathing, loud wheezing means that the child is moving a good amount of air with each breath. Quiet wheezing indicates that the lungs or airways are very tight, and very little air is moving through them. Therefore, quiet wheezing can sometimes indicate that the child is getting worse instead of better.

I ordered a double dose of albuterol by nebulizer for Tammy, and we kept observing her oxygen level with a fingertip monitor. We also gave her a dose of steroid tablets for further long-acting control of her wheezing.

After her first nebulizer treatment, Tammy's peak flow improved from 180 to 240 liters per minute. After a couple of hours and a few more nebulizer treatments, her peak flow rose to 270 liters per minute. Tammy also said that she felt 90 percent better than she had when she arrived.

Before she left, the nurses and I reinforced what Tammy and her parents knew about asthma. Fortunately, her pediatrician had taken the time to develop a thorough asthma management plan for her. As a result, they knew the signs for mild, moderate, and severe asthma attacks and for the corresponding green, yellow, and red danger zones when she does her peak flow measurements.

They also described to her the **signs of a severe attack**:

- **Shortness of breath while at rest**
- **Talking in words or phrases instead of complete sentences**
- **Peak flow under 50 percent** of the child's personal best.
- Sitting upright on the edge of a chair to use the accessory muscles in the neck to breathe

We also recapped the various asthma triggers. During this conversation, Tammy told us that, a couple of days before, she spent the night at the home of a friend who has several pets. Her asthma symptoms began the next morning.

I reminded Tammy and her parents that they need to check if friends have pets beforehand. I recommended that they schedule an appointment with Tammy's pediatrician to discuss situations like this. For example, she might have to avoid homes with pets entirely, or she might be able to take extra medication, such as a steroid, before she goes to visit or to spend the night.

Tammy's experience illustrates several key points to know about managing your child's asthma.

- Know your child's asthma triggers—whether it's pollen, dust mites, animal dander, or common colds.
- Know how to use your child's peak flow meter, and know the three zones for peak flow readings. Green is the safe zone, yellow is the caution zone, and red is the danger zone.
- Know how to treat your child when his peak flow indicates the yellow or red zone. For example,

a child in the yellow zone can use a short-acting inhaler. If the child is using the inhaler and not improving, call your child's doctor. Oral steroids or a steroid inhaler may be prescribed. A child in the red zone must go to a doctor or to an emergency room immediately.

What are some other clues to asthma in older children?

- A cough that seems to be worse at night
- Wheezing after running or exercise
- Wheezing or trouble breathing during a particular season of the year
- Wheezing or cough after exposure to certain irritants, such as animal hair or dust
- Colds associated with wheezing

Patient case no. 2: Miquel has a bad asthma attack

Fourteen-year-old Miquel went over to Ray's house after school. Miquel knows that his asthma usually gets worse when he goes over there, but he made sure that he had his inhaler with him. (Both of Ray's parents smoke cigarettes.)

While they are having fun with a new computer game, Ray's mom made them some deviled eggs for a snack.

About a half hour after being there, Miquel started to wheeze and became short of breath. He used his inhaler and was not feeling much better. He realized that he forgot his peak flow meter at home. He continued to wheeze and use his inhaler.

He used it five times in thirty minutes, and his breathing continued to become more and more difficult.

Miquel told Ray's mother that he had to go home and use his nebulizer machine. He was now talking in phrases instead of complete sentences, and his wheezing was getting worse. On a scale of one to ten his breathing severity is seven. During the three-to-four minute ride home, Miquel's breathing worsened and he became wide-eyed, scared, and anxious because he could not catch his breath.

When they arrived at Miquel's house, he was so short of breath he could not get out of the car. Ray's mother ran in to get Miquel's mother, and they called an ambulance.

When the paramedics arrived, Miquel was barely breathing. Instead of breathing fast, he was now breathing slowly, and he was barely conscious. The paramedics rapidly began to assist his breathing with an oxygen mask. His finger oxygen measurement by the paramedics was only 80 percent. (Normal is near 100 percent.) The paramedics tried to keep him breathing as well as possible. They gave him a shot of epinephrine to help with his severe wheezing.

The paramedics called the emergency room, and when they arrived, we had all of the equipment ready. We rushed Miquel into our special pediatric resuscitation room. I could see that Miquel was having respiratory failure and would not live unless I could put an airway tube into his trachea and put him on a ventilator.

I gave Miquel several medicines to make him sleep and temporarily paralyze his body so that I could intubate him. His asthma, however, kept his airways so tight that it was difficult to push air in and out of his lungs with the breathing bag. We also gave him steroids and more bronchodilator treatments. He was admitted to the intensive care unit, and a lung specialist was called in on his case.

Within twenty-four hours, Miquel was breathing much better, although he was still on a ventilator in the intensive care unit, kept asleep by a sedative.

The next day, the lung specialist removed the ventilator and airway tube. Miquel was awakened, and his normal breathing returned.

Miquel's parents told us that he's had severe attacks like this before that required him to be on a ventilator. (Children with a history of being on a ventilator have a high risk of having severe and rapid asthma attacks.) We also found out that Ray's mother had used peanut oil in her deviled eggs, and Miquel is allergic to peanuts.

Miquel left the hospital after three days. The doctors reminded him about his peanut allergy and the need to avoid cigarette smoke. They also gave him a new asthma management plan and two new medications.

Miquel learned that he cannot ignore what his body is telling him and must be more alert to danger signs and be more cautious about what he eats.

TOTAL PARENT POINTERS
ASTHMA

Every parent should know these **key facts about asthma.**

1. Each year, more and more children are diagnosed with asthma. About **six out of every one hundred children in the United States have asthma.**

2. **Children can die from severe attacks of asthma.**

3. Children with asthma should have an **asthma management plan** that has been developed by their physician. This plan should include:

   a. How to use current medications—quick-relief and long-term control medications.

   b. How to use a peak flow meter.

   c. Which peak flow readings indicate green zone, yellow zone, or red zone. See peak flow chart at the end of this section.

   d. How to respond to each zone. For example, readings in the yellow zone warn parents to call their physician. Any readings in the red zone mean that the child must go to a doctor or to an emergency room immediately.

4. **Know your asthma attack triggers and how to avoid them.** If exercise is a trigger, the child can learn to use his inhaler before exercising. Know the asthma triggers such as dust, mold, animal dander, cigarette smoke, foods that contain sulfites, certain medications such as aspirin, and strong odors.

5. **Create a trigger-free environment in your home.** Wash bedding at least once a week to avoid dust collection. Enclose your mattress and box spring with allergy protective covers. Use your inhaler before sports if you have exercise induced asthma.

6. **Know your personal best peak flow as well as you green, yellow, and red zones.** (Over 80 percent is green zone, 50–80 percent is yellow, and below 50 percent is red.)

TOTAL PARENT POINTERS
ASTHMA

FINDING YOUR PEAK FLOW ZONES

1. Find your personal best peak flow number and circle it.
2. The number to the right of it is your 80 percent peak flow. Circle it.
3. The number to the right of that is your 50 percent peak flow number. Circle it.

4. Set the yellow marker on your peak flow meter to the 80 percent number.
5. Set the red marker on your peak flow meter to the 50 percent number.

Peak Flow Number	80%	50%
100	80	50
110	88	55
120	96	60
130	104	65
140	112	70
150	120	75
160	128	80
170	136	85
180	144	90
190	152	95
200	160	100
210	168	105
220	176	110
230	184	115
240	192	120
250	200	125
260	208	130
270	216	135
280	224	140
290	232	145
300	240	150
310	248	155
320	256	160
330	264	165
340	272	170
350	280	175

Peak Flow Number	80%	50%
360	288	180
370	296	185
380	304	190
390	312	195
400	320	200
410	328	205
420	336	210
430	344	215
440	352	220
450	360	225
460	376	235
470	376	235
480	384	240
490	392	245
500	400	250
510	408	255
520	416	260
530	424	265
540	432	270
550	440	275
560	448	280
570	456	285
580	464	290
590	472	295
600	480	300

24

Autism Spectrum Disorders

What is autism?

Autism is a developmental disorder characterized by abnormalities in a child's social interaction, communication, and repetitive behaviors. This condition affects approximately one in every 166 children. Autism is one of five disorders under the title of autism spectrum disorders. We will talk about each of those disorders later.

When do the signs of autism usually occur?

Parents recognize the signs of autism when their child is between the ages of two and six. They first notice that something is not right with their child's communication skills. The National Institute of Child

Health and Human Development (NICHD)[1] lists five behaviors that can be early signs of autism:
1. The baby does not coo or babble by the age of twelve months.
2. The child does not gesture, point, wave, or grasp by the age of twelve months.
3. The child has not said a single word by the age of sixteen months.
4. The child does not say two-word phrases on his own (rather than just repeating what someone says to him) by twenty-four months of age.
5. The child exhibits ANY loss of ANY language or social skills at ANY age.

Some additional signs of autism detailed by the Autism Society of America[2] include:
1. A child who is insistent on sameness and resistant to change.
2. A child who has difficulty expressing her needs with words or gestures.
3. A child who prefers to be alone.

4. A child who avoids eye contact.
5. A child who does not want to be held.
6. A child who spins objects repetitively.
7. A child who has a very severe and strong reaction to loud noises, bright lights, or other sensory stimulation.
8. A child who has an undersensitivity to pain.
9. A child who plays with objects that appear to be odd or unusual.
10. A child who is unresponsive to verbal cues.
11. A child who demonstrates self-destructive behavior, such as hitting herself.
12. A child who makes repetitive body movements.
13. A child who repeats certain words or phrases.
14. A child with an inappropriate attachment to certain objects.
15. A child who exhibits obvious hyper- or underactive behavior.

What should I do if I think my child has autism?

It is normal for children to exhibit any of the above behaviors from time to time. However, the more of the above behaviors a child exhibits and the longer the time span, the more you ought to be concerned. If your child exhibits two or more of the above signs of autism, especially on an ongoing basis, talk to your pediatrician or contact your local grade school teacher and request an evaluation. If the child is a pre-schooler, your pediatrician may suggest contacting your local health department for an evaluation. But by school age, federal law requires your home school district to perform a full developmental evaluation upon a parent's written request within ninety working days. The written request should be submitted to the principal or special education coordinator at your child's home school. You may request an evaluation even if your child is too young to enroll in that school. All testing and subsequent treatment should be provided by the school district at no cost to the family. Schools and local health departments have trained staffs available to perform a complete assessment of your child. A specialist will also screen your child for any visual, hearing, or neurologic problems that could mimic autistic behavior.

Are there different types of autism?

Autism is one of five subtypes of autistic spectrum disorders:

1. Autism (autistic disorder)
2. Pervasive developmental disorder (atypical autism)
3. Asperger's syndrome
4. Rett's syndrome
5. Child disintegrative disorder

Autism (or autistic disorder) is considered the most severe condition, compared to Asperger's syndrome and pervasive developmental disorder. Rett's syndrome and child disintegrative syndrome are less common types of autistic spectrum disorders.

Autism is the most common of these disorders. Pervasive developmental disorder—NOS (not otherwise specified) is a less severe type of autism. This term is used when a child does not exhibit all of the criteria for autistic disorder. Asperger's syndrome is autism in a child with normal intelligence and fairly developed social skills. Rett's syndrome only occurs in girls and is characterized by hand-wringing motions and frequent leg movements. Child disintegrative disorder occurs in children between age three or four who have had a dramatic loss of verbal, motor, and social skills.

Is the incidence of autism increasing or decreasing?

Some experts claim that the incidence of autism in children is growing from an estimated 10 to 17 percent every year, according to the Autism Society of America.[3] However, other experts say that the incidence is not increasing, but we are better at identifying and diagnosing the condition than in the past.

What causes autism?

No one is really sure what causes autism. However, scientists believe there is a significant genetic component. Some environmental factors may play a role, but this is not proven. Some studies suggest that rubella (measles) before thirty weeks in a woman's pregnancy can cause autism in her unborn child.

The most important point for parents to understand is that autism has nothing to do with their parenting skills or their effectiveness as a good parent. Scientists have analyzed the brains of children with autism and have found that a four-year-old with autism has a brain the size of a thirteen-year-old.

There is also an increase in the number of neurons in the white matter. However, it appears that these neurons do not communicate very well over long distances within the brain. The neurons appear to be more jumbled. The neurons seem to be too short for adequate communication with more distant parts of the brain. The brain of an autistic child also appears to have a poor communication system between the right and left sides of the brain.

Basically this means that the brain of the autistic child has several areas that function almost independently and do not have a good feedback system with other parts of the brain.

What is the best treatment for autistic children?

Autistic children require treatment on several levels, such as speech, behavioral, and physical therapies. Two of the most popular behavioral therapies for autistic children are:

1. Applied Behavioral Analysis (ABA)—This is the popular behavioral therapy originally proposed by psychologist B. F. Skinner. This is a type of behavioral modification that provides rewards for correct behavior.

2. The second technique is called DIR (Developmental-Individual-Relationship) based therapy. This is based on the concept

of floor-time therapy originally developed by child psychiatrist Stanley Greenspan. This therapy is focused on teaching the child appropriate back and forth communication. This therapy focuses on both the verbal and emotional interactions between two people. Spending time on the floor facilitates communication and a bond between two people.

It should be noted that many of the more successful behavior and psychological treatments of autism involve a significant amount of sensory stimulation and sensory interaction with the child.

Can autistic children grow up to be normal adults?

There are several reports of children who have grown up to be functioning adults with normal lives. It has been demonstrated that early intervention, especially before kindergarten, correlates with a more positive outcome. High-functioning autistic children and those with a normal IQ tend to have a better long-term outcome. However, children with moderate to severe autism tend to have smaller degrees of improvement with therapy.

PERVASIVE DEVELOPMENTAL DISORDER

Pervasive developmental disorder—NOS (not otherwise specified) is a subtype of autism that fulfills all the criteria for an autistic disorder. This is also called atypical autism. These children's social skills are less impaired than those of children with an autistic disorder.

ASPERGER'S SYNDROME

Asperger's syndrome is considered the least severe of the five subtypes of the autism spectrum disorder. In fact, some researchers even place Asperger's syndrome in a separate category and do not include it as a subtype of autism. One of the most important aspects of Asperger's syndrome is that these children do not have delays in the area of communicational language.

A child with Asperger's syndrome typically has a severe and sustained impairment in social interaction, and the development of restricted, repetitive patterns of behavior and interest in activities. This impairment causes clinically significant impairment in social, occupational, and other important areas of functioning.

Asperger's syndrome occurs in children who have normal intelligence and fully developed interpersonal communication skills. These children also have normal language skills.

Many Asperger children may have an obsessive interest in a certain topic or area of interest. For example, they may be compulsive about collecting stamps, baseball cards, rocks, etc.

Children with Asperger's syndrome also have trouble with abstract ideas. They seem to be socially aloof, but they want to be socially active. They just don't have the intuitive social skills to know what to do.

RETT'S SYNDROME

Rett's syndrome is a subtype of autism that occurs only in girls. It affects one out of ten thousand to fifteen thousand females. Typically, someone notices that the child's development has deteriorated between the ages of six and eighteen months. The girl's mental and social development begins to regress. In addition, the child withdraws from social contact with her parents and others. A young child with Rett's syndrome will have a characteristic hand-wringing movement and trouble keeping her legs still.

Some studies have shown that a mutation of a single gene causes Rett's syndrome.

CHILD DISINTEGRATIVE DISORDER

Child disintegrative disorder is a type of autism that occurs in two out of one hundred thousand children, typically in boys between three and four years of age. After the age of three or four the child has a very dramatic loss in his verbal motor and social skills. The child may also lose control of his bowel or bladder function and have a low intellectual ability.

Is there any genetic testing for autism?
Parents should be aware that approximately 2 to 5 percent of children with autism spectrum disorder have Fragile X syndrome, a disorder that affects the X chromosome and is the most common form of mental retardation. All children with autism spectrum disorder should be tested for Fragile X syndrome. Parents need to be aware that if their autistic child has Fragile X syndrome, one out of two boys born in the future to those parents are likely to develop autism.

Seizures in autistic children
One percent of children with autism develop seizures. Approximately one out of four, or 25 percent, of children with autism will develop some type of seizure disorder. These can usually be managed very effectively with various antiseizure medications.

NOTES
1. Modified from National Institute of Child Health and Human Development's Autism Research.
2. Courtesy of the Autism Society of America, "Common Characteristics of Autism," www.autism-society.org
3. Ibid.
4. American Psychiatric Association, *Diagnostic and Statistical Manual of Mental Disorders: DSM-IV-TR* (Washington, DC: American Psychiatric Association, 2000).

TOTAL PARENT POINTERS
AUTISM SPECTRUM DISORDERS

1. **Autism** is **a condition that affects approximately one in 166 children.** Autism is a development disorder characterized by abnormalities in the child's social interaction and communication. It also involves repetitive behaviors.

2. Some of the **most common warning signs of autism are:**
   a. The baby does not coo or babble by the age of twelve months.
   b. The child does not gesture, point, wave, or grasp by the age of twelve months.
   c. A child has not said a single word by the age of sixteen months.
   d. The child does not engage in two-word phrases by the age of twenty-four months.
   e. The child has lost a significant portion of his language or social skills.

3. A child with signs of autism should have a complete **developmental screening evaluation** by specialists at his preschool, grade school, or local state health department. This screening is required by federal law, the Individual with Disabilities Education Improvement Act (IDEA). IDEA is a federally mandated program that requires that the family of a developmentally impaired child receive free public services for educational therapy, speech therapy, occupational therapy, behavioral therapy, etc.

4. **The five categories of autism spectrum disorder are:**
   a. Autism
   b. Asperger's syndrome
   c. Rett's syndrome
   d. Child disintegrative disorder
   e. Pervasive development disorder

5. The different therapies that are most likely to help children with autism include the following:
   a. Behavioral therapy
   b. Occupational therapy
   c. Sensory therapy
   d. Social therapy
   e. Communication therapy

Almost every successful therapeutic approach to autism involves some form of sensory stimulation or contact.

More Information About Autism
Listed below are several organizations that can be contacted for further information on autism or go to our Web site—*TheTotalParent.com.*

Association for Science in Autism Treatment
389 Main Street Suite 202
Maiden, ME 02148
info@asatonline.org
http://www.asatonline.org
Tel: 781.397.8943   Fax: 781.397.8887

Autism Network International (ANI)
PO Box 35448
Syracuse, NY 13235–5448
jisincla@mailbox.syr.edu
http://ani.autistics.org

Autism Society of America
7910 Woodmont Avenue Suite 300
Bethesda, MD 20814–3067
http://www.autism-society.org
Tel: 301.657.0881   Fax: 301.657.0869
800–3AUTISM (328.8476)

 TOTAL PARENT POINTERS
AUTISM SPECTRUM DISORDERS

MAAP Services for Autism, Asperger's and PDD
PO Box 524
Crown Point, IN 46308
chart@netnitco.net
http://www.maapservices.org
Tel: 219.662.1311   Fax: 219.662.0638

National Dissemination Center for Children with Disabilities
Special Education Programs
PO Box 1492
Washington DC 20013–1492
nichcy@aed.ort
http://www.nichcy.org
Tel: 800.695.0285   Fax: 202.884.8441

US Department of Education, Office of Autism National Committee (AUTCOM)
PO Box 429
Forest Knolls, CA 64933
http://www.auticom.org

Autism Research Institute (ARI)
4182 Adams Avenue
San Diego, CA 62116
http://www.autismresearchchinstitute.com
Tel: 619.281.7165   Fax: 619.563.6840

Autism Speaks
2 Park Avenue 11th Floor
New York, NY 10016
http://www.autismspeaks.org
Tel: 212.252.8584   Fax: 212.252.8676

Cure Autism Now (CAN) Foundation
5455 Wilshire Blvd Suite 2250
Los Angeles, CA 90036–4234
info@cureautismnow.org
http://www.cureautismnow.org
Tel: 323.549.0500   Fax: 323.459.0547
888.8AUTISM (828.8476)

National Alliance for Autism Research (NAAR)
99 Wall Street
Research Park
Princeton, NJ 08540
naar@naar.org
http://www.naar.org
Tel: 609.430.9160   Fax: 609.430.9163
888.777.NAAR (6227)
California: 310.230.3568

National Institute of Child Health and Human Development (NICHD)
National Institutes of Health, DHHS
31 Center Drive, Rm 2A32 MSC 2425
Bethesda, MD 20892–2425
http://www.nichd.nih.gov
Tel: 301.496.5133   Fax: 301.496.7101

National Institute of Deafness and Other Communication Disorders Information Clearinghouse
1 Communication Avenue
Bethesda, MD 20892–3456
nidcdinfo@nidcd.nih.gov
hhtp://www.nidcd.nih.gov
Tel: 800.241.1044
800.241.1055 (TTD/TTY)

National Institute of Mental Health (NIMH) National Institutes of Health DHHS
6001 Executive Blvd Rm. 8184, MSC 9663
Bethesda, MD 20892–9663
nimhinfo@nih.gov
http://www.nimh.nih.gov
Tel: 301.443.4513   Fax: 301.443.4279
301.443.8431 (TTY)
866.615-NIMH (6464)

25

Behavioral Problems

This chapter will help you identify the clues to some of the most
common psychiatric illnesses and
psychological problems that can
affect children and teenagers,
including the following:
1. Conduct disorders
2. Oppositional defiant disorder
3. Intermittent explosive disorder
4. Depression
5. Teen suicide
6. Bipolar disorder

CONDUCT DISORDER'S

All children have their moments
of acceptable and unacceptable
behavior. But at what point does
misbehavior become a significant
problem? One answer is that when
the child's behavior is significantly
unacceptable and lasts for more
than six months, the child may
have a conduct disorder. This
means he demonstrates a consistent pattern of hostile, aggressive,
and disruptive conduct that is
beyond what is expected of a child
at that age.

**What are the usual signs of a conduct
disorder?**
1. Doing poorly in school despite
   doing well previously
2. Frequent arguments and temper
   tantrums
3. A trend of consistent
   confrontations or arguments
   with parents, teachers, and
   other authority figures
4. Damaging or destroying other
   people's property
5. Persistent lying
6. Stealing
7. Sexual activity at an early age
8. Threatening or harming other
   children or pets
9. Disregard for commonly
   accepted rules of conduct or
   moral values
10. Insensitivity to the suffering or
    unhappiness of others

OPPOSITIONAL DEFIANT DISORDER (ODD)[1]

All children can be argumentative,
defiant, or uncooperative at times.
Young adolescents are particularly

prone to exerting their independence through oppositional behavior and rebellious communications. Children may misbehave as a result of a lack of sleep or stress. However, when the disruptive and argumentative behavior is far beyond the norm for other children of the same age, it may indicate what is called the oppositional defiant disorder (ODD).

The signs of oppositional defiant disorder are:[2]

1. Frequent temper tantrums
2. Excessive arguing with adults
3. Active defiance and refusal to comply with adult requests and rules
4. Deliberate attempts to annoy or upset people
5. Blaming others for his mistakes or misbehavior
6. Often being touchy or easily annoyed by others
7. Frequent anger and resentment
8. Mean and hateful when upset
9. Seeking revenge
10. An attitude of sullenness and an unwillingness to cooperate

Since rebelliousness is common among younger teenagers, it should be emphasized that not every oppositional adolescent has ODD. However, it is estimated that about 5 to 15 percent of school-age children may have the full ODD syndrome. Frequently the parents of these children report that since birth the child has shown more oppositional behavior than other children in the family.

What is the best means of dealing with a child who has ODD?

1. Provide positive reinforcement for good behaviors.

2. Try to avoid power struggles, especially over minor issues. It is especially a good idea to avoid power struggles over the child's attitude. Remember that the child has complete control over her attitude, and that arguing with a child about her attitude is fruitless and doomed to failure. As a parent, you have much more legitimate control when it comes to the child's behavior. An effective response to an ODD child is to say, "I'm sorry you don't understand and that you don't like it, and you can be as angry as you want, but you're still going to have to do . . ."

3. Model the type of behavior you want your child to learn. This means if the child becomes argumentative, you can compose yourself and speak to her in a soft, comforting, and reassuring tone of voice. If necessary, take a brief time-out or create some distance between yourself and your child to avoid an escalation of the issue. When you return five or ten minutes later, you can deal with the issue in a calm and controlled manner. This will also help your child to learn how to calm down and to learn the appropriate means of communicating. Sometimes simply agreeing with the child is an effective response: "You're right; I'm a lousy parent. But you're stuck with me, and you've got to do the dishes."

4. Set limits and rules for the

child's behavior. This may involve enforcing a bedtime rule of being in bed at 8 or 9 p.m., limiting computer time to a certain number of minutes per day, etc. The best way to do this is to sit down with all family members and allow everyone to provide input to creating these rules. Talk to each other about the reasons for certain rules such as bedtimes and curfews.

5. Set up a reward system. Allow family members to provide ideas about what type of realistic rewards can be used. This may include the reward of getting one or more extra hour of TV time on the weekend for doing daily chores and homework without being reminded. Or it might mean an extra hour of computer time during the week. In particular, recognize and praise appropriate acts of responsible, independent decision making and behavior.

6. Write down the rules and rewards on a piece of paper and post it where everyone can see it.

7. Be prepared to strictly enforce the rules that you have made. Be careful not to make rules that are too strict to enforce. Start out with a few basic rules that can be easily observed and reinforced with rewards. As time goes on, you can add more rules to the list.

8. Focus on maintaining your own mental health. This means allowing yourself adequate time for sleep, relaxation, and exercise. You may also need to creatively utilize some separation time from your child. This may involve allowing your child to go to a friend's house for a few hours while you take a break. It may also mean that your spouse will take over care of the children while you do something to relax and refresh yourself. Talk to other moms and dads who may be having a similar experience. Remember, children do not mind being punished if the parent is being punished along with them. So make sure that you are not the one suffering by setting limits on your child.

INTERMITTENT EXPLOSIVE DISORDER

Childred with this disorder express anger in very aggressive outbursts, often resulting in injuries to other people or destruction of property. These outbursts are frequently unprovoked and the child's reaction is out of proportion to the precipitating event. These disorders, which tend to be more common in boys, are a type of impulse control disorder. The child has an uncontrollable urge to act out and be destructive.

How can I teach my child self-control and anger control?

Model the behavior you want your child to have. Remember, you and your spouse are the most important and powerful examples of adulthood that your children live with and adopt. If you have a problem controlling your temper, your child will learn and mimic your behavior.

This is actually an opportunity for your own self-development. Ask yourself: Do I want my child to act like me when I am upset? If the answer is no, then think about how you can change your own behavior. This may be as simple as being aware of it, but usually it takes a dedicated effort to find new ways of dealing with your own anger and frustration. Try to develop the values of patience and understanding. The key concept here is commitment. If you are committed to changing your behavior, it will happen. Think about how positively this will impact your child's character and his future happiness. Keep in mind that you are the one person whom the child will learn from. The way that you behave means one hundred times more to him than what you tell him. You need to show him how to behave by setting a good example.

Help your child understand that everyone experiences anger at some time. Teach your children how to engage in creative problem solving to deal with difficult situations. It may be a matter of simply having empathy for the other person, understanding that accidents can happen, or learning about patience. The key here is to develop the right attitude. Sometimes interpreting the child's problem as one of learning self-control rather than changing bad behavior makes the problem easier both for you and your child.

Use time-outs. Time-outs can be used differently for different ages.

Children under the age of five or six can usually be sent to a quiet area for a few minutes until they compose themselves. Distracting them is also a good technique.

Children in the seven-to-twelve age group can understand actions and consequences. Talk to them (when they are calm) about how bad behavior can have bad consequences (such as the loss of something valued when they are punished). If you recall from an earlier chapter, the key is to find out what they like most, and then consider taking that away first as a punishment. It may be loss of TV viewing, computer time, playtime, or it might mean missing a sports game or not being able to go to a friend's house.

Age thirteen to seventeen: Reinforce your child's problem-solving skills. Teach her that it is better to sit back and think about how to deal with an upsetting situation than to react impulsively to it. Reacting impulsively usually results in an emotional outburst instead of a thoughtful and reasonable response to a situation. Emotional outbursts frequently result in a poor solution to the problem, a loss of friends, alienation of other people, unhappiness, and a tarnished image or reputation.

Make sure that your children are getting enough sleep. In this age of laptops, e-mails, chat rooms, iPods, handheld devices, computer games, and TVs, there are a multitude of distractions to keep your child up at night. (It is not a good idea to allow children to have a TV in their room. This is too tempting for them to resist. It also prevents you from monitoring what they watch.) Check to make sure that your children are getting to bed at a reasonable hour. This usually means around 8 p.m. for school-age children and 9 p.m. for junior high or seventh and eighth graders. Bedtime hours for high-school age children can be flexible, such as from 9 p.m. to 10 p.m. on school nights, depending on home-work and activities. Don't allow your children to fall into the trap of staying up later and later each night. This will result in fatigue and diminished learning ability at school as well as poor behavior. They will be irritable when they come home, and before you know it, things will escalate into an argu-ment. When they stay up late on weekends, they will need to catch up on their sleep on Saturday or Sunday before the school week begins again.

DEPRESSION

Depression affects almost every-body at some point. Along with emotions such as anxiety, love, and anger, depression or extreme sad-ness is one of the most common human emotions and can be a reaction to very small, minor events or to very big, important events or relationships. Approximately 5 percent of children experience sig-nificant depression at some time in their lives. The diagnosis of clinical depression is usually made when strong and often uncontrollable feelings of depression interfere with the child's ability to function normally.

Keep in mind that drug use is high on the list of the causes of depression in children. Children who use drugs frequently go into a depressed mood as they withdraw from the drug or stimulant. In some cases, sedatives, narcotics, and cocaine cause a drug-induced depression.

Some of the signs of depression include the following:

1. Frequent and intense sadness, tearfulness, crying
2. Extreme hopelessness
3. Decreased interest in activities, inability to enjoy previously favored activities
4. Persistent boredom, low energy
5. Social isolation, poor communication
6. Low self-esteem and guilt
7. Extreme sensitivity to rejection or failure
8. Increased irritability, anger, or hostility
9. Difficulty with relationships
10. Frequent complaints of physical illnesses, such as headaches and stomachaches
11. Frequent absences from school or poor classroom performance
12. Poor concentration
13. A major change in eating and/ or sleeping patterns
14. Talking about running away from home
15. Thoughts or expressions of suicide or other self-destructive behavior

If one or more of these signs persist, especially if they are intense, parents should seek an evaluation.[3]

What should I do if I think my child is depressed?

Focus on identifying what may have caused the depression. In some cases it may be a loss (usually of a loved one or a close friend), drug abuse, a difficult home situation, troubles at school, parental pressure to succeed, or a difficult romantic relationship.

Talk to your pediatrician, family doctor, or school counselor. If your budget or insurance permits, make an appointment with a private counselor (child psychiatrist, psychologist, or social worker).

Listen carefully for comments suggestive of suicidal thoughts and observe closely any changes in appearance or behavior.

TEEN SUICIDE

What do I need to know about the risks and warning signs of teen suicide?

Parents need to be aware that suicide is the third leading cause of death in the fifteen-to-twenty-four-year-old age group. Youngsters in this age range can be highly sensitive and emotional and react to every problem as if it is a crisis. If the problem is severe enough, they may feel that suicide is the only way to escape their unhappiness.

Warning signs of suicidal thoughts in a child or teenager include the following:[4]

1. A unusual change or neglect in personal appearance
2. A significant personality change
3. A loss of enjoyment or pleasure in things that were previously enjoyed
4. Withdrawal from various activities, friends, social groups, etc.
5. Abusing drugs and/or alcohol
6. Sudden deterioration in school work
7. Frequent physical complaints such as stomachaches, headaches, insomnia, loss of appetite, etc.
8. Making such statements as, "You won't have to worry about this when I'm not around anymore," or "You won't have to worry about me anymore."
9. Hopeless statements such as, "It is no use trying anymore."
10. A recent significant loss in a relationship (such as rejection by a boyfriend or girlfriend) or of something of significant value to the child

What should I do if my child's behavior suggests suicidal thoughts?

You should try to bring your child to his doctor. Also make an appointment with a counselor, psychiatrist, or psychologist. However, if you feel that a suicide attempt is imminent, it is better to be safe than sorry. Without any hesitation, call an ambulance or bring your child to the nearest emergency room. Keep your child away from dangerous weapons, chemicals, medicines, etc. Keep in mind that children can die from overdoses of several over-the-counter pain medicines.

BIPOLAR DISORDER

Bipolar disorder is characterized by extreme swings in mood, energy, and behavior that significantly interfere with normal life. Bipolar disorder is a new term for what was previously called manic-depressive illness. It can occur in children and teenagers, but it is often difficult to recognize in children because the symptoms seem to be part of a child's normal moody behavior. The key difference, however, is that the mood changes in bipolar disorder are extreme and significantly interfere with normal functioning at home and at school.

Symptoms of bipolar disorder include:[5]

1. Persistent irritable mood
2. Loss of interest in activities previously enjoyed
3. Significant change in appetite or body weight
4. Difficulty sleeping or oversleeping
5. Physical agitation or a slowing down
6. Loss of energy
7. Feelings of worthlessness or inappropriate guilt
8. Difficulty concentrating
9. Recurring thoughts of death or suicide

Manic symptoms of bipolar disorder include:[6]

1. Severe changes in mood: either extremely irritable or overly silly and elated

2. Overly inflated self-esteem, grandiosity
3. Increased energy
4. Decreased need for sleep, being able to go about the day's events with little or no sleep without tiring
5. Increased talking, talks too much, talks too fast, changes topics too quickly, cannot be interrupted
6. Distractibility, attention constantly swings from one thing to the next
7. Hypersexuality, increased sexual thoughts, moods, or behavior, use of explicit sexual language
8. Increased goal-directed activity or physical agitation
9. Disregard of risk, excessive involvement in risky behaviors or activities
10. Difficulty sleeping or oversleeping

Approximately 1 percent of adolescents between the ages of fourteen and eighteen have bipolar disorder.

What kind of medications are used to treat bipolar disorder?

Mood-stabilizing medications are used to treat the child. Ideally, this should be handled by a child psychiatrist. Medications include:

1. Lithium
2. Valproate
3. Various new mood-stabilizing medications

NOTES

1. Modified from: "Child Behavioral Disorders," Medline Plus, National Library of Medicine, National Institutes of Health, http://www.nlm.nih.gov/medlineplus/childbehaviordisorders.html.
2. "Children with Oppositional Defiant Disorder," Facts for Families, American Academy of Child and Adolescent Psychiatry, no. 72, updated December 1999, http://www.acap.org/cs/root/facts_for_families/children_with_oppositional_defiant_disorder.
3. "The Depressed Child," Facts for Families, American Academy of Child and Adolescent Psychiatry, no. 4, updated July 2004, http://www.aacap.org/cs/root/facts_for_families/the_depressed_child.
4. "Teen Suicide," Facts for Families, American Academy of Child and Adolescent Psychiatry, no. 10: updated May 2008, http://www.aacap.org/cs/root/facts_for_families/teen_suicide.
5. Child and Adolescent Bipolar Disorder: An Update from the National Institute of Mental Health, Publication no. 001-14778, 2000, http://hsc.virginia.edu/internet/psychiatric/PDFs/BipolarDisorder/NIMHbiploarupdate.pdf.
6. Ibid.

TOTAL PARENT POINTERS
BEHAVIORAL PROBLEMS

1. **Conduct disorder** is characterized by extreme acting out, immoral, at times even illegal behavior. The child may damage property or injure someone, persistent in lying or stealing, hold hostility toward authority figures, exhibit poor school performance, skip school, and engage in early sexual activity.

2. **Oppositional defiant disorder** occurs in children who have a high degree of argumentative and defiant behavior that persists over six months. The best treatment is positive reinforcement of good behaviors. Avoid power struggles.

3. **Intermittent Explosive Disorder.** These children have uncontrollable and extreme outbursts of anger and violence that are out of proportion to the inciting event. **The key is teaching these teenagers how to manage their anger.** An important part of this is **being a good role model.** This means that parents must set a good example in dealing with their own anger and frustration. **Time-outs** can be used for both younger and older children. **Problem-solving discussions** are important with older children and teenagers.

4. **Be aware of any signs of depression in children and teenagers.** These include a persistent depressed mood, change in energy level, poor school performance, loss of interest in previously enjoyable activities, loss of appetite, drug use, lack of interest in social activities, etc.

5. Be aware of **the warning signs of a potentially suicidal teenager**: suicidal comments, loss of weight, sleeping or staying in his room all day, loss of friends, lack of social interests, a recent emotional loss such as a girlfriend, neglect of personal appearance or hygiene, drug or alcohol use, persistent physical symptoms (abdominal pain, headaches).

6. **Bipolar Disorder** (formerly called manic-depressive disorder) is characterized by severe mood swings and irritability. Mood-stabilizing drugs are very helpful for many of these children.

26

Childhood Cancers

EARLY WARNING SIGNS OF CANCERS

No parent wants to think about the possibility of his child having cancer. And although cancer in a child is rare (about 12,400 children and adolescents are diagnosed every year in the United States), it's still wise for you to know the symptoms, because early diagnosis and treatment is key to the best possible outcome.

What are the most common cancers that affect children?

The most common cancers in children are:

- Leukemia—36 percent
- Tumors of the brain and spinal cord—26 percent
- Lymphoma—15 percent
- Neuroblastoma—9 percent
- Muscle tumors—8 percent
- Kidney tumors (Wilms tumor)—8 percent
- Bone tumors—6 percent
- Tumors of the eye (retinoblastoma)—3 percent[1]

LEUKEMIA

Acute leukemia is the most common childhood cancer (41 percent) and is due to a rapid rate of production of certain white blood cells called lymphoblasts. As a result of this rapid multiplication of lymphoblasts in the bone marrow, there is bone marrow failure. The red blood cells decrease, and the child becomes weak, pale, and anemic. The platelets that control bleeding also decrease, and the child can develop bleeding gums. The lymph nodes also enlarge because these cells are also in the lymph nodes.

How common is leukemia in children?

Acute lymphoblastic leukemia (ALL) accounts for 77 percent of all cases of childhood leukemia.

Other causes of leukemia in children include:

1. AML—acute myelogenous leukemia—11 percent of cases
2. CML—chronic myelegenous leukemia—2 to 3 percent of cases

3. Juvenile chronic myelegenous Leukemia—1 to 2 percent of cases.

The other 7 to 9 percent of cases are difficult to classify in the above categories.

HODGKIN'S DISEASE

Hodgkin's disease is a cancer of the lymph glands, making it a type of lymphoma cancer. Lymphoma is classified as either Hodgkin's or non-Hodgkin's lymphoma. Lymphoma is the third most common cancer in children in the United States.

Hodgkin's disease is diagnosed by imaging tests, which show the presence of tumors in the lymph nodes. Hodgkin's disease usually occurs in patients between the ages of thirteen and thirty-five, and the disease begins with a painless enlarged lymph node in the neck or upper shoulder area. If your child has a painless lymph node over one inch in size on the neck and it does not decrease over a four-to-five-week span, make sure your doctor has it evaluated and biopsied.

The overall cure rate for advanced cases is 60 to 70 percent. The survival rate for children with early diagnosis is 90 percent.

BRAIN AND SPINAL CORD TUMORS

What are the symptoms of brain and spinal cord tumors?

Twenty-nine percent of all childhood cancers occur in the brain or the spinal cord. Tumors of the brain and spinal cord typically cause the following symptoms:

- Trouble walking
- Headaches that awaken the child at night
- A significant change in the child's behavior
- A change in the parallel alignment of the eyes
- Persistent headaches that do not stop after several days, especially in children less than six years of age

What should I know about brain hemorrhage from brain tumors?

Sometimes a child with tumors may develop bleeding in the brain, also called a brain hemorrhage. This is one of the most serious complications a cancer patient can face. A hemorrhage can occur when a tumor has spread to the brain or when the child's blood has become thin. Thinning of the blood can be caused by a low platelet count. Platelets help the blood to clot, so thin blood does not clot properly.

When a hemorrhage or bleeding occurs in the brain, a seizure may occur or the brain may swell. That brain swelling can also compress parts of the brain that control breathing. If the brain swells, the child can stop breathing and die. Patients who have brain swelling are frequently placed on a ventilator or may be given medications such as steroids (dexamethasone) to decrease swelling of their brain.

MUSCLE TUMORS

Muscle tumors can also occur in children. They begin in a muscle as a firm area that is nontender.

The most common location is in the head or neck area. Symptoms include a swollen, raised area. If symptoms don't improve within four to five weeks, the area should be biopsed. A malignant tumor of the muscle tissue is called a rhabdomyosarcoma.

BONE TUMOR

Bone tumors begin in long bones, especially in the bones around the knee. Two examples of bone tumors include Ewing's sarcoma and osteosarcoma. Children with this type of bone tumor may develop a limp and pain in the area of the bone. Sometimes this may include some slight swelling. If a child has bone pain and the pain does not resolve in approximately a week, the child should be referred to her pediatrician or family doctor. An x-ray may reveal signs of a tumor.

EYE TUMORS

Parents who notice a white discoloration in the black pupil of their child's eye are typically first to find this rare eye tumor called a retinoblastoma. This is the most common tumor found within the eye in children. Unfortunately in 30 percent of the cases, children will have tumors in both eyes. Tumors that originate in the eye can also spread to the brain, liver, or kidneys. Unfortunately, since this is a malignant tumor, the affected eye must be surgically removed to prevent spread of the disease to other parts of the body.

COMPLICATIONS OF CANCERS

The most frequent complications of childhood cancer include:
- Infections
- Spinal cord compression
- Low sodium level in the bloodstream
- Tumor destruction syndrome
- Obstruction of the veins to the heart
- Brain hemorrhage
- Abdominal emergencies

INFECTIONS IN CANCER PATIENTS

Children with cancer often have a reduced immunity, which makes them vulnerable to infectious complications. In many cases, the white blood cells are decreased as a result of the tumor, chemotherapy, or radiation. In such cases, children can develop infections such as pneumonia, urinary tract infections, skin infections called cellulitis, and airway infections. Infections may also occur at sites of an IV catheter or other types of catheters used for chemotherapy. Any young cancer patient who has a fever should be evaluated immediately by a physician. A fever is defined as an oral temperature above 99.5°F or a rectal temperature or 100.4°F or more.

Other infections that can occur in cancer patients include:
- Bacterial infections
  - Strep infections
  - Bacteria that infect the lungs and cause pneumonia
  - Bacteria that infect the urine
- Fungal infections
  - Yeast infections that can infect the upper airway

- Viral infections
  - Herpes
  - Simplex virus
  - Chicken pox virus that can cause severe disease

Other types of infections include parasites, which can affect the lungs.

TUMOR DESTRUCTION SYNDROME

Tumor destruction syndrome occurs when there is a sudden destruction of cells involved with the tumor. This can occur shortly after chemotherapy is administered. As a result, there is a sudden destruction of cells and an increase in certain chemicals of the blood, such as uric acid and phosphate. This can result in kidney failure, acidity of the blood, and low calcium levels.

Needless to say, kidney failure is a severe complication. Low calcium can result in spasms of the muscles and an abnormal heartbeat. Low calcium can also cause muscle weakness and evulsions. The best treatment for tumor destruction syndrome is large amounts of IV fluids and medications that decrease the production of chemicals such as uric acid.

What should I know about low sodium in the blood stream?

Children with low sodium can develop:
- Confusion
- Fatigue
- Seizures

Treatment of low sodium is important because this can cause seizures and breathing troubles. Children with low sodium are treated with an IV of normal saline to increase the sodium level. In addition, oral fluids may be restricted in order to allow the blood to become more concentrated with sodium again.

SVC SYNDROME

Obstruction of the veins to the heart is called SVC syndrome or superior vena cava syndrome. Compression of the tumor against the veins that return blood to the heart restricts this blood flow. When blood cannot return to the heart, the heart will try to compensate by beating faster. Unfortunately, since not enough blood is returning to the heart, the blood pressure may drop and the child's face can develop swelling. They can go into shock or die.

This type of obstruction can also affect the upper airway going to the lungs. Treatment for this is radiation as well as other techniques that open the compressed veins to the heart. Medicines to dissolve blood clots will be used, or a stent will be inserted to open a blood vessel.

SPINAL CORD COMPRESSION

Spinal cord compression can occur with tumors that spread to other areas of the body, such as muscle tumors, Hodgkin's disease, and neuroblastoma. Most patients develop weakness on both sides of the body. For example, a child may develop weakness in his legs to the point that he is unable to walk. This type of weakness is due to compression of the spinal cord by an enlarging tumor near the spinal cord. The most effective treatment for this is radiation to shrink the tumor and decrease the compression on the spinal cord. IV steroids such as Decadron are also given to decrease the swelling of the tumor that is pressing on the spinal cord.

What causes abdominal pain in a child with cancer?

Abdominal pain in a child with cancer may be caused by a complication of the cancer. The pain may be due to the cancer spreading to the intestine, a bowel obstruction, inflammation of the pancreas, or inflammation of the bowel lining. Lab tests and CT scans may be needed to determine the cause of the pain.

TOTAL PARENT POINTERS
CHILDHOOD CANCERS

1. The **most common cancers in children are**:
   - **Leukemia**—36 percent
   - **Tumors of the brain and spinal cord**—26 percent
   - **Lymphoma**—15 percent
   - **Neuroblastoma**—9 percent
   - **Muscle tumors**—8 percent
   - **Kidney tumors** (Wilms)—8 percent
   - **Bone tumors**—6 percent
   - **Tumors of the eye** (retinoblastoma)—3 percent[1]

2. **Clues to tumors**:
   - **Pale skin with enlarged lymph nodes, bleeding gums, and weakness**—signs of leukemia
   - **Trouble walking, headaches that awaken child at night, confusion, change in behavior, nonparallel eyes**—possible brain tumor
   - **White area in black part of pupil**—possible retina tumor called a retinoblastoma
   - **Persistent bone pains** that awakens child at night or lasts more than one week not associated with known trauma

3. **Acute leukemia is the most common childhood cancer** (41 percent). Acute leukemia is due to the rapid production of certain white blood cells called lymphoblasts. Children with leukemia may be weak and pale. They will sometimes having bleeding gums.

4. **Hodgkin's disease** usually occurs in patients between the ages of **thirteen and thirty-five**. The disease begins with a painless enlarged lymph node in the neck or upper shoulder area. If your child has a painless lymph node over one inch in size on her neck that does not decrease over a four-to-five-week span, make sure your doctor has it evaluated and biopsied.

5. 29 percent of all childhood cancers occur in the brain or the spinal cord. **Tumors of the brain and spinal cord** have the following symptoms:
   - Trouble walking
   - Headaches that awaken the child at night
   - A significant change in the child's behavior
   - A change in parallel alignment of the eyes
   - Persistent headaches that do not stop after several days, especially in children less than six years of age

6. **Bone tumors** usually begin in long bones, especially around the knee. Two examples of bone tumors include Ewing's sarcoma and osteosarcoma. Children with bone tumors may develop a limp and pain in the area of the bone.

7. The most frequent complications of childhood cancer include:
   - Infections
   - Spinal cord compression
   - Low sodium level in the bloodstream
   - Tumor destruction syndrome
   - Obstruction of the veins to the heart
   - Brain hemorrhage
   - Abdominal emergencies

8. **Tumor destruction syndrome** involves a sudden destruction of cells involved with a tumor. This can occur shortly after a chemotherapy treatment. In addition to a sudden destruction of cells, there is an increase in certain chemicals in the blood, such as uric acid and phosphate, which can result in kidney failure, acidity of the blood, low calcium levels, irregular heartbeat, and muscle spasms.

9. **Spinal cord compression** can occur in tumors that spread to other areas of the body, such as muscle tumors, Hodgkin's disease, and neuroblastoma.

27

Cystic Fibrosis

What is cystic fibrosis?

Cystic fibrosis is an inherited disease that affects approximately one out of three thousand children born in the United States. About thirty thousand people in the United States have cystic fibrosis. Children with this illness have an abnormality in the secretion of their sweat glands, the secretions of their lungs, and the pancreas. It causes their sputum to be thick, and it makes their sweat very salty.

Children with this condition have frequent coughs and frequent lung infections. They also have trouble digesting fats because the tube from their pancreas gets blocked by the thick secretions. As a result, these children may fail to gain weight because they are unable to absorb fats and certain vitamins such as A, D, E, and K.

How is cystic fibrosis diagnosed?

If your child has had frequent infections or pneumonias, persistent coughs, and slower growth than other children, your pediatrician or family doctor should be notified.

If your doctor suspects cystic fibrosis, she will order a sweat test. This test measures the amount of salt in his sweat. A repeat test is usually required to confirm the diagnosis.

How is cystic fibrosis treated?

Children with cystic fibrosis are treated per their symptoms. The goal of the treatment is to:
- Reduce lung secretions
- Open the airways and help with wheezing by using inhaler medications
- Treat lung, sinus, and upper respiratory infections early
- Administer enzyme medicines to help with the digestions of fats
- Replace the salt that is lost through sweat
- Loosen the secretions in the lungs with medications and exercise
- Treat with steroids to help with wheezing or inflammation

What are some good preventative ideas for people with cystic fibrosis?
- Get an annual flu vaccination
- Avoid tobacco smoke
- Take vitamins to prevent a deficiency of vitamins A, D, E, and K
- Exercise regularly

TOTAL PARENT POINTERS
CYSTIC FIBROSIS

1. Cystic fibrosis affects one in three thousand children.
2. This **genetic disease** is due to a defective gene that regulates the secretion of salt in the glands of the body. This results in thick secretions in the lungs, salty sweat, and blockage of the tube that releases fat-absorbing enzymes in the intestines.

3. Cystic fibrosis is treated with some or all of the following methods.
   a. Inhaler medicines for wheezing
   b. Avoiding tobacco smoke
   c. Early treatment of any lung or sinus infections.
   d. Steroids at times for wheezing and lung inflammation.
   e. Regular exercise.
   f. Taking enzyme medicines to help dissolve fatty foods.
   g. Taking vitamins since some may not be absorbed.

28

Developmental Problems

CEREBRAL PALSY, DOWN'S SYNDROME AND SPINAL BIFIDA

Cerebral palsy is a condition caused by damage to the part of the brain that controls muscles and body movements. This damage, typically a result of a lack of oxygen to the baby's brain, can occur during pregnancy, during delivery, or immediately after the child is born. Children who are premature have an increased risk of cerebral palsy, but in about half of all cases, the cause is unknown.

Sometimes an extremely high bilirubin blood level can cause cerebral palsy, which is one reason why newborns are tested and monitored closely. Other causes of cerebral palsy include meningitis, head injury, lead or other poisoning, chromosomal abnormalities, or substance abuse by the mother during pregnancy.

What are some signs of cerebral palsy or developmental problems in my two- to five-month-old?
- The child is very floppy.

- The child feels very stiff.
- The child tosses his legs and they become very stiff in a scissor-type position.
- When you pick the child up, his head lags because it seems as if the muscles in his neck are not strong enough.

What is a sign of cerebral palsy or a developmental problem in my six- to nine-month-old?
- Using one hand to reach while keeping the other hand in a tight fist.

What are some signs of cerebral palsy or developmental problems in a child over ten months old?
- The child does not crawl on all fours.
- The child crawls unevenly using one arm or one leg while pulling the other arm or leg.

If you see any of the signs listed above, call your pediatrician or family doctor for a further evaluation.

How is cerebral palsy treated?

Treatment for cerebral palsy is focused on physical, occupational, speech, language, and educational therapy.

What IQ level do children with cerebral palsy usually have?

Some children with cerebral palsy have above average intelligence, some are average, and some are mentally challenged. Approximately one half of children with cerebral palsy have a problem with their intellectual functioning.

What other problems are associated with cerebral palsy?

- Partial or complete hearing loss.
- Stiffness or contraction of the muscles.
- One out of three children with cerebral palsy has seizures.
- Three out of four children have one eye turned slightly in or out. This condition is called strabismus.
- Some may have shortening of bones on one side of the body, which is caused by muscle weakness on that side. This sometimes causes tilting of the pelvic bone and curvature of the spine, called scoliosis. If a child has more than a two-inch difference in length between her two legs, an orthopedic surgeon or neurosurgeon should be consulted for corrective treatment and possible surgery.
- Frequent dental cavities. Children with cerebral palsy have more than the average number of cavities.

- Difficulty sensing movement on one side of the body. Children with cerebral palsy may not know the position of their hand or foot on one side of the body. As a result, these children frequently do not use the hand, arm, or leg on that side. Physical or occupational therapy is useful for teaching these children how to use the other side of their body.

DOWN'S SYNDROME

Down's syndrome is the most common genetic cause of mild to moderate mental retardation. It occurs in one in eight hundred live births. It is named after John Langdon Down, the first physician to recognize the disorder.

Down's syndrome is characterized by varying degrees of mental retardation, a flat facial profile, an upward slant to the eyes, a single crease in the center of both palms, and white spots on the iris of the eye.

What causes Down's syndrome?

Down's syndrome is a genetic disease caused by an extra chromosome number 21. It is well known that the chances of giving birth to a child with Down's syndrome increases with the mother's age. Under the age of thirty, the chances of having a baby with Down's syndrome are one out of one thousand. At age thirty-five, the chances are one out of four hundred.

Is there any testing for Down's syndrome done during pregnancy?

Yes. Your doctor may order a blood test called a multiple marker screen

to check for the presence of genetic problems. These include:
1. Down's syndrome
2. Spina bifida
3. Trisomy 18
4. Abdominal wall defect

This test is sometimes referred to as an AFP (alpha-fetoprotein) test, although it measures other substances besides AFP. These include the levels of alpha-fetoprotein, hCG-human chorionic gonadotropin, and estriol, a type of estrogen in the blood. It plots the levels and determines your risk of having a child with one of the conditions noted above.

- Alpha-fetoprotein is made by the growing fetus.
- HCG is a hormone made by the placenta
- Estriol is a hormone made by the placenta and the baby's liver

What if my AFP test comes back indicating a possible high risk for Down's syndrome?
An abnormal AFP test is only a guideline and does not confirm that your child will have Down's syndrome. My wife had an abnormal AFP test before our last child was born. She scheduled an amniocentesis, which came back normal. Subsequently, after our son was born, he showed no signs of Down's syndrome.

Are there any tests to confirm whether my baby has Down's syndrome or not?
Your doctor may suggest having one of three tests to check for the presence of Down's syndrome if you have a high AFP test. The tests are:
1. Amniocentesis—This involves removing some amniotic fluid from within the uterus to do a chromosome analysis.
2. CVS (chorionic villus sampling)—This is a biopsy of the placenta to do a chromosome analysis.
3. PUBS (percutaneous umbilical blood sampling)—Blood from the umbilical cord is drawn in order to do a chromosome analysis.

The advantages and disadvantages of each technique are noted below.

How is the diagnosis of Down's syndrome made?
An initial diagnosis of Down's syndrome is based on the child's appearance: a characteristically flat facial profile, an upward slant to the eyes, a short neck, a single crease on the palm, characteristic ear shape, and white spots on the iris of the eye. Your doctor will order a blood

Amniocentesis	CVS Chorionic Villus Sampling	PUBS Percutaneous Umbilical Blood Sampling
14–18th Week of Pregnancy	9–11th Week of Pregnancy	18–22nd Week of Pregnancy
Lower Risk of Miscarriage than CVS	1–2 Percent Risk of Miscarriage	Most Accurate Greatest Risk of Miscarriage

test, called a chromosome karyotype, to confirm the diagnosis. This test usually takes several weeks.

What other medical problems occur in children with Down's syndrome?
Children with Down's syndrome may also have some hearing loss, congenital heart problems, and seizure disorders (5 to 13 percent).

Infants with Down's may also have feeding problems due to poor muscle tone and protruding tongue. Mothers who are breast-feeding should consult with a specialist if they are having breast-feeding problems.

Children with Down's have a higher risk for leukemia, pneumonia, and ear infections. They also have a much greater risk of becoming seriously ill from infections due to a poorly functioning immune system.

Children with Down's may have a delay in their developmental milestones also. Early educational intervention is available in all states. Some children are able to be placed in regular classrooms. Some can eventually live relatively independently.

SPINA BIFIDA

Spina bifida is a defect in the spinal cord and vertebral column. There are mild, moderate, and severe forms. Mild cases may cause no problems. Mild cases have a missing part of a bone in a vertebrae. In severe cases, the child may have a large bulge on the lower back that encloses the protruding spinal cord and nerves. Severe cases can result in leg paralysis and trouble with bladder and bowel function.

Can taking folic acid help to prevent spina bifida and other spinal cord defects?
Yes. Taking folic acid every day before a woman is pregnant can help prevent spinal bifida and other so-called neural tube defects. It is important for women to do this before they are pregnant because the child's organs begin to develop in the first twelve weeks of age.

How much folic acid should I take each day?
Taking a multivitamin with folic acid or eating a breakfast cereal fortified with folic acid is usually adequate. The general recommendation is to take four hundred micrograms of folic acid every day. Folic acid is a B complex vitamin found in dark green vegetables, egg yolks, and some fruits.

TOTAL PARENT POINTERS
DEVELOPMENTAL PROBLEMS

1. **All women of childbearing age should take a multivitamin with four hundred micrograms of folic acid per day. Folic acid helps prevent spina bifida and other congenital nervous system problems.**

2. **Down's syndrome** occurs in one out of eight hundred births. The risk increases with maternal age.

3. An **alpha-fetoprotein (AFP) test** may be done during pregnancy to see if there is risk for a genetic disorder in the child.

4. **Chromosome testing for genetic defects during pregnancy can be done by:**
   a. Amniocentesis
   b. CVS—chorionic villus sampling
   c. PUBS—percutaneous umbilical blood sampling

5. Children with Down's syndrome can be happy, productive, and caring members of society.

29

Diabetes

What is childhood diabetes?

In general, in today's medical world, more and more attention is being paid to diabetes as not only a serious disease in it's own right but also as a precursor to heart attack, cancer, and other life-threatening diseases. As with adults, childhood diabetes is an illness in which the child's body is unable to produce insulin, a hormone needed to digest glucose, or blood sugars. Normally, insulin is produced in the pancreas, an endocrine gland just behind the stomach.

In type 1 diabetes the child must take insulin to keep his blood sugar levels normal. Each year, more than thirteen thousand young people are diagnosed with type 1 diabetes.

Type 2 diabetes begins when the body develops a resistance to insulin and no longer uses insulin properly. This type of diabetes is on the rise in children and is a growing problem because the disease can often be a result of physical inactivity and obesity. (See chapter 32 on obesity in children.) Unfortunately, it's part of the emerging obesity epidemic in children and adults.

Who is at risk for childhood diabetes?

Parents who have a history of diabetes or have diabetes in their family need to be aware of the warning signs that can indicate diabetes in children of any age. Even if you are not aware of diabetes in your family, check with your doctor if you notice the warning signs in your child.

What are the warning signs of diabetes?

- Failure to grow or failure to thrive
- Excessive thirst
- Excessive urination
- Weight loss
- Dehydration

Children who have elevated blood glucose may be diagnosed with diabetes. Diabetes can be either type 1 or type 2. A person with type 1 diabetes requires insulin. type 2 diabetes can be managed with an improved diet, regular exercise, and sometimes medication.

How is diabetes treated?

Children with diabetes need to eat a balanced diet and accurately monitor the number of calories eaten each day. Meeting with a nutritionist or diabetes education specialist is recommended.

A balanced diet for a child with diabetes should include the same types of food recommended for an adult: a balance of complex carbohydrates (bread and fruit), fats, and protein. The child should eat approximately the same number of calories with each meal as well as between-meal snacks to prevent a drop in blood sugar. Children should also eat additional calories if they are involved in strenuous exercise. Children with diabetes should always keep healthy snacks with them, such as granola bars and fruits.

Children with type 1 diabetes who require insulin will need to do finger-stick blood tests one to several times a day. If your child is diagnosed with type 1 diabetes, you will need to be educated regarding the medical and emotional needs of your child. If finger-stick blood tests are needed, you will need to do them until your child is old enough to do them. You will also need to teach your child about proper nutrition and oversee your child's diet. Your pediatrician or family doctor can recommend resources to help you learn about the disease and help your child cope with the disease.

What are the complications of diabetes?

Children with diabetes can develop two major complications:

- Low blood sugar (hypoglycemia)
- Diabetic coma (diabetic ketoacidosis, DKA)

What are the signs of hypoglycemia? (low blood sugar)

The symptoms include:

- Sweating
- Confusion
- Change in mental status
- Fatigue
- Occasionally passing out
- Sometimes vomiting

Hypoglycemia is a serious illness because low blood sugar impairs the brain's functioning and must be corrected before there is a prolonged loss of glucose to the brain.

How is hypoglycemia treated?

The treatment for hypoglycemia is to give your child orange juice with several packets of sugar or have the child eat a candy bar if she is able to do so.

What is diabetic ketoacidosis?

The symptoms of diabetic ketoacidosis, or diabetic coma, include:

- Fatigue
- Elevated blood sugar, usually over four hundred
- Rapid breathing
- Lower than normal temperature (unless an infection is causing the diabetic coma)
- Fruity odor to the breath

• Presence of ketones in urine. (Detected with simple test strips found in drug stores.)

Diabetic ketoacidosis (DKA) is a complication of diabetes due to an abnormally high blood sugar and the buildup of acids in the blood-stream. For example, if a child does not receive her insulin injections for one or two days, her blood sugar level will increase, but there will not be enough insulin in her body to release the energy in the blood sugar. Her body will then start to break down fat tissue and turn it into sugar. Unfortunately, this process causes acids to be released into the blood. These acids are called keto acids or ketones. One way of checking for this condition is to test the child's urine with a dipstick for ketones or keto acids. If these are present, the child has diabetic ketoacidosis. Severe cases can be life threatening. Children can die if not treated early and properly with insulin and IV fluids.

Signs and symptoms of diabetic ketoacidosis are:

1. High blood sugar (usually over 300—normal is under 120)
2. Rapid breathing
3. Thirst due to dehydration
4. Fruity breath odor
5. Weakness and fatigue
6. A history of missed insulin injections for one or more days
7. Sometimes an infection (such as pneumonia) may be a precipitating factor. When an infection occurs, the body needs more insulin or the blood sugar will increase.

How is diabetic ketoacidosis treated?

If your child has very high blood sugar and altered mental status, call 911 and get your child via ambulance to the nearest emergency room. The child will be given a large amount of IV fluids, additional insulin, and potassium. If an infection is present, antibiotics may be ordered.

What are the complications of diabetic ketoacidosis?

Children with diabetic ketoacidosis can develop:
• Severe dehydration
• Brain swelling, which is called cerebral edema
• Seizures

TOTAL PARENT POINTERS
DIABETES

1. **Signs of diabetes** are excessive thirst, frequent urination, and an excessive appetite. There is usually a family history or diabetes.
2. **Complications of diabetes** include:
   a. Low blood sugar (hypoglycemia)
   b. Diabetic ketoacidosis (DKA)
3. **Symptoms of low blood sugar** are fatigue, confusion, sweating, and sometimes passing out.

4. **Symptoms of diabetic ketoacidosis (DKA)** are rapid and deep breathing, thirst, dry mouth, fatigue, fruity breath odor, and dry skin. These children have a high reading (usually over four hundred) on glucose monitors and their urine test shows ketones. DKA can be life threatening in some children. DKA requires IV fluids, close glucose monitoring, insulin dosing in the hospital, and treatment of any precipitating events, such as an infection.

30

Dyslexia

Dyslexia is a learning disability that makes it difficult for a child to read. For example, there is often difficulty in learning to put together the different phonic sounds of the written word. Poor spelling, trouble rhyming, and difficulty in following directions can also be symptoms of dyslexia. Many children with dyslexia have trouble understanding that words can be broken down into smaller sounds (called phonics or phonemes). The good news, however, is that children with dyslexia usually have at least average and often above average intelligence.

How common is dyslexia?

As many as 15 to 20 percent of the population may have a reading disorder. It is estimated that four out of five of that number have dyslexia. It is, in fact, a rather common, if unrecognized, problem. Anywhere from 5 to 10 percent (and possibly as much as 17.5 percent) of the population may have varying degrees of dyslexia.[1]

Some famous people who had dyslexia were Albert Einstein, Leonardo da Vinci, Winston Churchill, and Thomas Edison.

What are some of the early clues that my child may have dyslexia?

Most children are ready to read by the age of six. If your child is six or older and having unusual difficulty with reading, there are several clues that raise the question of whether dyslexia may be the cause:

- Difficulty learning to read
- Difficulty learning the different sounds of letters, or phonics (or phonemes)
- The child reverses letters such as *b* or *d*
- The child passes over small words while reading
- Difficulty rhyming words
- Trouble sounding out long words
- The child reads very slowly
- Frequent spelling mistakes (These children may occasionally do well on spelling tests in which there is intense preparation

before the test. However, they tend to have many misspelled words on a typical essay.)

- The child may also have difficulty with math and counting accurately
- The child may have difficulty understanding a rapid sequence of directions or instructions

What do the words look like to a child with dyslexia?

Almost all very young children have word reversals, letter reversals, or number reversals. Since human neurological functioning matures through the early grade school years, most children grow out of these kinds of reversals. However, these reversals tend to persist in children with dyslexia. A dyslexic child will continue to tell you that the words she is trying to read appear to be backward, reversed, or jumbled. For example, the word *dog* may be confused with the word *god.* The sentence, "The cat ran away" may look like this to a dyslexic child: "Teh tac nar waya."

Many children with dyslexia have trouble understanding the different phonics or phonemes involved with each word. For example, the word *dog* is comprised of three phonemes'; "da," "ah," and "gh." Children with dyslexia may have trouble putting these three phonemes together into a fluent and smooth word, such as dog.

What causes dyslexia?

Nobody is sure about the cause of dyslexia, but it is generally agreed by most experts that it is something physiological rather than psychological. Some research is focused on chromosomes number 6 and 15. Dyslexia also tends to run in families; if one child has dyslexia, there is a 40 percent chance that a sibling will have it.[2] If one of the parents has dyslexia, there is a 23 to 65 percent chance of at least one of the children having it.

The key point to keep in mind, however, is that there are varying degrees of dyslexia. Children may have mild, moderate, or severe forms of this learning disorder.

Are there any other medical problems that can be mistaken for dyslexia?

Yes, this is one of the most important first steps in arriving at a final diagnosis of dyslexia. Whenever a child with a learning disability is identified, it is important to determine if there is some other condition that makes it appear that the child has dyslexia. The key problems to look for that can mimic dyslexia include:

1. Hearing problems
2. Visual problems
3. Neurological problems
4. Psychiatric problems (such as depression)
5. Developmental lags

If parents feel that their child has a learning disability, they should notify a teacher or school administrator immediately. School administrators in the United States are required by federal law to evaluate a child to determine if there are any problems with the child's hearing, vision, neurologic function, or reading ability. This evaluation usually needs to be completed within a certain period of time, such as two to three months. This evaluation may include a vision test, a hearing test, a psychological test, and an intelligence test. If all the tests are negative, then the diagnosis is more supportive of dyslexia.

Parents need to be aware that dyslexia is not due to a lack of intelligence. The main problem is that these children have trouble processing the different phonemes or phonics of words, but they possess normal intellectual ability (the ability to understand, reason, and comprehend). Rather than being due to lack of intelligence, dyslexia is due to a neurological condition that affects specific neurological or perceptual motor skills in the process of reading. It is like a broken link in a chain. For example, the brain may have a specific problem processing how the different sounds of a word come together, and therefore it cannot apply its intellectual understanding to reading the word (since it cannot recognize the word for what it is).

Is dyslexia more common in boys than in girls?

The actual rates of dyslexia are about equal in boys and girls.

Does an early identification of dyslexia improve the child's ability to read?

Yes. The earlier the child's condition is identified, the earlier treatment can be started. However, the overall prognosis is based on several factors: early intervention, a supportive home environment, a strong self-image, and a good remediation program.

The main strategy in treating dyslexia is focused reading to compensate for the particular deficit. This may include, for example, specific practice in teaching the child the different sounds of different letters.

What are the most effective treatments for dyslexia?

The most effective treatment for dyslexia, if the specifics are identified, actually can be performed at home or (if the child is being tutored by a learning disability specialist) made more effective through the involvement of the parents. In most ordinary circumstances, some of the key techniques that parents can use to help their child to read include:

- Read with your child at least twenty to thirty minutes each night.
- Teach your child how to sound out each letter of a word.
- Teach your child what each of the letters sounds like.
- Teach your child how to blend each sound into a complete word, such as the three sounds of cat: "ca," "ah," and "te."
- Focus on showing your child the difference between words such as *was* and *saw*.
- Encourage your child to write down some of the most common words: *the, it, was, and, is, for, be*, etc.
- Reassure your child that her reading problem is not an intelligence problem.

- Teach your child coping skills to deal with her frustration at school. Let her know that many famous people such as Leonardo da Vinci and Winston Churchill had dyslexia.
- Provide a positive and supportive environment for your child at home.
- Be sure to compliment your child for her talents and her accomplishments.

Let your child know that her problem requires a more focused approach to reading. One of the keys is spending as much time as possible reading with your child at an early age. A fun and interactive way to do this is to have the child pick a book that is suitable for her reading level and then alternate who reads each page. The parent reads one page, and the child reads the next page.

This opportunity of listening to your child read is extremely important because it enables you to hear her word fluency. (Fluency means how she pronounces different words.) If you hear her having trouble pronouncing many words, this provides you with the feedback to help her pronounce those words properly. It also provides you with an opportunity to give the child some positive and supportive feedback about her reading ability.

What are the three most important recommendations to improve my child's reading ability?

1. Read with your child at least twenty to thirty minutes each night.

2. Read with your child at least twenty to thirty minutes each night.

3. Read with your child at least twenty to thirty minutes each night.

These three recommendations are not a typographical error. The key element of success in school is spending this focused reading time with your child. This does not diminish the importance of obtaining a complete evaluation for a child with a learning disability, but it emphasizes the critical importance of one-on-one time with your child each night.

The final element of your home education program involves instilling in your child a sense of enjoyment, excitement, and fun about reading. Use whatever techniques are at your disposal to help your child feel that reading is a fun and interesting experience. Show her how much you enjoy the different stories that she reads to you. In addition, look for an opportunity to talk about the story afterward to emphasize how much you enjoyed her reading. This also gives you an opportunity to evaluate her comprehension of what she read. By doing this, you will teach your child how to understand what she has read and prepare her for a future of successful reading and life skills.

SCHOOL-BASED REMEDIATION PROGRAMS

The second component of treatment is a school-based professional remediation program. This program should be tailored to fit each child's specific reading needs. Reading specialists will spend time teaching your child about word sounds, phonics, and word fluency, or whatever else will help the child compensate for any deficits caused by dyslexia. They will also provide a supportive environment for learning and for improving your child's self-image.

NOTES

1. Sally E. Shaywitz. "Current Concepts: Dyslexia," *New England Journal of Medicine* 338, no. 5 (1998): 307–12.
2. Ibid.

TOTAL PARENT POINTERS
DYSLEXIA

1. **Dyslexia** is a learning disorder in which the child has trouble reading due to specific deficits in the reading process, such as understanding the different phonics that make up a word. It is also difficult for these children to put these different sounds together into one smooth-sounding word.

2. The **clues to dyslexia** include:
   a. Trouble with reading at the age of six or more
   b. Trouble sounding out long words
   c. Difficulty rhyming
   d. Difficulty pronouncing words
   e. Slow reading
   f. Poor spelling
   g. Letter, number, or word reversals that do not disappear with age

3. If you suspect that your child may have dyslexia, contact your child's teacher and indicate that you would like your child to have a **complete learning evaluation.**

4. Focus on teaching your child the different sounds or **phonics** that make up each word.

5. **Read with your child at least thirty minutes each night.** Take turns reading so he that you can hear how he pronounces each word. Correct his pronunciation when indicated.

6. For further resources and more information about dyslexia, please see below for helpful resources and Web sites.

Many thanks to the National Institute of Neurologic Disorders in Children for providing some of the research and other information used for this chapter. Below you will find additional resources.

ORGANIZATIONS

National Center for Learning Disabilities
381 Park Avenue South, Suite 1401
New York, NY 10016
http://www.ld.org
Tel: 212–545–7510   Fax: 212–545–9665
888–575–7373

Learning Disabilities Association of America
4156 Library Road, Suite 1
Pittsburgh, PA 15234–1349
info@ldaamerica.org
http://www.ldaamerica.org
Tel: 412–341–1515   Fax: 412–344–0224

National Institute of Child Health and Human Development (NICHD)
National Institutes of Health, DHHS
31 Center Drive, Rm. 2A32 MSC 2425
Bethesda, MD 20892–2425
http://www.nichd.nih.gov
Tel: 301–496–5133   Fax: 301–496–7101

International Dyslexia Association
8600 LaSalle Road
Chester Building, Suite 382
Baltimore, MD 21286–2044
info@interdys.org
http://www.interdys.org
Tel: 410–296–0232 800-ABCD123
Fax: 410–321–5069

National Institute of Mental Health (NIMH)
National Institutes of Health, DHHS
6001 Executive Blvd. Room 8184, MSC 9663
Bethesda, MD 20892–9663
nimhinfo@nih.gov
http://www.nimh.nih.gov
Tel: 301–443–4513   Fax: 301–443–4279
866–615-NIMH (6464)
301–443–8431 (TTY)

31

Heart Problems

EARLY WARNING SIGNS OF CONGENITAL HEART PROBLEMS

Congenital heart disease is diagnosed annually in approximately eight out of every one thousand children in the United States. Some of the causes of congenital heart disease are:

1. Genetic disorders—10 to 14 percent of cases (Down's syndrome or other chromosome defects)
2. Infections during pregnancy (rubella or German measles during the first fourteen weeks of pregnancy)

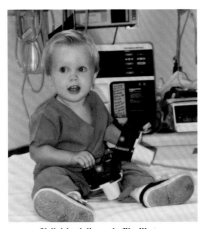

Child holding defibrillator paddles in ER resuscitation room

3. Medications whose side effects can cause heart defects (lithium, warfarin, and certain antiseizure medications)
4. Fetal alcohol syndrome (ingestion of moderate to high amounts of alcohol by the mother during pregnancy)

However, the majority of congenital heart problems have no known cause. Thankfully, advances in diagnostic imaging and in the medical and surgical management of even the most complex congenital heart problems have lead to a marked increase in survival into adulthood as well as a better quality of life for those with congenital heart problems. However, as with many conditions, the sooner the problem is diagnosed the better.

What are the early warning signs of pediatric heart problems?

Key signs and symptoms during the first four weeks of life that indicate a possible heart problem are:

- Poor feeding or increased time to feed

- Sweating
- Weak cry
- Turning blue or experiencing blue spells
- Fast breathing rate
- Chronic cough or wheezing
- Irritability or excessive sleepiness
- Poor growth or weight gain
- Nasal flaring

Listening to child's heart with a stethoscope

Some children with heart disease have symptoms immediately after birth. About 50 percent of children with congenital heart problems will be diagnosed in the first week of birth. Another 10 percent will be diagnosed by the end of the first month. In some cases, symptoms may not emerge until several months after birth.

The three primary congenital heart problems include:

1. VSD (ventricular septal defect)—a hole between the heart's two ventricles

2. ASD (atrial septal defect)—a hole between the heart's two atria

3. Aortic coarctation—narrowing of the aorta

What is a ventricular septal defect (VSD)?

A VSD is a hole between the two large ventricles at the bottom of the heart on the right and the left (see illustration below). The right ventricle is supposed to contain only nonoxygenated blood. The left ventricle is where oxygenated blood returns after it is pumped through the lungs. When there is a

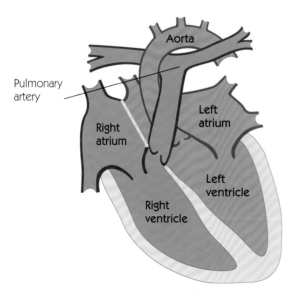

Normal heart

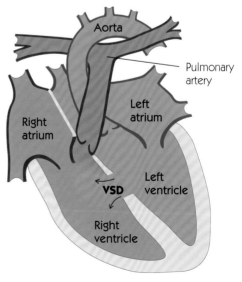

Ventricular septal defect (VSD)

hole between the left and right ventricles, oxygenated blood is pushed into the right ventricle, where it is mixed with nonoxygenated blood and pumped through the lungs again. Small VSD defects may cause only minimal problems. Larger VSD defects may cause congestive heart failure and high pressures in the blood vessels to and from the lungs. This is called pulmonary hypertension. Children with larger defects may have poor weight gain and development problems. Your doctor will usually be able to hear a heart murmur with this condition.

What is an atrial septal defect (ASD)?

An atrial septal defect is a hole or defect in the wall between the two upper chambers of the heart called the atria. This occurs in up to 10 percent of congenital heart problem cases. As noted in the illustration below, an ASD is a hole between the right and left atrial chambers.

This allows oxygenated blood from the left atrium to move to the right atrium, which contains nonoxygenated blood. Fortunately, this is less serious than VSD.

This condition will cause problems in only about 10 percent of infants who have the defect. The chances of it causing a problem depend on the size of the hole or defect. Some of these holes will close on their own. Others may require surgery.

What is aortic coarctation?

Aortic coarctation is a narrowing of the aorta, the large artery that contains blood being pumped out of the heart to the entire body (see illustration below). If this artery is narrowed, it results in a slower and more restricted flow of blood out of the heart. This can result in shock and congestive heart failure.

These children may have rapid breathing and/or feeding difficulties

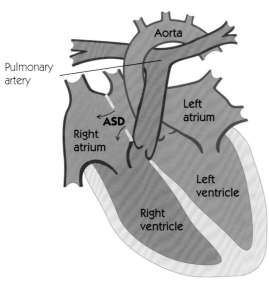

Atrial septal defect (ASD)

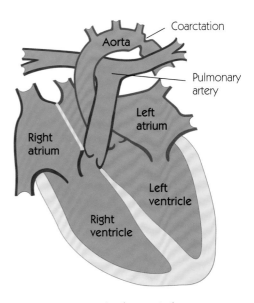

Aortic coarctation

due to the complication of congestive heart failure.

Which congenital heart problems can be corrected by surgery?

Complete repairs are possible for:
- Ventricular septal defect (VSD) (25 percent of cases of congenital heart disease)
- Tetralogy of Fallot (9–12 percent)
- Transposition of the great vessels (10–11 percent)
- Aortic coarctation (8–11 percent)
- Patent ductus arteriosus (10 percent)

What does it look like if a child turns blue or cyanotic from congenital heart disease?

Blue spells, or cyanotic spells, are caused by certain congenital heart problems that result in low levels of oxygen in the blood.

These blue spells can be caused by the tetralogy of Fallot, transposition of the great vessels, and other congenital heart problems. When a child with congenital heart disease turns blue, this is called cyanotic heart disease.

For a review of other causes of cyanotic heart disease, see the sidebar on the following page.

It is important for parents to know what to look for to differentiate between cyanosis of heart disease and the normal acrocyanosis of newborns. Newborns under the age of one to two months tend to have episodes of blue hands and feet (but not the lips or tongue) if exposed unwrapped to the cold. The key thing to focus on is any bluish tint to the lips or tongue. If the lips and tongue are blue, that is your cue to check for possible congenital heart disease.

Rather than looking for blueness, think instead of looking for the absence of pinkness of the lips and tongue. Another tip is that some children may not have any signs of cyanosis or blueness until the end of their first year.

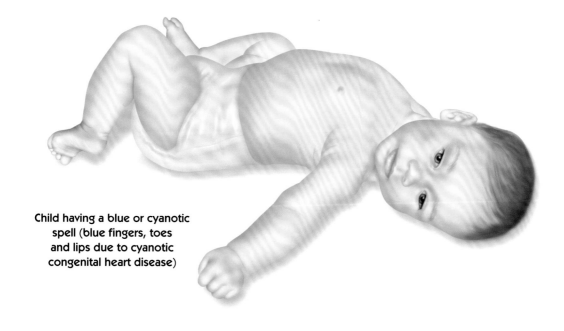

Child having a blue or cyanotic spell (blue fingers, toes and lips due to cyanotic congenital heart disease)

OTHER CAUSES OF CYANOTIC HEART DISEASE

The five congenital heart problems that cause cyanosis or blue spells are called the Five Ts:

1. Tetralogy of Fallot
2. Transposition of the great arteries
3. Tricuspid atresia
4. Total anomalous pulmonary venous return
5. Truncus arteriosus

For more information on other causes of cyanotic heart disease see the sidebar.

Do all children with congenital heart problems have blue spells?

No. Some forms of congenital heart disease do not cause blue spells. These are called noncyanotic congenital heart disease.

What are some of the other complications that can occur in children with congenital heart problems?

Complications that can occur in children with congenital heart problems include:

- Abnormal or irregular heart rhythms called arrhythmias
- Endocarditis—an infection of the heart muscle or heart valves
- Poor growth
- Electrolyte disorders due to medications (such as a low potassium level)
- Strokes
- Fatigue and trouble keeping up with other children in activities

To recognize complications early and to prevent even greater problems, it is very important for parents to continue to follow up with the child's cardiologist—even after surgery.

Children whose heart valves have been replaced with mechanical valves will need to have surgery in the future to replace the valve with a larger one to match their growing body.

 ## OTHER CAUSES OF CYANOTIC HEART DISEASE:

It's not widely known that the five congenital heart problems that cause **cyanosis or blue spells** are called the Five Ts:

1. **Tetralogy of Fallot**—This consists of four heart problems, hence the term tetralogy, which include:
   a. VSD (ventricular septal defect)—a hole between the two ventricles
   b. Narrowing of the artery that goes to the lungs (pulmonary artery)
   c. An overriding aorta
   d. Enlargement of the right ventricle
2. **Transposition of the great arteries**—the aorta and the artery to the lung come out of the opposite ventricles in the heart.
3. **Tricuspid atresia**—this means that the tricuspid valve between the right atrium and the right ventricle is not present
4. **Total anomalous pulmonary venous return**—the veins that should bring oxygenated blood from the lungs to the left atrium bring it to the right atrium instead.
5. **Truncus arteriosus**—the arteries that go to the lungs and the body come off one large artery.

ABNORMAL HEART RHYTHMS

Some children with or without congenital heart disease can develop very fast or very slow heart rhythms. The child below is an example of a child with a very fast heart rhythm called SVT (supraventricular tachycardia). This very fast heart rhythm originates above the ventricles of the heart.

A ten-year-old boy told his parents that he felt like his heart was fluttering or beating really fast. This is sometimes referred to as palpitations. He and his parents knew that he had experienced this several times before. He had been treated for it at another hospital. His hearts' electrical system has abnormal wiring. It's like having an extra electrical wire that shouldn't be there. This wire goes from the atria to the ventricles of the heart and causes the heart to beat very fast at times.

When he came to our ER, his heartbeat was around 200 beats per minute. His heart rate should be less than 120. We could tell by the heart monitor and his EKG that this was SVT (supraventricular tachycardia).

Since his blood pressure was normal, we were able to give him an IV medication to slow down his heartbeat. After two doses, his

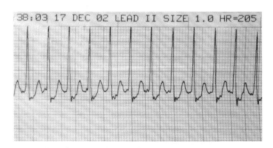

Cardiac monitor strip of boy with SVT

heart beat returned to normal. We released him after speaking with his pediatric cardiologist and setting up an appointment.

What precautions should children with heart problems take?

Children with certain heart and valve problems sometimes need to receive an antibiotic prior to various invasive and/or dental procedures, because bacteria can enter the bloodstream during the procedure and attach to the heart valves. This can cause an infection of the heart valves that can lead to valve damage and other complications. Bacteria that attach to the heart valves or muscle can cause bacterial endocarditis.

The guidelines for prescribing antibiotics prior to certain types of procedures in congenital heart disease children change periodically. In general, children who have the following conditions usually need antibiotics before certain invasive (such as a bronchoscope examination of the airway and lungs) or dental procedures:
1. Artificial heart valves
2. Prior episode of bacterial endocarditis
3. Heart transplant with heart valve disease
4. Heart shunts

To be safe, if your child has heart disease, even after surgical correction, always check with your doctor or pediatric cardiologist about the need for antibiotics prior to any surgical, invasive, or dental procedure.

TOTAL PARENT POINTERS
HEART PROBLEMS

1. The key signs and symptoms during the first four weeks of life that indicate a **possible heart problem** are:
   - Poor feeding or increased time to feed
   - Sweating
   - Weak cry
   - Turning blue or having blue spells
   - Fast breathing rate
   - Chronic cough or wheezing
   - Irritability or excessive sleepiness
   - Poor growth or weight gain
   - Nasal flaring
2. **Congenital heart disease** is diagnosed annually in approximately eight out of every one thousand children in the United States. While the majority of congenital heart problems have no known cause, some causes of congenital heart disease include:
   - **Genetic disorders**: 10–14 percent of cases (Down's syndrome or other chromosome defects)
   - **Infections during pregnancy** (rubella or German measles during the first fourteen weeks of pregnancy)
   - **Medications** whose side effects can cause heart defects (lithium, warfarin, and certain antiseizure medications)
   - **Fetal alcohol syndrome** (ingestion of moderate to high amounts of alcohol by the mother during pregnancy)
3. **Blue spells** (also known as cyanotic spells) are caused by certain congenital heart problems that result in low levels of oxygen in the blood.
4. An **atrial septal defect** (ASD) is a hole or defect in the wall between the atria, the two upper chambers of the heart. This occurs in up to 10 percent of children with congenital heart disease.
5. A **ventricular septal defect** (VSD) is a hole between the two ventricles, the two lower chambers of the heart, which allows a mixing of oxygenated and nonoxygenated blood. The severity of the symptoms depend on the size of the hole between the two ventricles.
6. **Coarctation of the aorta** is a narrowing of the large artery that carries blood out of the heart to the body. If this artery is narrowed, it results in a slower, more restricted blood flow out of the heart, which can result in shock and congestive heart failure. These children may have rapid breathing and/or feeding difficulties due to the complications of congestive heart failure.
7. **Complications** that can occur in children with congenital heart problems include:
   - **Abnormal or irregular rhythms of the heart** (arrhythmias)
   - **Endocarditis** (an infection of the heart muscle or heart valves)
   - **Poor growth**
   - **Electrolyte disorders** due to medications (such as a low potassium level)
   - **Stroke**
   - **Fatigue** and trouble keeping up with other children during physical activities

TOTAL PARENT POINTERS
HEART PROBLEMS

8. Some children with congenital heart problems need an **antibiotic before certain procedures** (such as specific dental and invasive procedures) to prevent bacteria from entering the bloodstream that could attach to and damage the heart valves (bacterial endocarditis).

9. **The guidelines for prescribing antibiotics prior to certain procedures in congenital heart disease children change periodically.** In general, children who have the following conditions usually need antibiotics before certain invasive or dental procedures:
   • Artificial heart valves
   • Prior episode of bacterial endocarditis
   • Heart transplant with heart valve disease
   • Heart shunts

If your child has heart disease, even after surgical correction, always check with your doctor or pediatric cardiologist about the need for antibiotics prior to any surgical, invasive, or dental procedure.

10. You should always **consult with your child's cardiologist** prior to:
    • Long-distance travel, especially by airplane
    • Participation in vigorous exercise or sports
    • Starting new medications

32

Obesity in Children

How big is the problem?

Obesity is receiving more and more attention, not only because of its seriousness as a medical, social, and psychological problem, but also because it is unavoidably obvious, especially in children.

It is estimated that at least nine million children between the ages of six and nineteen are overweight. In fact, the incidence of obesity in this age group has tripled in the last twenty years. In 1980, 5 percent of children twelve to nineteen were overweight. In 2004, that number of overweight children more than tripled to 17 percent. The epidemic is even worse in Hispanic and African American communities where 25.5 percent of African American and 21.8 percent of Hispanic children are overweight.

The reason? Kids are eating too much fast food, exercising less, and sitting in front of the TV and computer too much.

When we look at the national dietary recommendations, it is obvious that kids are not eating right.

In fact, scientists in one study found that the national recommendations for the minimum fruit, vegetables, meat, and whole grains servings were met by only 1 percent of children. In fact, the fat intake of many kids on a daily basis greatly exceeds the suggested 30 percent of daily calories.

What are the complications of obesity in children?

The complications of childhood and adolescent obesity are severe. Parents need to be aware that an obese child's life expectancy decreases by seven years. In addition, the child will have an increased statistical probability of acquiring the following diseases:

- Heart disease
- Stroke
- Kidney problems
- Some forms of cancer

What is causing this obesity epidemic?

Kids are less active today. They are more focused on computer games and TV shows and are less active in sports and other outdoor activities. There has been a dramatic increase in the amount of time children spend in nonexercise activities. This includes watching TV, using the computer, playing video games, etc.

Working parents tend to rely on high fat, low nutrient fast foods for meals. The National Health Department recommends that children have five servings of vegetables or fruits every day. In addition, the calories from fats should be limited to 30 percent or less of the day's total calories.

How can I solve my child's obesity problem?

There are several things you can do to help your child.

First, educate your child about the fat content of various foods. Indicate to them that he will feel better and will feel more energetic by eating fruits and vegetables five or six times a day. High-fat foods tend to make people feel sluggish and will add more weight to their bodies.

Let them know that obesity is viewed as a negative aspect of their appearance. Being overweight or obese might mean that they will not be chosen to be on a particular team at school. This can be devastating to kids who are trying to fit in with their peers.

Give them healthy, enjoyable food choices. Instead of offering ice cream, choose a low-fat yogurt for desert. Better yet, don't buy ice cream. Buy the frozen yogurt. Let them know that if they order a double cheeseburger, this will exceed their fat allowance for the entire day. Offer healthy choices such as a salad with chicken, and chicken or turkey sandwiches on whole-grain breads.

Increase their activity level. Children are drawn to the excitement of computers, television, and various other electronic devices. In many cases, you need to take away these electronic distractions in order to motivate your child to become involved in outdoor activities.

In my household, as our children have become more and more involved with computers and television, we have developed specific techniques to deal with this problem. The main computer cannot be used without a password. In some cases, we have removed the Internet connection on certain days or at certain times of the day. We have also removed the power cord so they cannot use the computer at all. We have even unplugged the television or turned off the power fuse to the television outlet to prevent unsupervised television viewing.

The result? Our children find activities to do outside. They now go to a friend's house to play baseball or football, and that means burning calories. The give-and-take of playing with other kids also helps them to develop their social skills rather than their already quite handy hand-eye coordination skills by playing computer games.

Use time on the computer as a reward for good behavior.

When our children have behaved exceptionally well, they can earn a half hour or more of computer time.

We also have a rule that for every hour they read, they can have one hour of computer time or an hour of TV.

The bottom line is our children are more active, more appreciative of their computer time, and more motivated to earn this privilege. Remember, as parents, it's up to you to set the rules and rewards so that your child appreciates and understands the importance of becoming a well-rounded individual.

Food choices

Parents need to be aware that your food choices while grocery shopping will impact your child's obesity. If you load up on pizza, cheeseburgers, cookies, and ice cream, the children will obviously get used to eating these types of foods. However, if you teach your children to enjoy chicken and vegetables, whole-grain breads, fruits, and milk, your children will develop healthy dietary habits that will last the rest of their lives. In order to establish these good dietary patterns, parents need to serve as good role models. This means changing your own eating habits in order to be a positive role model for your children. Instead of having soda with a meal, you should have a glass of milk to be a good example for your children. Parents should also think about making a comment about how good vegetables or fruits taste during dinner.

Moms and dads can use their spare time to search the Internet for appetizing and creative recipes that utilize chicken, fruits, and vegetables that are appealing to the entire family.

Low-fat food tips

1. Come up with creative ways of making fruits and vegetables more appealing. Offering your children some carrots and celery with a low-fat ranch dip gives the veggies a much more fun and appetizing appearance. You might also consider melting some low-fat cheese on the broccoli to make it look more yummy.

2. When your children are getting hungry, make a low-fat sandwich, such as turkey on whole-grain bread. Don't ask what they want to eat; just make it. If they are hungry and it's right in front of them with a glass of milk—who knows? They just might eat it and like it.

3. Buy low-fat fast foods, such as a salad with grilled chicken, when you are with your children. When they ask for some, be sure to share it with them. Next time, they might order one for themselves.

Creative techniques for teaching your children about foods

Sit at the dinner table and get some large white paper plates. Have your child draw a line down the middle of the plate. Draw a line that divides one of the halves into quarters. The full half of the plate is the section that should be used for green, yellow, or orange fruits and vegetables. The two one-quarter sections are left for protein and carbohydrates or starches. The protein section includes meat such as chicken, pork, beef, beans, cottage cheese, or tofu. Remind your children that the Department of Health and Human Services has a five-a-day campaign, which recommends that children have five servings of fruits and vegetables each day.

Fast food pitfalls and tips

Keep in mind that most fast foods are loaded with extra fat and can sabotage your family's diet. However, educated choices about fast foods can actually be part of a significant diet education program. For example, choosing low-fat grilled chicken, vegetables, salads, or turkey sandwiches on whole-wheat bread can all be smart choices to a good diet program. Many of the fast-food restaurants now offer low-fat yogurt as well as fruit as part of their menu. The key is to avoid white breads and excessive red meat and other fatty foods, such as french fries.

Exercise really works!

Keep in mind that you are the parent and anything that you can do to get your children to exercise is a plus. Getting your children involved in any kind of sports activity helps them lose weight, develops team spirit, teaches them to share with others, and helps establish new friendships. Encourage your children to become involved with sports they are interested in. The results of being involved in sports may last throughout their life, enabling them to lose weight, lower their cholesterol, and increase their life expectancy. It will also decrease their risk of heart disease, stroke, and diabetes.

TOTAL PARENT POINTERS
OBESITY IN CHILDREN

1. Teach your children about having five servings of fruits and vegetables every day.

2. **Get your children involved in some type of sport or activity** that keeps them moving, such as sports, dance lessons, walking, bicycling, etc. Taking swimming lessons provides exercise and helps teach your child how to stay safe in the water.

3. **Disconnect the TV and computer and other video games if necessary.** Keep the TV out of your child's bedroom. This is too distracting for children. In addition, studies have shown that the amount of food a person consumes increases as they watch more TV.

4. Come up with **creative and appealing low-fat foods** for meals and snacks.

5. **Pack the children's lunch box with healthy but fun foods** such as granola bars, chicken sandwiches on whole-grain bread, and low-fat yogurt.

6. **Eat dinner together.** This enables you to control what your children eat and provides time to talk about healthy food choices.

7. **Exercise together as a family.** Go for a bike ride or go swimming together. Go hiking for a day or two at your local forest preserve or state park (or even around the neighborhood). Walk to the nearest playground or play basketball, soccer, or baseball with your children.

33

Sickle-Cell Anemia

What is sickle-cell anemia?

Sickle-cell anemia is an inherited blood disorder that occurs in approximately one in six hundred people of African American descent. However, it can also affect children of Mediterranean, Indian, and Middle Eastern origin. Some people only have sickle-cell trait, which by itself usually does not cause the complications of sickle-cell disease.

In sickle-cell anemia, the red blood cells that are normally disc-shaped become crescent-shaped (see diagram below). This is due to the fact that the individual inherited a different form of the protein (hemoglobin) that carries oxygen in his red blood cells. This protein tends to form long strands, which causes the red blood cells to assume a crescent or sickle shape.

Anemia means that the individual has less than the normal amount of red blood cells. This is due to the fact that they don't live as long as normal red blood cells.

PAIN CRISIS

Children with sickle-cell disease usually develop an acute pain crisis one or more times per year. This is a result of a blockage of the blood flow to their bones and to other parts of their bodies because the sickle-shaped red blood cells tend to clog up the small blood vessels. When the arteries get clogged or blocked, the decrease in blood flow causes a decrease in the amount of oxygen that can be delivered to those body tissues. A lack of oxygen to the bones and other tissues causes severe pain.

Children with pain crises complain of severe pain in their long bones, back, or abdomen.

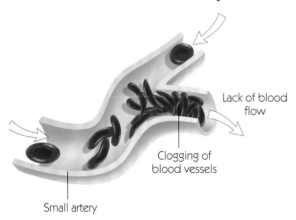

Lack of blood flow

Clogging of blood vessels

Small artery

Sickled red blood cells

How is sickle-cell anemia diagnosed?

Any child with bone pain and a family history of sickle-cell disease should receive medical treatment if the parents suspect sickle cell may be a possible diagnosis.

Young children may develop pain or swelling in their hands and feet (called dactylitis) during the first few years of life. The swelling is usually most visible on the top of the hands and feet. This is how some infants are initially diagnosed with sickle-cell anemia. Older children may develop severe pain in the bones of the back, arms, thighs, chest, or abdomen.

Your doctor will make the diagnosis of sickle-cell anemia based on a blood test and a blood count. If the blood test is positive for sickle cells, your physician will determine whether your child has sickle-cell trait or sickle-cell disease. Sickle-cell trait is not as severe as sickle-cell disease. Sickle-cell disease means that the child has two doses of the sickle-cell gene. Sickle-cell trait indicates that the child only has one dose of the sickle-cell gene. These patients generally do not have symptoms, but they are carriers of the gene for sickle-cell. This is important to know for genetic counseling. If two people with the trait have children, their children can have sickle-cell disease.

What are the complications of sickle-cell anemia?

- Infections due to reduced immunity
- Pain crisis
- Acute chest syndrome
- Pneumonia
- Bone infections (called osteomyelitis)
- Strokes
- Gallbladder infections
- Gallstones
- Blood clots in the lungs (pulmonary embolism)
- Persistent erection of the penis (priapism)
- Delays in physical growth and the onset of puberty

What are the four main crises that can occur in sickle-cell anemia?

1. Pain crisis
2. Aplastic anemia (bone marrow stops producing red blood cells, white blood cells, and platelets)
3. Sequestration crisis (blood fills up the spleen and can cause shock or rupture of the spleen)
4. Hyperhemolytic crisis (red blood cells are being destroyed at an extremely fast rate, and the child is becoming extremely anemic)

APLASTIC ANEMIA

The bone marrow stops producing white blood cells, red blood cells, and platelets. Red blood cells are important for carrying oxygen to all areas of the body. Platelets are important for blood clotting. White blood cells are important for fighting infections. These patients are at high risk of dying from an overwhelming infection. Aplastic anemia is frequently caused by a viral infection that suppresses the bone marrow and prevents the production of blood cells.

SEQUESTRATION (SPLEEN BLOCKAGE CRISIS)

Swelling and pooling of blood in the spleen causes severe anemia, possible bleeding of the spleen, or even shock. Some patients require removal of their spleen in order to prevent the anemia from getting worse. (The spleen filters an individual's blood and removes red blood cells that are more than three to four months old.) When blood is sequestered in the spleen, it has been cut off from circulating through the rest of the body.

HYPERHEMOLYTIC CRISIS

Hyperhemolytic crisis occurs when the child experiences super rapid destruction of his red blood cells. As a result, the child's anemia can become very severe and can result in shock.

ACUTE CHEST SYNDROME

Symptoms of acute chest syndrome include chest pain, an abnormal chest x-ray, and sometimes pneumonia or a blood clot in the lungs. Most of these children will recover with proper treatment. But some children with acute chest syndrome who develop blood clots in their lungs or severe cases of pneumonia can die.

The key is to watch your child for symptoms of chest pain, shortness of breath, fever, coughing up blood, and chest pain with deep breathing.

TREATMENT

Painful crises need to be treated with pain relievers and oral or IV fluids. Severe anemia (low blood count of red blood cells) is treated with blood transfusions. Infections are treated with antibiotics.

Prevention is paramount. Making sure that your child does not become dehydrated is a key element in preventing pain crises.

TOTAL PARENT POINTERS
SICKLE-CELL ANEMIA

1. The sickle shape of red blood cells is due to the fact that these children have an additional hemoglobin protein in their red blood cells. (Hemoglobin carries oxygen in the red blood cell.) This protein tends to form long strands that stretch the red blood cell to a sickle or crescent shape. These cells tend to clog up arteries, which cuts off the blood flow. The lack of blood flow to bones and other tissues causes a **pain crisis.**

2. Children with sickle-cell disease who have a **fever** (100.4°F rectal or higher—99.6°F oral or higher) need prompt evaluation by a physician.

3. Young children of African American, Mediterranean, Middle Eastern, or Indian descent with painful swelling of the hands and feet and a family history of sickle-cell disease should be suspected of sickle-cell anemia.

4. Children with **chest pain and difficult breathing** or fever should be evaluated immediately in the emergency room or by your doctor. This may be an acute chest syndrome.

5. **Sickle-cell disease** occurs in children who have two doses of the sickle-cell gene. They can develop painful crises one or more times per year.

6. **Sickle-cell trait** occurs in children with only one dose of the gene for sickle cell. They do not have symptoms, but they are carriers of the gene.

34

Urinary and Genital Problems

What is a urinary tract infection?

Urinary tract infections (UTIs) are a common source of infection for all children. Kids who are old enough to talk are obviously easier to diagnosis because they can describe their symptoms. Children under the age of one can also have urinary tract infections, but their age and inability to communicate means more sleuthing and prompt follow up on our part to make sure the UTI is diagnosed and treated.

The signs of a UTI in children twelve months and under include:

- Frequent urination
- Fever over 100.4°F rectal
- Irritability
- Fussiness
- Poor appetite

Girls experience UTI's four times more frequently than boys because of the short urethra that leads to their bladder. A shorter urethra allows bacteria to enter the bladder more easily. Also, circumcised boys have UTIs about five to twenty times more frequently than uncircumcised boys.

URINARY INFECTIONS—KEY POINTS

1. Older children with a urinary infection will complain of:
   - Painful burning during urination
   - Frequent urination; every one to two hours or more
   - An urgent need to get to the bathroom to urinate
   - Fever over 100.4°F rectal or 99.5°F oral
   - Occasional nausea and vomiting
   - Occasional lower abdominal pain or pain in the sides (or flanks)
2. Young infants with a urinary tract infection may have only symptoms of poor feeding, irritability, fussiness, and a fever above 100.4°F rectal.

What causes a urinary tract infection or UTI?

Typically, a UTI is caused by bacteria from the bowel and rectal area getting into the urethra. In addition, congenital abnormalities of the kidney or the ureters (the tubes that drain the kidneys) can cause blockage and pooling of the urine.

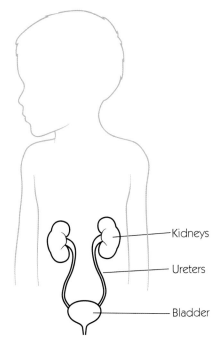

Kidneys and ureters

One of these is called reflux or VUR (vesicourethral reflux). This means that there is backflow of urine from the bladder into the ureteral tubes.

When the flow of urine is blocked, this causes an accumulation of bacteria. Therefore, when a child has a UTI, your physician may want to do a special x-ray to see if urine is not flowing properly or flowing backward. (The doctor may not order this x-ray for an initial infection but for recurring infections.) Most cases clear up after the child reaches the age of ten.

What is the treatment for UTIs?

Very young children who have a high fever or appear sick will usually be hospitalized. Older children can frequently be given oral antibiotics as an outpatient. Several antibiotics can be used; your doctor will discuss the options with you.

TESTICULAR TORSION

Testicular torsion is a twisting of the testicle that results in lack of blood flow to a testicle. If this lasts for over six to twelve hours, the testicle may die and will not produce sperm.

The key symptoms of a twisted testicle (testicular torsion) are:

1. Sudden onset of severe pain in one testicle in a child or adolescent (torsion is most common in teenagers but can occur at any age)
2. The boy may complain of pain in the lower abdomen, flank, or testicle.
3. Nausea and vomiting may occur.
4. Swelling and tenderness of one testicle.
5. If the diagnosis is made in the first four hours of pain, the save rate of the testicle is around 96 percent. If the diagnosis is not made after twelve hours, the save rate of the testicle is only 20 percent.

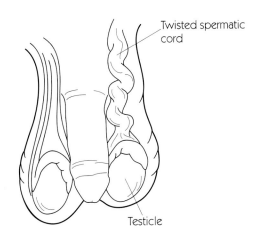

Testicular torsion

KIDNEY STONES

Kidney stones are fairly rare in children, occurring in approximately in one in seventy-five hundred children. Kidney stones are caused by a buildup of certain chemicals in the urinary tract, which forms stones. Some of these chemicals include calcium oxalate, uric acid, and cystine. Many children who have kidney stones have an abnormality of the urinary tract or a metabolic problem, which has caused a buildup of certain substances in the urine.

What are the symptoms of a kidney stone?

Some children will experience the following:

- Sudden severe pain in their side or flank
- Blood-colored or pink-tinged urine
- Vomiting

How is a kidney stone diagnosed?

Symptoms of a kidney stone include sudden pain in the side and pink-tinged urine. A CT scan is done to confirm the diagnosis.

Many children with kidney stones will pass the kidney stone within twenty-four hours. In more severe cases, the child is hospitalized and treated with IV pain medications. In some cases, the kidney stones can be shattered with special ultrasound equipment as the child lies in a tub of water. This is called ultrasonic lithotripsy.

Unfortunately, 10 to 15 percent of children with kidney stones will have recurring episodes. If the child is sent home before passing the stone, the parents will be instructed to use a strainer to catch the stone when it passes through the urine. The stone is usually about the size of a grain of sand. Once the stone is passed, the stone can be sent to a laboratory to determine its composition.

Acute glomerulonephritis (AGN)

AGN is a disease of the kidneys that occurs approximately one to two weeks after a strep throat infection. It is believed that certain proteins that help the immune system to fight infection become deposited within the kidney, leading to a decrease in the kidney's function. Nearly 80 percent of these patients recover completely. However, some children can develop severe complications or permanent renal (kidney) disease.

The symptoms of AGN include:

- Decreased urine output
- Swelling of the face, hands, or feet
- High blood pressure
- Blood in the urine

Many children will complain of fatigue and may have a fever.

How is AGN diagnosed?

Your physician will order blood and urine tests and will see certain characteristic findings in lab results. Clues to AGN include:

- Red blood cell casts in urine
- White blood cell casts in urine
- Signs of a prior strep throat infection based on a throat culture (or rapid strep swab) or an elevated blood test called an ASO (Antistreptolysin O) titer.

What are the complications of AGN?
Children with AGN can develop the following complications:
- High blood pressure
- Fluid retention
- Kidney failure
- Increased potassium level in the blood
- Congestive heart failure

Children who have this illness may be treated with medications for high blood pressure, as well as a restricted diet to limit salt intake.

VAGINAL DISCHARGE
Vaginal discharge and vaginal irritation in children or teenagers can be due to:
- Vaginal irritation due to poor hygiene or bath products
- Foreign bodies in the vagina, such as tissue, crayons, small toys
- Vaginal discharge secondary to yeast infections
- Intestinal worms
- Sexually transmitted diseases
- Pelvic inflammatory disease

How are these discharges and irritations treated?
Vaginal irritation due to poor hygiene can be corrected by instructing the child on cleaning the vaginal area. Teach your child how to wipe from front to back rather than from the rectum toward their vaginal area. These cases usually clear up with proper attention to hygiene.

FOREIGN BODIES
IN THE VAGINAL AREA
Children will sometimes place pieces of tissue or small toys or other objects in the vaginal area without your knowing it. This will result in a foul smelling discharge from the area. A parent or physician can find the object by examining the area carefully. The infection will usually clear up after the object is removed and proper hygiene is observed.

YEAST INFECTIONS
Yeast infections of the vaginal area are uncommon. They may be a sign of diabetes in older children or adolescents.

VAGINITIS DUE TO
INTESTINAL WORMS
Sometimes intestinal worms (roundworms, pinworms, and whipworms) can cause vaginal as well as rectal irritation. Parents can check for these worms by inspecting the child's rectal area at night. A tape test can also be used to diagnose intestinal worms. A tape test involves placing a piece of cellophane over the rectal area early in the morning when a child wakes up to see if any small eggs or worms are found. This can then be brought to the doctor's office where the tape can be inspected under a microscope for parasites.

How are intestinal worms treated?
A medication usually kills the worms within one to three days. Please see chapter 7 for more information.

SEXUALLY TRANSMITTED DISEASES
Children who have been sexually abused may have a discharge due to gonorrhea or chlamydia.

TOTAL PARENT POINTERS
URINARY AND GENITAL PROBLEMS

1. **Signs of a urinary tract infection** are:
   a. Burning with urination
   b. Frequent urination
   c. A need to get to the bathroom quickly to urinate; a feeling of "I can't hold it."
   d. Sometimes blood- or pink-tinged urine

2. **Vaginal discharge in young girls** can be due to:
   a. Poor hygiene or irritating bath products
   b. Foreign bodies placed in vaginal opening
   c. Yeast infection
   d. Intestinal worms
   e. Sexually transmitted disease from sexual abuse

3. **Kidney stones in children** are characterized by:
   a. Sudden onset of pain in the side of flank
   b. Bloody or pink-tinged urine
   c. Family history of kidney stones

4. Important clues to **Testicular torsion** (twisted testicle) are:
   a. Usually occurs in adolescence but can occur at any age
   b. Sudden onset of pain and tenderness in one testicle
   c. Swelling of the painful testicle in some cases
   d. The diagnosis must be made in the first few hours or the testicle will die and will not produce sperm.

PART 4

Keeping Your Child Safe

35

Preventable Deaths in Children

SECRETS TO SAVING YOUR CHILD'S LIFE

Unintentional deaths and injuries in children are so sad because most of them are preventable. As an emergency physician for over twenty-five years, I have seen far too many injuries that could have been prevented by closer supervision of a child, proper use of car safety seats and riding helmets, and the safe storage of poisons, medications, and firearms.

What's so regrettable to me and my colleagues is that many of these serious injuries and deaths could have been avoided if only we all worked harder at prevention. Research shows that accidental injury and death is a national epidemic that needs to be immediately addressed for the safety of our children.

Accidental deaths usually occur because of a failure in the chain of decision making, behavior, or knowledge. It may have been a distraction while driving, leaving a door open to the swimming pool, or not holding a child's hand in a parking lot for a few seconds.

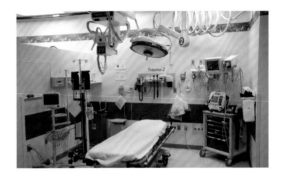

Resuscitation room in an emergency room

You are about to learn a wealth of information that can save your child's life.

What are the most preventable causes of injuries and death in children?

The most common preventable causes of injury and death include:
1. Falls
2. Choking
3. Drowning
4. Motor vehicle collisions (MVC)
5. Poisoning
6. Bicycle injuries
7. Burn injuries
8. Heat stroke
9. Firearm injuries

There is some good news here. From 1987 to 2000 there was a 39 percent decline in the death rate from injuries in the United States in children fourteen and younger.[1] But the bad news is that the death rate in the one and under age group decreased only 10 percent in that same fourteen-year period.

What are the three main causes of accidental death in children fourteen and under?

1. Motor vehicle collisions—28 percent of all children's deaths
2. Drowning—16 percent of all children's deaths
3. Choking and airway obstruction—14 percent of all children's deaths

Think about those three situations. If we can focus on preventing those types of deaths, we can impact 58 percent, or six out of ten, accidental (and preventable) deaths of children.

What is the number-one cause of injuries in children age fourteen and under?

The answer may surprise you, but it's falls—falls down stairs, falls out of strollers, falls off patio decks, and other types of accidental falls.

What's the main cause of accidental (preventable) death in children under the age of one?

Airway obstruction accounts for 60 percent of deaths in this age group. Small infants and children suffocate on small toys, pieces of food, candies, and other objects they put in their mouth, making them unable to breathe. The key point to remember is that anything approximately the same size as a child's finger can cause an airway obstruction.

The key to prevention is keeping small objects away from children under the age of one. You should also keep beads, peanuts, and small candies away from infants in this age group.

Children can also choke and suffocate from the drawstrings on their clothing, so be especially vigilant about removing these from their clothes. There have also been cases of young children who have been strangled by the cords from window blinds and curtains. We've all heard the sad stories of small children who accidentally get their neck stuck or tied up in a cord that causes strangulation.

Suffocation can also occur when infants and young children are put in the same bed as their parents and a parent unintentionally rolls on top of them. In addition, if small infants are placed on water beds or very cushy surfaces, there is a potential for them to sink into the water mattress or cushions, resulting in suffocation when their nose and mouth are covered.

Prevention of choking and suffocation in children age one and younger

1. Keep infants away from small objects, toys, or candies, anything small enough to cause choking.
2. Remove drawstrings from your child's hooded clothing.
3. Keep window blind cords out of reach of your child.

4. Take a CPR course. In the event that your child sustains a choking injury, you will know how to perform chest thrusts and back blows to dislodge the objects.

5. Avoid placing infants on extremely soft or cushy pillows, bedding, or water mattresses.

6. Keep the phone number of your closest ambulance handy. 911 is the universal number to call in an emergency and to summon EMS. (There are some areas within the country that do not have 911 service, and for those areas you need to know your local emergency number.)

For a brief overview of CPR and the procedures for dislodging a choking object in infants, please see chapters 36 and 37. You can also visit our Web site at *TheTotalParent.com* and click on Emergencies and CPR.

FALLS

Falls are the number-one cause of accidental injuries in children. In 2000, eighty-one children died as a result of injuries from a fall.

What are some of the most common reasons for falls?

1. Stairs
2. Open windows
3. Baby walkers
4. Unsafe playgrounds

The key to fall prevention is close observation of your children and locking doors to stairs, windows, and the safe use of baby walkers on a flat surface.

The National Program for Playground Safety has been involved in a research program to develop safety guidelines for the construction of playgrounds. These guidelines have recommendations for certain surface materials that can decrease the severity of injury from a fall. Currently, seven states have mandatory playground safety standards in place.

What can I do to prevent injuries from accidental falls?

Examine your home carefully and in detail, looking for areas of danger. These include unlocked doors to stairways, loose objects on the floor that can cause a child to slip, and hard surfaces that the child can fall on.

Tips for preventing falls include:

1. Install safety gates at the tops and bottoms of all stairs.
2. Always make sure to strap your child into his highchair, stroller, or baby swing.
3. Never leave your child unattended in his highchair, stroller, or baby swing.
4. Whenever possible, place a nonslip rug over hard floor surfaces such as tile and hardwood floors.
5. If possible, put padding over the sharp corners of coffee tables, benches, fireplaces, etc.
6. Children falling out of windows is also a serious problem, especially in low-income apartment buildings. Safety latches should be placed on windows allowing the window to open a few inches.

There is a campaign called Kids Can't Fly that has programs in hospitals throughout the country. Window latches and educational materials are provided at no cost.

CHOKING
Swallowed foreign bodies

If your child swallows something he shouldn't have, the most important question to ask yourself is, "Does he have any trouble breathing?"

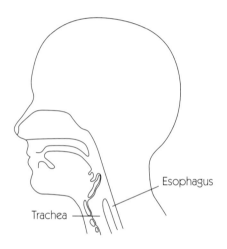

Trachea and esophagus

This is critical because we want to know which tube the object went down. Did it go toward the airway (the trachea) or into the esophagus?

If the child demostrates any of the following after swallowing or inhaling an object, call 911 or your local emergency number immediately:

1. Trouble breathing
2. Hoarseness
3. Change in voice (indicates the object is against the vocal cords)
4. Wheezing
5. Persistent cough (indicates the object is irritating the airway)

If none of the above are present, you should bring your child to the ER for x-rays to determine where the object is and whether it needs to be removed.

In many cases, if the object is in the esophagus or swallowing tube, it will pass through the stool over the next couple of days.

Swallowed button batteries

One particular worrisome object is the small button battery used in calculators and other electronic devices. These batteries can release a harsh alkaline chemical and burn a hole through the stomach or intestines within six hours.

These batteries must be removed within a few hours if they are still in the stomach. They are removed by a GI (gastrointestinal) specialist who uses an upper GI scope to retrieve the battery. If the battery has moved past the stomach and into the intestines, the child can be observed for the next twenty-four to forty-eight hours with x-rays to follow the progress of the button battery.

CHOKING CASE STUDIES
Case no. 1

An eight-month-old infant was brought to the ER with a history of crawling on the floor and putting coins in her mouth. She then started to cry and had a persistent cough. Her parents called for an ambulance and brought her to the ER immediately. She did not appear to have an airway obstruction. We took an x-ray, which is pictured on the following page.

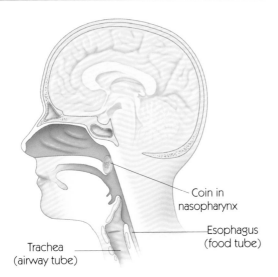

Coin in nasopharynx

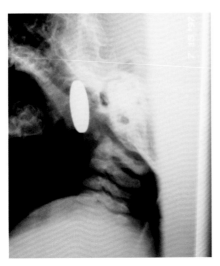

X-ray of coin in nasopharynx

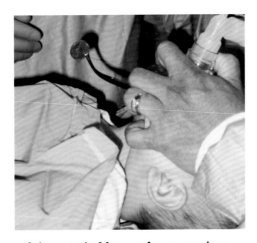

Coin on end of forceps from x-ray above

A coin can be seen in the area above the soft palate in the mouth, the area above the uvula where postnasal drip occurs. I could not visualize the coin when I looked in her throat, so I called an ear, nose, and throat (ENT) specialist, and the child was taken to surgery. The ENT specialist removed the coin as seen in the photo.

Case no. 2

A four-year-old boy told his dad that he swallowed a quarter that he found in the garage. I asked one of the hospital security guards to let me use his metal detector. When I waved it over the boy's belly, it responded. (See photo below.) I also ordered an x-ray, which showed the quarter in the intestines.

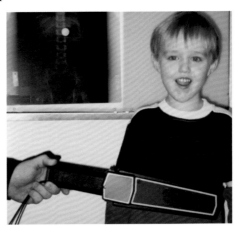

Child with metal detector over abdomen and x-ray of coin

The boy had no signs of a bowel obstruction such as vomiting or abdominal pain.

I asked the parents to check his stool every day to see when it passed. I also told them to bring him back if he experienced any of the following:

1. Abdominal pain (especially if it was progressively severe)
2. Vomiting
3. Swelling or distention of the abdomen
4. Blood in the stool

Two days later, he passed two dimes and a nickel instead of the quarter he swallowed! (I'm kidding. The parents found the quarter two days later.)

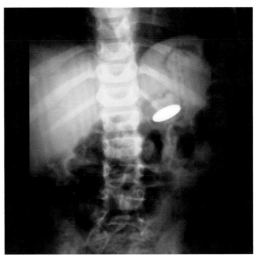
X-ray of the coin in the intestines

Case no. 3

A boy told his dad that he swallowed a nail. He had no abdominal pain, no vomiting, and no trouble breathing. I ordered an x-ray, which is to the right.

Since this nail had already moved into the intestines, I gave the parents the same advice as for case no. 2. The child passed this nail about one and one-half days later without complications.

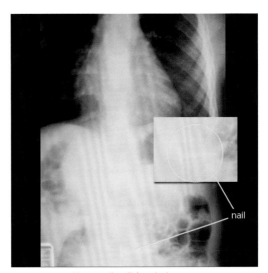
X-ray of nail in abdomen

Case no. 4

A young teenager had picked up a sewing needle and held it between her teeth for just a few seconds. She was just starting to sew when someone startled her. She gasped and swallowed the sewing needle. Her parents brought her to the ER. By then the needle was covered with stool and was moving through the intestines.

We told the parents to bring her back if she had abdominal pain, blood in the stool, vomiting, or if her belly became larger or distended.

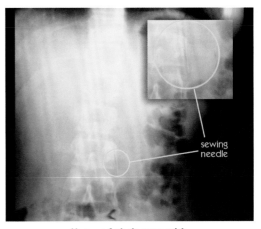
X-ray of abdomen with sewing needle in intestines

Case no. 5
A child told his dad that he was playing with some tools and swallowed a socket from a socket wrench. The child passed it in his stool the next day.

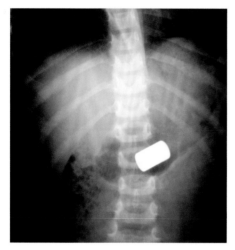

X-ray of ratchet socket in child's abdomen

DROWNING

The reasons for drowning in this age group are fairly obvious. First, children in this age group have discovered the joy of walking. They can go wherever they want, and they want to see as much as they can. Second, children in this age group are very curious, but they have no concept of danger. Water, of course, is a natural attraction. In addition, most of these children have not had any swimming lessons, and they are unable to save themselves if they fall or jump into the water. Once in the water, they cannot shout loudly enough for help because they panic and lack sufficient breath to yell for help.

It only takes one or two seconds for a child to fall into a pool, lake, or pond. Children have even drowned in buckets of water that have been left unattended.

How can I prevent my child from drowning?

1. Keep your child in view at all times whenever you are near any body (even a bucket) of water.
2. Hold onto your child's hand whenever you are near any type of lake, lagoon, or pond.
3. Have reliable locks on your doors if you have a pool outside. Also keep a locked gate around the pool to prevent neighborhood children from wandering into the pool area.
4. Install door alarms that go off when the doors to the pool area are opened. Keep doors to the pool area locked at all times.
5. Install pool alarms that will detect movement in the water.
6. Cover your pool when it is not in use.
7. Have your child take swimming lessons at an early age so that she can respond properly if she has an accident and falls into a body of water. Contact your local YMCA, park district, or health club for swimming classes in your area.
8. Tell your children to never go near water unless you or a responsible adult are there with them.

MOTOR VEHICLE COLLISIONS

What are the key points to prevent accidental deaths due to motor vehicle collisions?

The keys are prevention and the proper use and installation of car seats.

1. Motor vehicle collisions account for 35 percent of deaths in children in the five-to-nine-year-old age group.
2. Car crashes are responsible for 40 percent of deaths in the ten-to-fourteen-year-old age groups.
3. Four out of five car seats (82 percent or more) are used incorrectly or installed incorrectly.
4. Only one out of five children who should use a booster seat actually has a booster seat.
5. Parents need to be aware that adult seat belts should not be used on children until they are eight years of age and over four feet nine inches in height.
6. Never place an infant in a rear-facing car seat in the front passenger seat of a car. If a front-end collision occurs and the airbag deploys, a child in a rear-facing car seat can be killed by the forceful deployment of that airbag.
7. Infants should ride in rear-facing car seats until they are at least one year old and weigh at least twenty pounds. Children should ride in rear-facing car seats as long as possible—to the upper weight limit of the car seat. This can be anywhere from twenty-two to thirty-five pounds. Check the manufacturer's specifications.
8. Rear-facing and forward-facing car seats can be secured with seat belts.
9. Another system for attaching car seats is the LATCH (Lower Anchors and Tethers for Children) system. All cars built since September 2000 are required to have the LATCH for child car seats. The LATCH system allows your child's car seat to be installed without using seatbelts. The diagram below illustrates how the top of a forward-facing seat is secured with the top tether.

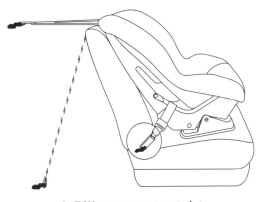

LATCH system seat restraint

10. Booster seats are for children who have outgrown their forward-facing seat with a harness. Children should be at least four feet nine inches tall before they move into an adult seat belt. This usually occurs between eight and twelve years of age.
11. Never put the shoulder strap of the seat belt under your child's arm or behind his back.

How do I know if my child's car seat is installed correctly?

Contact a local hospital or fire department. Some of the larger hospitals and police departments have a certified child passenger safety technician on staff. This person can check your car seat to make sure it is installed correctly. In addition, many hospitals have annual safety events where child safety experts will check your car seat for free. (However, do not wait for an annual safety fair to make sure that your car seat is attached properly.)

We have several articles on our Web site written by a certified car seat technician with instructions on installing child car seats properly. In general, there should be no more than one inch of movement to the right, left, or from front to back if you pull against the car

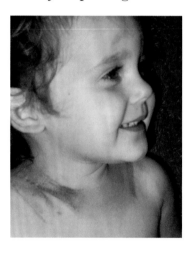

This child shows abrasions of both shoulders from restraint belts after a motor vehicle collision. **She survived a head-on collision** thanks to the proper installation and use of a child restraint seat.

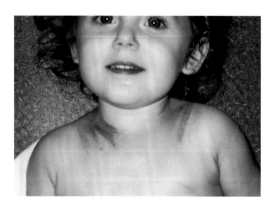

seat near the belt path. In addition, you should not be able to pinch a piece of the child's harness and fold it upon itself. If you can, then the harness is too loose.

To find a certified child seat inspector in your area, visit the National Highway Traffic Safety Administration Web site at www.nhtsa.dot.gov. Search for the Child Safety Seat Inspection Station Locator. If you have trouble finding one, visit our Web site and search for Car Seats. Our site has a direct link to the Child Safety Seat Inspection Station Locator.

MOTOR VEHICLE ACCIDENTS AND OLDER CHILDREN

Motor vehicle accidents are a major cause of death and disability in the ten-to-eighteen-year-old age group. Many of these injuries could be avoided by wearing seat belts, not talking on cell phones while driving, and limiting the number of teenage passengers in the car. Several states have enacted laws that limit the number of children who can be in a car with a sixteen- to eighteen-year-old driver.

Case study—car crash

A sixteen-year-old was driving on a highway at forty-five to fifty miles per hour and crashed into the side of another car. The teenager was not wearing a seat belt. He was also texting someone on his cell phone at the time.

He was pinned inside the car, and it took paramedics ten minutes to extricate him. The boy had a blood pressure of 110/70 (normal is 120/80), a rapid pulse of 110, and rapid breathing. He was complaining of pain in the upper left quadrant of his abdomen.

When I examined him in the ER, his left upper abdomen was tender to touch. His blood pressure remained stable, but his pulse was over 100. A CT scan revealed a lacerated spleen.

This boy's blood pressure then started to drop. We rapidly transfused him with blood and quickly transported him to the operating room for surgery. The trauma surgeon found that the spleen had severe lacerations that could not be repaired. The blood vessels to the spleen were tied off and the spleen

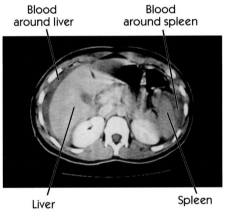

CT scan of lacerated spleen

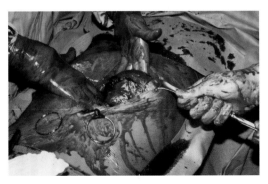

Spleen being removed in surgery

was removed. The boy was released from the hospital a few days later.

If this teenager had been wearing a seat belt, it is very likely that he may not have required surgery. If he had not been text messaging, he may not have had the accident.

If you are involved in an accident such as this, the police will obtain your phone records. They will know what you were doing on the phone at the time of the accident. So teach your children not to be distracted and to always wear their seat belts.

Teen driver safety program

Provena St. Mary's Trauma Center (my hospital) has developed its own teen driver safety program geared toward high school students just before prom season. It consists of a reenacted collision and a demonstration of what really happens after an accident by the fire, police and paramedic departments.

The students watched from the football stands as six teenagers with fake blood were removed from the cars by the paramedics. The paramedics use the Jaws of Life to cut open the cars to extricate the teenagers. One teenager was permanently

Car set up for mock accident for teen driver safety program

Two teenagers in makeup in backseat of car after mock accident

Firefighters using the Jaws of Life to cut through a car door

The boy in body bag who "died" in the mock accident during a teen driver safety program

High school car safety program with Dr. Kurzejka and ER staff caring for the teenager while her mother comforts her daughter, who is paralyzed below the waist.

paralyzed from the waist down and one died in the accident.

One of the teenage drivers was arrested by the state police for driving under the influence of alcohol.

After the car extrication, the students reconvened in the gymnasium, where a mock courtroom convened. The teenagers heard several students and parents testify about how this accident changed their lives forever. They also spoke of how much they missed the student who died. The girl who was paralyzed came to court in her wheelchair.

BICYCLE INJURIES

The key to injury prevention is knowing and obeying bicycle safety techniques, which include avoiding busy highways with fast moving vehicles and a narrow shoulder to ride on. In addition, safety helmets significantly reduce the chance of head injuries. If a child is struck by a car, usually 50 percent of them sustain significant head injuries.

On the average, more than 100 children die in bicycle crashes every year. In 2004, 130 children under the age of fourteen died from bicycle-related injuries. About 297,728 children suffered injuries due to bicycle accidents in that year. A recent survey indicated that four out of five children did not wear helmets when riding their bicycles. As of 2006, 20 states plus the District of Columbia and 148 municipal localities have laws mandating the use of bicycle helmets—most for those sixteen and under.

When you go bike riding with your family, be a good example

for your child by wearing a helmet yourself.

Help your children understand the rules of the road when they ride bicycles. Teach them to look both ways before crossing busy streets, avoid riding on busy highways, and to signal when turning.

Child wearing bicycle helmet

BURN INJURIES

What can you do to prevent accidental burn and fire injuries?

1. Smoke detectors and carbon monoxide detectors are a must-have for every home. Smoke alarms, which are appropriately located in the main rooms of the house, decrease the chance of dying in a house fire by 50 percent.
2. Test your smoke detectors and carbon monoxide detectors on a regular basis. The National Fire Protection Association (NFPA) recommends that battery-operated smoke detectors be checked once a month. They also recommend that the batteries be changed at least once a year.
3. Practice fire drills with your children at least twice a year. Blindfold your older children and see if they can find their way out of the house. This would simulate a house full of smoke in which the child could not see.
4. Teach your children the best escape routes in the event of a fire.
5. Make sure your children's pajamas are not flammable.
6. Keep fire extinguishers in key locations around the house such as the kitchen, garage, and near the outdoor grill. You should also check your extinguishers to make sure they have adequate pressure and are ready to use.
7. Lower the temperature of your water heater to 120°F to prevent burning or scalding injuries.
8. Lock away matches and lighters.

HEAT STROKE

Children who are left in cars on warm or even semi-warm days can die from heat stroke within thirty to sixty minutes. In 2004, thirty-four children who were left in cars died from heat stroke. Some parents have asked if it helps to leave the windows slightly open to help the air circulate. They wonder if this prevents the temperature in the car from rising. The answer is no.

The temperature of a car can increase over 41°F in just one hour. This can occur whether the outside temperature is in the low 90s or even in the low 70s. Whether it is cool or cloudy, the temperature inside the car can rise to over 100°F within sixty minutes. Infants' age one and under are especially prone to heat stoke because their body's temperature control system is not developed enough to maintain their body temperature. Their bodies have not learned how to produce enough sweat to cool them off when exposed to a hot environment such as the inside of a warm or hot car.

Never leave a child unsupervised in a car while you run errands in a store—even if you are only going to be gone for a few minutes. Along with heat-related injuries, you will also risk the possibility of someone abducting your child while stealing your car. There have been many reports of cars stolen with babies in the backseats while the parent ran into the gas station to pay for gas or grab a gallon of milk.

FIREARM INJURIES

Unfortunately, sixty children age fourteen and under died from gun injuries in 2002. However, another eight hundred children in that age group were treated in emergency rooms for gun injuries in that same year.

There are an estimated 3.3 million children who live in homes that have guns, which are kept loaded and unlocked. As a result, several states have passed child gun access prevention laws. These laws enable states to hold the parents liable for any injury to a child that comes from having a loaded firearm in the house.

What can I do to prevent firearm injuries from occurring in my house?

1. Keep all firearms locked and out of reach of children.
2. Keep ammunition in a safe and locked location separate from the firearms.
3. Do not tell children where the firearms are located.
4. Remove all bullets from firearms.
5. Make sure that a safety lock is connected or a safety lock is attached.
6. Make sure you have a permit for the firearm.
7. Make sure that you are trained in the safety rules of using a firearm.
8. Children should be taught what to do if they find a gun: they should never touch the gun. Instead they should immediately leave the room and go find an adult.

POISONING

Poisoning is discussed in chapter 42, "Poisoning and Overdoses."

NOTES

1. National Safe Kids Campaign, *Report to the Nation: Trends in Unintentional Childhood Injury Mortality,* 1987–2000 (Washington, DC: National Safe Kids Campaign, 2003), 2.

TOTAL PARENT POINTERS
PREVENTABLE DEATHS IN CHILDREN

The information in this chapter is important in preventing your child from sustaining accidental injury or even death. The key concepts to remember are:

1. **Prevent falls.**
   Falls are the number-one cause of accidental injuries in children. Keys to fall prevention include:
   - Install safety gates at the top and bottom of stairways.
   - Always keep your child strapped in his highchair, stroller, or baby swing.
   - Never leave a child unattended in a highchair, stroller, or baby swing.
   - Place nonslip carpets over hard floors such as marble, tile, or hardwood.
   - Use protective padding over sharp corners of tables, chairs, etc.

2. **Prevent choking and strangulation. Airway obstruction and choking is the number-one cause of death in children age one or less.** Keep small objects out of their reach, tie up all curtain cords, and remove drawstrings from any hooded clothing. Other suggestions:
   - **Take a CPR course** so that you know how to deal with a choking child or a child who is drowning and needs CPR.
   - Keep the telephone number for your local ambulance and fire department available.

3. **Prevent drowning.**
   - Keep your child in sight at all times while near any lakes, ponds, or streams. Taking your gaze off of your young child can mean the difference between life and death.
   - **Hold your child's hand while near any body of water.**
   - Avoid having buckets of water in your home or even outside
   - Lock doors to prevent access to any pool area.
   - Cover your pool when it is not in use.
   - Take your child to a swimming class at your local park district or YMCA.

4. **Prevent motor vehicle injuries.**
   - Have your child's car seat checked for proper installation by a certified child passenger safety technician at your local hospital.
   - **Never place a rear-facing seat in the front passenger seat of a car.**
   - **Never allow a child under the age of eight to use an adult seat belt.**
   - **Never allow a child to place a shoulder strap under her arm or behind her back.**
   - Use a booster seat for older children until they are at least eight years old and over four feet nine inches tall.
   - Make sure that your car seat is installed correctly in your vehicle with the seat belt or the LATCH system.
   - Rear-facing car seats can be used until your child reaches the upper weight limit of the seat. This may be up to thirty to thirty-five pounds. Check your car seat specifications.

5. **Prevent bicycle injuries.**
   - Make sure your child wears a helmet. Be a role model by wearing a helmet yourself.
   - Teach your child the rules of the road for bicycle riding.

TOTAL PARENT POINTERS
PREVENTABLE DEATHS IN CHILDREN

6. **Prevent burn and fire injuries.**
   - Smoke detectors and carbon monoxide detectors are a must for every house. Smoke detectors decrease the chances of dying in a house fire by 50 percent. Check your detectors every month and change batteries every year.
   - Practice fire drills with your children twice a year.
   - Keep fire extinguishers in key locations around the house and the garage.
   - Lower the temperature on your water heater to 120°F.
   - Lock away matches and lighters.

7. **Prevent heat stroke.**
   - Never leave a child in a car unattended. The temperature on even a 70° day can increase to 100°F within sixty minutes.

8. **Prevent firearm injuries.**
   - Lock and secure all firearms away from children.
   - Keep a safety latch or gunlock in place on all firearms.
   - Keep ammunition locked in a separate location away from firearms.
   - Keep in mind that several states have child firearm access prevention laws that hold parents liable for injuries to children as a result of access to their parents' firearms.

36

Choking

Approximately 17,550 children age fourteen or younger are treated in United States emergency rooms each year for choking. Almost 200 children die in the United States each year from choking or airway obstruction. Most of these deaths occur in children younger than four years old.

Are choking deaths preventable?

Although many people refer to choking as accidents, the sad reality is that many are preventable.

Your mission as a parent is to keep small objects away from your young children. This includes small toys, small parts that can be removed from or broken off of larger toys, hard foods, and hard candies.

Besides hard candies, there is also a choking risk from semi-hard or gooey candies, which can mold to the child's airway and cause blockage. These types of candies are very difficult for paramedics and physicians to remove.

Children should be encouraged to sit while eating. Never let them run or play with candy, gum, or lollipops in their mouths. Teach

Child on carpet

them to chew, chew, chew, and swallow before talking. Parties for adults can be especially dangerous, as candies and nuts may be dropped or left where small hands can find them later.

A toilet paper tube can be used to test toys. If a toy can fit inside the tube, then it is small enough to pose a choking hazard for infants and toddlers.

What are the most common causes of choking deaths?

1. Hard or firm foods, such as peanuts, seeds, gum, hot dogs, meats, carrots, cookies, or foods with nuts.

2. Small toys and other small objects on the floor, such as necklace beads, small parts for toys, buttons, or latex balloons.
3. Hard or gooey candies.

What are the most common causes of suffocation deaths?

Suffocation occurs when a child is choked by a tight band around the neck or an object blocks the child's nose and mouth so that air cannot move in and out.

1. Window blinds, and curtain or drape cords can accidently get wrapped around a child's neck and cause airway obstruction and death. Always keep these cords wrapped and placed out of reach of small children.
2. Suffocation can occur if small infants are in bed with their parents. These children can suffocate if a parent rolls on top of them while sleeping.
3. Cords on hooded clothing have been known to cause choking deaths if the child's neck gets wrapped in them while asleep. You need to remove all cords from hooded clothing.
4. Suffocation can occur if pillows and bulky bed linens are placed in bed with an infant. These items can obstruct the child's face while sleeping and result in suffocation.

Why do children age four years and younger have the highest number of choking deaths?

1. Their chewing teeth are not yet fully erupted.

2. Their chewing muscles are not fully developed and coordinated.
3. They incompletely chew their food before swallowing.
4. They are more likely to experience the startle reflex, which refers to their instinct to inhale quickly if they are suddenly startled. If this occurs while there is food in their mouth, they may inhale a piece of it into their airway, or trachea.

The diagram below shows a peanut lodged above a child's vocal cords.

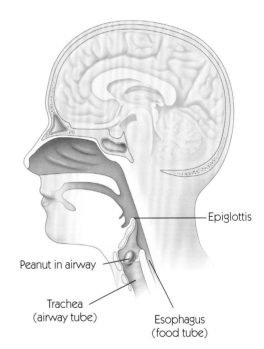

Peanut in airway above vocal cords

An ear, nose, and throat collague said that one of the most difficult cases he has had was a young girl who was choking on a small doll shoe. An illustration of how this would look to a physician

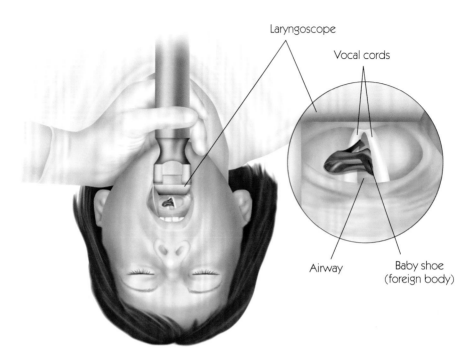

Laryngoscope

Vocal cords

Airway

Baby shoe
(foreign body)

Girl with toy shoe lodged between her vocal cords

or paramedic using a laryngoscope can be seen in the diagram above.

How quickly can a child choke on an object?

A mother was changing her eight-month-old son's diaper on a changing table. Before she realized what was happening, she saw him put something in his mouth. A few seconds later he began coughing severely and acting as if he was choking. She rushed him to the ER. I used a laryngoscope to look inside his mouth. He then coughed up a piece of broken tile. His breathing returned to normal, and his mother was overjoyed. They went home relieved that this emergency was quickly resolved.

Child who choked on tile

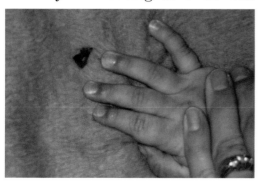

Piece of broken tile

What can I do to prevent my children from choking?

1. Get down on your hands and knees and look at all the floors of your house for any small objects, toys, etc. that could be chokers.
2. Cut up solid and firm foods for young children, such as grapes, hot dogs, meats, and harder vegetables. Hot dogs should be cut lengthwise and then into small pieces. The round cut of a hot dog or grape is just the right size to get stuck in a child's airway.
3. Don't give young children hard or gooey candies or potato chips.
4. Instruct baby-sitters about all of the above.
5. Take a CPR class so you know how to treat a choking child with abdominal thrusts (the Heimlich maneuver) or chest thrusts.
6. Make sure that your baby-sitter is CPR certified.

How can I tell if my child is choking?

Some of the important signs of choking are:

1. The child cannot talk or make any age-appropriate vocal sounds.
2. There is no air movement in and out of the mouth and nose.
3. An older child will make a choking sign (holding the neck with one or both hands) and look panicky.
4. Persistent and severe coughing or gagging.
5. Very difficult breathing.
6. Turning blue (especially the lips).
7. The child suddenly has a hoarse voice.

Child over age one being given abdominal thrusts (heimlich maneuver)

What should I do if my child is choking?

If the child is not speaking, turning blue, not moving air in and out, or has severely labored breathing, you must immediately:

1. Do the Heimlich maneuver, also referred to as an abdominal thrust on children older than one year. Continue until the object is coughed up or the child becomes unconscious (limp). If the child becomes unconscious, begin CPR and have someone call 911 or the emergency response number.
2. In infants age one year or younger, do five back blows followed by five chest compressions. See diagrams below for location

of chest compressions in infants. Continue until the infant coughs up the object or becomes unconscious (limp). If the infant becomes unconscious, begin CPR and have someone call 911 or the emergency response number.

3. Call 911 or your local emergency number for an ambulance as soon as possible.

CPR COURSE

Take a CPR course for hands-on training about caring for a choking infant, child, or an adult. For three hours of your time, you can learn how to save the life of your children and adult family members. Be a leader and help organize a course in your office or workplace. Invite your friends and co-workers to join you for a few hours of fun and education! Call your local hospital and ask for the education department to help set up a CPR course at your workplace.

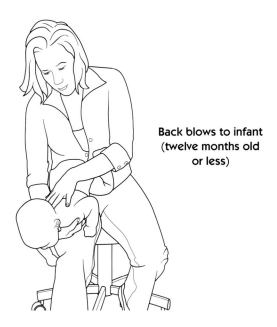

Back blows to infant
(twelve months old
or less)

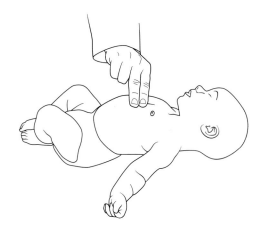

Chest compressions on infant
(twelve months old or younger)

TOTAL PARENT POINTERS
CHOKING

1. **Choking is preventable.** The key is to understand and identify potential choking risks in your home and elsewhere.

2. **Most children who die from choking are age four years or younger.**
   a. Their **chewing teeth have not fully erupted.**
   b. Their **chewing muscles are not yet fully developed** and coordinated.
   c. They **incompletely chew their food** before swallowing.
   d. They are more likely to experience the **startle reflex** and inhale a foreign object into their airway.

3. The **most common causes of choking** are:
   a. Hard or soft and gooey candies
   b. Hard or firm foods
   c. Small objects on the floor, tables, etc.

4. The **most common causes of suffocation in children are:**
   a. Strangulation due to window blind or drape cores
   b. Suffocation while sleeping in bed with an adult.
   c. Strangulation due to cords on hooded clothing
   d. Suffocation due to cushy pillows in the child's bed.

5. **The treatment for a choking child is:**
   a. Five back blows followed by five chest compressions in infants age twelve months or younger until the object is coughed up.
   b. Abdominal thrusts (Heimlich maneuver) in children over the age of one year.

6. **Take a CPR course** for hands-on training about caring for a choking infant, child, or an adult. For three hours of your time, you can learn how to save the life of your children and adult family members. Be a leader and help organize a course in your office or workplace. Invite your friends and co-workers to join you for a few hours of fun and education! Call your local hospital and ask for the education department to help set up a CPR course at your workplace.

37

CPR (Cardiopulmonary Resuscitation) and Cardiac Arrest

Cardiac arrest means that the heart stops and is unable to pump blood through the body. Within minutes, the individual isn't breathing. The consequences of not intervening in the first few minutes after cardiac arrest can be very serious. Brain damage—potentially irreversible—may begin if the brain is without oxygen for more than four to six minutes. The person may die. In an adult, it's a tragedy. In a child, it's worse than a tragedy.

Approximately sixteen thousand children die each year in the United States from unexpected cardiac arrest. About 45 to 70 percent of pediatric cardiac arrests occur in children

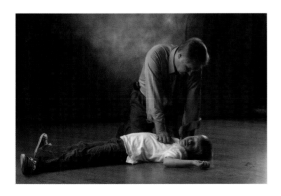

younger than twelve months of age. The most common causes are:

1. Asthma
2. Airway obstruction (choking and suffocation)
3. SIDS (sudden infant death syndrome)[1]—infants should be put to sleep on their back
4. Drowning
5. Meningitis (an infection of the spinal fluid and the brain)
6. Congenital heart disease
7. Sepsis (an overwhelming infection in the bloodstream)
8. Trauma (this becomes a major cause of death after age one)
9. Suicide and drug overdoses (in adolescents)
10. Bronchiolitis (RSV infections), severe cases

In most cases, the cause of cardiac arrest in children is usually a breathing or medical problem that has become so severe that the child's body could not get enough oxygen, causing the heart to stop beating. In general, about 90 percent of childhood cardiac arrests are due to breathing or medical problems, and the other 10 percent are due to primary heart problems.

In adults, the cause of cardiac arrest is usually a primary heart problem, such as a heart attack, which can cause an abnormal beating of the heart.

What are the signs of cardiac arrest?

The signs of cardiac arrest are the sudden onset of:

1. No breathing (or very shallow, or agonal, breathing)
2. Pale or ashen-looking skin
3. No movement or occasional jerky movements
4. Cool hands and feet
5. No response to painful stimulation
6. No pulse (nonmedical persons are not expected to know how to check for a pulse.) If you have the appropriate training, however, check for a pulse in the crease of the elbow or the neck.

What is CPR?

CPR is the technique of doing chest compressions and artificial ventilation (breathing) in children whose heart has stopped (cardiac arrest).

What do I need to know about doing CPR?

You should take a brief course that has been developed for parents and laypersons to learn about CPR and choking. Call your local hospital, the American Red Cross (www.redcross.org/services/hss/courses/), the American Heart

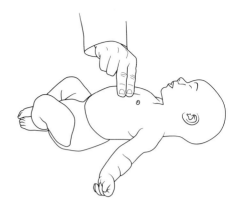

Proper position for doing CPR on an infant (twelve months old or less)

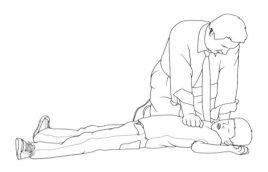

Proper position for doing CPR on a child age one to eight

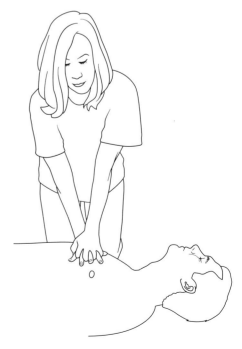

Proper Position for doing CPR on an adult or child over age eight

Association (www.americanheart.org), or the Emergency Care Safety Institute (www.ECSInstitute.org) for information on the nearest course offering.

We will review some of the key concepts here, but this is not a substitute for taking a course. Taking a CPR course will enable you to practice the proper techniques with a certified instructor on an infant and child CPR mannequin.

How do I position my child's head properly to open the airway?

Opening the airway before starting mouth-to-mouth breathing is an important concept to understand. Children have a relatively large head compared to the rest of their body. This causes their head and chin to flex forward and down when they are lying on their back. When this occurs, the airway can become kinked so that air cannot get through.

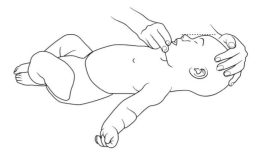

Infant head tilt to open airway

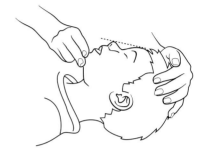

Child head tilt to open airway

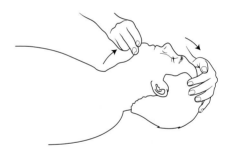

Adult head tilt to open airway

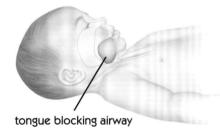

tongue blocking airway

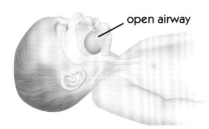

open airway

Tongue being lifted up by tilting the head back and opening the airway

In addition, the tongue may move back and block the airway. It is important to tilt the head back just enough to straighten the airway and to lift the jaw in order to lift the tongue and open the airway. The diagrams above demonstrate how this is done.

It is generally recommended to only tilt an infant's head up slightly. Older children (age one to eight) should have a bit more tilt to open the airway. Adults can have full extension—or tilting of their head and neck—to open their airway.

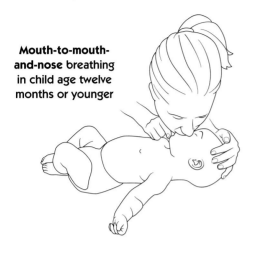

Mouth-to-mouth-and-nose breathing in child age twelve months or younger

Mouth-to-mouth breathing in child age one and older

What do I need to know about doing mouth-to-mouth breathing?

The first thing to do when a child is in cardiac arrest is to open the airway and begin mouth-to-mouth (or mouth-to-mouth-and-nose) breathing (also called ventilation).

The three points to keep in mind are:

1. Mouth-to-child's-mouth-and-nose breathing is done with infants age twelve months or younger.
2. Mouth-to-mouth breathing is done with children age one or more.
3. Begin your rescue breathing by giving two breaths (one second each).

Remember to pinch the child's nose closed when doing mouth-to-mouth breathing.

What do I need to know about doing chest compressions for CPR?

1. Do chest compressions with two fingers on the breastbone (sternum) just below the nipple line for infants age one year or younger.
2. Do chest compressions on children over age one with one or two hands over the breastbone (sternum) between the nipples.
3. Do about one hundred compressions per minute.

During CPR, you need to alternate giving two breaths (or ventilations) for every thirty chest compressions.

What is an automatic external defibrillator (AED)?

An AED is a portable electrical device used to shock the heart out of the deadly rhythm that may be causing the cardiac arrest.

Can AEDs be used on children?

Yes, but only in children age one year or more. Use the pediatric size pads if available. If these are not available, use the adult pads.

These portable units now have voice instructions that tell you what to do for the child. All you really need to know is:

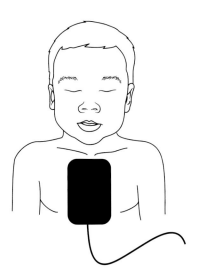

Location of automatic external defibrillator (AED) pad on front of child's chest

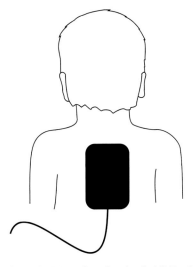

Location of AED pad on back of child's chest

1. How to identify cardiac arrest.
2. Where to place the electrode pads on the child (see diagram).
3. Only use AEDs on children age one year or older.
4. Use the smaller pediatric-sized pads if available. If these are not available, use the adult pads.

Once you place the electrode pads on the front and back of the chest, the computer in the AED will analyze the child's heart rhythm. It will instruct you to do one of two things:

1. Press the button to charge the AED and give a shock (after making sure that everyone is clear and not touching the child during the shock)
2. It will instruct you not to give a shock because the computer senses a rhythm that should not be shocked. You will then be instructed by the AED to begin or continue CPR.

AED units can be seen on the walls at various stadiums, shopping malls, health clubs, businesses, and schools.

AED on wall at a shopping mall

AED next to fire extinguisher at a grade school

Taking a brief three-hour heart-saver AED class can provide you with the skills to save the life of adults as well as children. Cardiac arrest is much more common in adults as compared to children. CPR can double or triple a cardiac arrest victim's chances of survival.

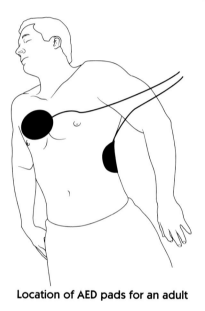

Location of AED pads for an adult

For every minute that passes for an adult in cardiac arrest, before being defibrillated (shocked), the chances of survival decrease by about 10 percent per minute. This means that if it takes five minutes to shock an adult in cardiac arrest, his chances of surviving will decrease by 50 percent (five minutes times 10 percent). Comparable statistics for children are not known.

What is bystander CPR?

Bystander CPR refers to a person's chance of surviving cardiac arrest being critically linked to the time CPR begins, because CPR is needed to keep blood and oxygen flowing to the heart, brain, and vital organs. Brain damage can begin after four to six minutes if there is no blood flow to deliver oxygen to the brain.

NOTES
1. The death rates from SIDS have decreased by about 40 percent since the recommendation of placing infants on their backs to sleep.

TOTAL PARENT POINTERS
CPR AND CARDIAC ARREST

1. CPR stands for **cardiopulmonary resuscitation**.
2. **CPR** is the technique of performing mouth-to-mouth breathing and chest compressions on a child in cardiac arrest (the heart has stopped).
3. The first thing to do when a child is found in cardiac arrest is to **open the airway** and begin mouth-to-mouth (or mouth-to-mouth-and-nose) breathing (also called ventilation or rescue breathing).
4. The main concepts to remember about rescue breathing during CPR are:
   - Place your mouth over the **child's mouth and nose** when doing rescue breathing on infants age **twelve months or younger**.
   - **Mouth-to-mouth breathing** is done with children **age one or more**.
   - **Begin rescue breathing by giving two breaths** (one second each).
   - Do **two rescue breaths** for every **thirty chest compressions**.
5. The key things to remember about doing chest compressions during CPR are:
   - **Age one year and younger:** Do chest compressions with two fingers on the breastbone (sternum) just below the nipple line. Compress one-third to one-half the depth of the chest.

   - **Children age one to age seven:** Do chest compressions using the heel of your hand with one or two hands over the breastbone (sternum) between the nipples. Compress one-third to one-half the depth of the chest.
   - **Children age eight and over:** Do two hand-locked compressions on the breastbone between the nipples. **Compress one and a half to two inches.**
   - Do about **one hundred compressions per minute**.
   - Give **two breaths** (ventilations) for every **thirty chest compressions**.
6. An **automatic extended defibrillator** (AED) can be used on children one year old and older. If specific cardiac rhythms are present, the AED will prompt the user to deliver a shock to restore the heart's normal rhythm. Make it a point to note where AEDs are located when you go to a mall or shopping center.
7. Learn how to do CPR, manage a choking child or adult, and use an AED by taking a **CPR course**. This course can provide you with the skills and confidence you need to save children and adults from choking or cardiac arrest.

Cardiopulmonary Resuscitation (CPR)

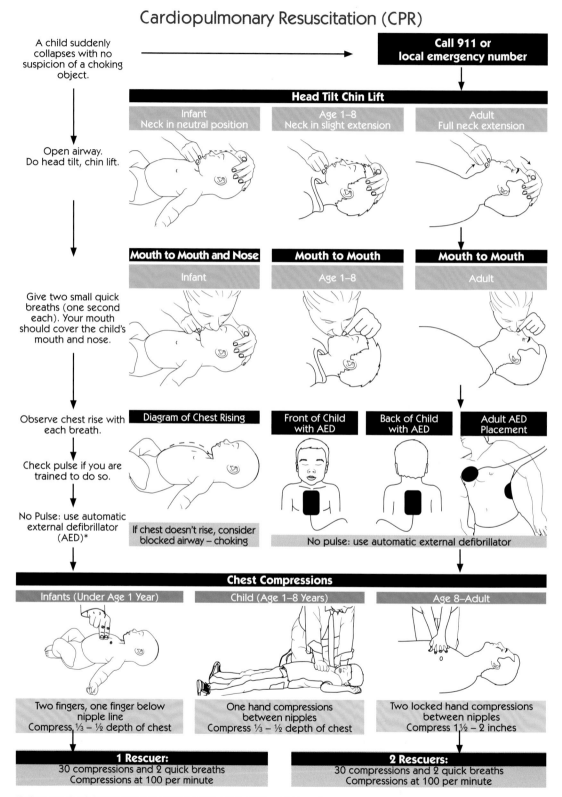

A child suddenly collapses with no suspicion of a choking object.

Call 911 or local emergency number

Head Tilt Chin Lift

| Infant Neck in neutral position | Age 1–8 Neck in slight extension | Adult Full neck extension |

Open airway. Do head tilt, chin lift.

| Mouth to Mouth and Nose | Mouth to Mouth | Mouth to Mouth |
| Infant | Age 1–8 | Adult |

Give two small quick breaths (one second each). Your mouth should cover the child's mouth and nose.

Observe chest rise with each breath.

| Diagram of Chest Rising | Front of Child with AED | Back of Child with AED | Adult AED Placement |

Check pulse if you are trained to do so.

No Pulse: use automatic external defibrillator (AED)*

If chest doesn't rise, consider blocked airway – choking

No pulse: use automatic external defibrillator

Chest Compressions

| Infants (Under Age 1 Year) | Child (Age 1–8 Years) | Age 8–Adult |

Two fingers, one finger below nipple line
Compress, ⅓ – ½ depth of chest

One hand compressions between nipples
Compress ⅓ – ½ depth of chest

Two locked hand compressions between nipples
Compress 1½ – 2 inches

1 Rescuer:
30 compressions and 2 quick breaths
Compressions at 100 per minute

2 Rescuers:
30 compressions and 2 quick breaths
Compressions at 100 per minute

*Deliver one shock followed by two minutes of CPR, but not if the child is under age one

38

Internet Safety for Children

The Internet is one of the greatest educational resources in the world. It allows us to access information from all over the world within seconds, and it is the most accessible, open, free communication pathway ever invented. However, as someone observed, "The greatest thing about the Internet is that anybody is free to say anything they want to; the worst thing about the Internet is that anybody is free to say anything they want to."

Children (as well as adults) can be exposed to a world of online predators. This chapter is devoted to teaching you how to protect your children from online predators and to inform you about viruses and spyware that can harm your computer.

The keys to prevention are education and action based on that knowledge. I will outline several of the most important concepts that you need to know to protect your child while she uses the Internet.

PERSONAL INFORMATION

Tell your child never to put any personal information on the Internet, such as their name, address, phone number, school, city, birth date, etc. This information can enable others to find them.

ONLINE FRIENDS

Let your child know that a new online friend who sends a photo and claims to be a thirteen-year-old boy or girl with a nice personality may actually be a thirty-five-year-old child molester. Let your child know that online predators are skilled at being very friendly and nice in order to obtain personal information from children and teenagers.

ONLINE PHOTOS

Tell your child never to post a photo of himself on the Internet. The only exception to this would be a protected private-access Web site that only allows certain people to access the site. This should only be done with your permission after you have reviewed the picture and the Web site. An example would be a school Web site with access limited only to students.

DOWNLOADING PROGRAMS FROM THE INTERNET

Let your child know that any program he downloads from the Internet can contain a virus or spyware.

Spyware are software programs that are automatically downloaded into your computer when you visit various Internet sites. These programs track the computer sites that you visit.

Viruses are a type of computer software that will either completely shut down your computer or create varying degrees of computer malfunction.

Let your child know that when she downloads software games, the programs may contain viruses or spyware, and this can cause the computer to crash. If your computer crashes, you will have to pay somebody to fix it, and potentially they may need to reinstall the operating system, which can be costly.

FIND OUT WHAT WEB SITES, CHAT ROOMS, INSTANT MESSAGING, AND BLOG SITES YOUR CHILD VISITS

Web sites can include various popular interactive sites such as MySpace or Facebook. Blogs are a type of mininewsletter that contains commentary by anyone who wishes to post a message on the blog site. A chat room is used for discussion among the various visitors to the chat room about whatever topic is being discussed. Instant messaging is a service available on some Internet sites that allows children to instantly text message several of their friends at the same time. Each of them can be involved in the same online discussion, and their text messages appear as soon as they are sent. If you contact your Internet provider, you can monitor the instant messaging and also receive copies of what is being sent in the messages. Talk to your Internet service provider or e-mail the provider to learn how to set up this type of parental control.

If you want to monitor the Internet sites that your child is visiting, visit our Web site at *TheTotalParent.com* and look up the article on Internet safety. We have reviewed several software programs that enable parents to monitor the sites their children are using.

The latest fad is online video Web sites, which allows anyone to post a video on the Web. Two of the most popular video Web sites are Myspace and YouTube.

Inform your child that any sexual comments or suggestions by people on the Internet should be immediately reported to you. You can make a copy of the commentary and take it to your local police department. You can also report this to the National Center for Missing and Exploited Children by calling 1-800-846-5678.

COMPUTER LOCATION IN THE HOUSE

It is a good idea to keep the computer in a very public location where you can monitor your children's

Web site visits. This will help prevent children from visiting any sites that contain adult-oriented or inappropriate material. It also helps you to keep track of when the children are using the computer to do their homework or when they are using the computer to visit other sites or instant message friends.

COMPUTER USAGE TIME LIMITS

Set down some basic rules for computer usage. This may be as simple as saying only fifteen to thirty minutes of personal usage during the week and perhaps one or two hours on the weekend. Or you may decide to limit computer usage on school nights to only educational purposes. It is up to you to establish the guidelines and enforce them.

Of course, the actual enforcement is the hard part, the time-consuming part. Children's brains are trained to push the limits beyond the rules. Your goal as a parent is to enforce the rules. If your child ignores the rules, then it may be necessary for you to terminate their computer or Internet usage for a certain period of time. To do this, disconnect the Internet cord or wireless connection. In some cases, we have resorted to removing the power cord to the computer or removing the cable that goes to the monitor. This is the easy way to prevent the child from using the computer, because if she doesn't have a cable for the monitor, she obviously cannot use it. We will usually keep the cable locked in a secret location that only my wife and I know.

Sometimes stopping the computer usage is a great incentive for kids to get back in the habit of playing outside, playing with their friends, and getting to know the people in the neighborhood. It is also an opportunity for them to read books and tackle their schoolwork.

SETTING UP MEETINGS WITH FRIENDS FROM THE INTERNET

As parents, we know that this is something that is fraught with problems and potential danger. Anybody on a computer can pretend to be a thirteen-year-old girl. All you need is a photo and a computer. In reality, that thirteen-year-old can be a middle-aged pedophile with a long criminal record.

Tell your children that if anyone suggests meeting or calling them, you should be notified immediately. Some online predators give the child a number to call instead of asking the child for her number. When the child calls the online predator, the number cannot be tracked. The predator then uses caller ID to track the child's phone number and therefore obtains the child's home address or cell phone number.

Remind your children that it is much better to get to know the children in your neighborhood and at school rather than someone they meet online. In fact, if your child seems to be unusually interested in a friend they have met on the Internet, I would strongly suggest investigating this so-called friend. If necessary, you may need to stop your child's computer usage for a time while this so-called Internet friend can be investigated further.

Are you spending enough quality time with your children?

This is a great opportunity to reflect on the amount and the quality of time that you are spending with your children. Perhaps one of your children needs some special attention at the moment. It may be that she is looking for someone to talk to because of some personal issues. It might also be the beginning of a drug or emotional problem. This is a great time to step in, take charge, and do something just with her.

SPECIAL TIME WITH DAD OR MOM

My children have special time with Dad. And they also have special time with Mom. As a physician, I have a very busy schedule, but I try to spend at least one night per month doing something special with each one of our five children. This gives us time to bond, talk about things, and do something memorable together.

Be sure to take advantage of the time that you and your children are in the car alone. Turn off the radio and just talk. Be sure to tell your children how much you love them. Compliment them for some recent good behaviors or accomplishments in school or in sports.

Your special time together can be as simple as going to a state park for a walk or a bike ride and some ice cream afterward. Or it can be something like bowling, going out to a restaurant, going to a sports game

or the theater, or doing something they really enjoy.

Be sure to bring your camera and take pictures to capture the moment. A simple tripod can allow you to take a great picture of the two of you at the park. Make a four-by-six or a big eight-by-twelve photo for your child to remember your day together, and put it on his desk or wall.

One of my favorite teaching tips for children is having them write short two-page essays. I tell my child that if he reads a short article or reads about a certain topic, he can then write an essay and qualify for a reward. The first draft is usually handwritten. I then edit the essay for grammar and punctuation. His second version can be done on the computer. In some cases, a third version may be needed for final acceptance. Once this is completed, our kids qualify for a trip to a dollar store or a low-fat yogurt at the ice cream shop.

In conclusion, the Internet is a tremendous educational and communication tool, but its use by children needs to be monitored carefully. I hope these tips have given you some insight into the problems that can occur when children are approached by online predators. I have also developed an Internet safety contract for children that you can use with your children. Have your child read through the contract and check off each box to show that he has read and understood it.

TOTAL PARENT POINTERS
INTERNET SAFETY CONTRACT FOR CHILDREN

- I will not give out any personal information on the Internet such as my name, address, phone number, city, name of my school, places where I like to hang out, or the name of our school teams. I understand that some not-very-nice people who use the Internet may use this information to locate my house and could do something dangerous to my family or me.

- I will not put my photo on the Internet unless my parents approve it. The only type of secure site for my photo is an approved private-access site such as my high school Web site that is limited to the kids at school who have password access.

- I understand that a fourteen-year-old who sends me a nice picture of herself may actually be an online predator and child abuser. I will not be fooled by this type of trick. I understand that they will also say nice things to me on the Internet in order to obtain my phone number or other information about where I live.

- If anyone I meet on the Internet asks to have a meeting with me in person, I will let my parents know immediately. In addition, if he asks me to call him or asks for my phone number, I will also tell my parents immediately. This may be a trick to do something dangerous. I understand that children have been harmed or kidnapped by these types of tricks in the past.

- I will never call any new friends that I have met online because they can locate my house and my name by using caller ID.

- I will give my parents a list of the Web sites, chat rooms, blog sites, and instant messaging sites that I use so that they can feel safe about the sites that I visit.

- I will not download any software games or programs to our family's computer because these may contain dangerous software viruses or spyware programs. A virus can make a computer crash. Spyware programs enable businesses and other people to secretly track what Web sites I visit. Malware programs are software programs with a mean intent.

- I promise that when I am using the computer for schoolwork that I will keep my promise. I understand that computer time should be limited on schooldays and weekends. This is important because I need to grow as a complete person. This involves socializing in person with my friends and with other people in the neighborhood. Spending too much time on the computer may distract me from doing other fun things with my friends and family.

- I will look for educational Web sites to help me with my schoolwork.

Child's signature _____

Parent's signature_____

TOTAL PARENT POINTERS
INTERNET SAFETY FOR CHILDREN

1. Tell your child that the alleged thirteen-year-old girl on the Internet who has a nice photo may actually be an **online predator** and pedophile. Explain to your children what those terms mean.

2. **Tell your children never to give out any personal information** such as their name, address, phone number, city, school name, or places where they hang out.

3. **Set up rules for limiting the time allowed for computer usage each day.**

4. Tell your children never to download any programs through the computer because they may contain viruses or spyware.

5. **Check to see what Web sites, chat rooms, blog sites, and instant messaging services your child is using.** Check the sites and find out what parental controls are available. Ask for whatever information you need to monitor your child's Internet communication. This may include asking for copies of e-mails, instant messages, or even a list of the Web sites they have visited.

6. **Keep the computer in a public location in the main area of the house.** This will enable you to monitor the Web sites your child is visiting and also to monitor their educational usage.

7. **Tell your children to never post a photo of themselves on the Internet unless they check with you first.** Photos should only be placed on secure sites that have limited access, such as a school Web site.

8. **Tell your children to inform you if anyone on the Internet suggests that they meet someplace to get to know each other.** Also, tell them to inform you if the person asks your child to call them on the phone.

For a list of helpful educational and informative Web sites, please visit our Web site at *TheTotalParent.com* and click on the education section under Help Your Child; then click on Educational Web sites.

39

My Child Is Lost

AN EMERGENCY ACTION PLAN

When we hear a child is missing, our heart aches because we can only guess how terrified the parents must be. We don't want to think about something so awful happening to our child, but the reality is that thinking about it is the key to preparation and prevention. Prevention means watching your child at all times, and preparation means having a plan in case your child is abducted or lost.

What is the most common cause of child abduction?

Most child abductors are divorced parents in a conflicting relationship with custodial parents. In 1999 approximately 203,900 children were abducted by a family member. Approximately 90 percent of these children were found or returned home; none of these children died. There were 58,000 other abductions in 1999 that were not family related. Almost all of these children were found safe and returned home. About 115 of these abductions were by strangers, and the children were abducted for ransom or molestation purposes. Approximately 60 percent of these children returned home safely; 40 percent were either killed or were never found.

How can abductions be prevented?

Some of the key educational points to convey to your children include:

1. Older children should always stay in a group. They should be encouraged to use the buddy system so that, if a stranger approaches, they will have strength and support to resist an abduction because they are with their buddy. In addition, if anything happens, the friend can describe the assailant to the police.

2. Children should always be suspicious if an adult approaches them to ask for directions or to ask for help in finding a lost dog. Children should be taught that predators might be trying to trick them into getting into their car.

3. Children should be taught to never get into a car with

a stranger unless they have prior instructions from their parents. That holds true even if the person tells the child, "Your mom sent me to get you."

4. Children should never be left alone in an automobile. Leaving children in the car while you run into a store is dangerous, and in many communities it is illegal.

5. Children should be taught how to call home. They should learn their phone numbers, including their area code, as soon as they are old enough to do so.

6. The child should be taught how to find a trusted adult, such as a police officer or teacher. If there is a hospital nearby, the child can be taught to go there for help.

7. Avoid placing a child's name on visible areas of his clothing or backpack. This may allow someone to pretend he already knows the child.

8. Children should be taught to just say no if someone tries to talk to them or touch them in a way that makes them feel uncomfortable. If a child feels that an adult is being too friendly and is making them feel uncomfortable, they should be told to walk away.

9. Know where your children are at all times. Children should be taught to contact you and ask for your permission if their plans change. You should have the home telephone numbers of your children's friends. It is also a good idea to get the parent's cell phone numbers and/or pager numbers.

10. Older children should have a cell phone if this fits in with the family budget. You can call your children periodically to check on how they are doing and where they are.

11. Older children, such as teenagers who are left at home for short periods of time, should be told never to open a door for anyone. This includes postal workers, delivery workers, and neighbors.

12. Children should be instructed how to answer the phone. They should never tell a caller that their parents are not home. They should say that their parents are busy and cannot come to the phone. They can offer to take a message.

How can I be prepared to find my child quickly if we are separated?

A good way of preparing for losing touch in a crowd is to always carry a recent picture (within the last six months) of each of your children in your wallet or purse. In the event one of your children is missing, this picture can be turned over to the police who can quickly transmit it to neighboring police departments.

An even better idea is to take a digital photo of each child before you go on a trip and e-mail the photos to yourself and to someone else you trust with easy computer access. In the event of a missing child, you or your friend at home can access the Internet, pull up your e-mail with the photo attachment and forward the child's photo to the proper authorities for immediate distribution to the local police departments and news agencies. You can do the same with a digital camera or a cell phone camera.

Before you go on a trip or into a crowded public area, make five to ten copies of each child's recent photo. To maximize easy identification, take a photo of the child in the clothes the child is currently wearing.

Having ten copies of your child's photo in the first few minutes after a kidnapping is extremely helpful. If one of your children is lost, you can immediately pass out the pictures to law enforcement and security personnel.

It is also a good idea to have a record of the age of your child, as well as approximate height, weight, skin color, hair color, and type of clothing they are wearing.

At the time of an abduction, it is sometimes difficult to remember what shirt or pants the child was wearing. Some parents buy the same color shirt for all of their children so they are easier to recognize in a crowded area. When the family is going on an outing, it might be a good idea to have the kids dress in similar colors. It helps to keep track of two or three children in a crowd if you know that they all have orange shirts and white pants. An example of a photo record (available at *TheTotalParent.com*) is included below.

It is also a good idea to keep the following records of your children:

- Fingerprints
- Child's DNA
- Medical records
- Dental records

If your child has been abducted, you should immediately:

1. Inform the local police department.
2. Initiate a Code Adam Alert or an AMBER Alert.
3. Pass out pictures to security personnel or people who are assisting in finding your child.
4. Call the National Center for Missing and Exploited Children

MY CHILD'S DESCRIPTION
Name: Maggie Smith
Age: 3-year-old
Clothes Wearing: white blouse and green shorts
Description:
blond hair, blue eyes, caucasian, red birthmark on the back of neck
Approximate Weight: 35 pounds
Location Last Seen:
Last seen at ABC amusement park on the Ferris wheel in Toledo, Ohio

Photo Record

at 1-800-THE-LOST (843-5678) and visit the center's Web site at www.missingkids.com

AMBER ALERT

What is an AMBER alert?

A man in Arlington, Texas, developed the AMBER (America's Missing: Broadcast Emergency Response) Alert when nine-year-old Amber Hagerman was kidnapped while riding her bicycle and was later killed. The community, in conjunction with local radio stations, coordinated their efforts to develop a local notification network via radio and TV stations. This eventually became a national program and was signed into federal law. AMBER alerts are coordinated through radio and TV stations via the Emergency Awareness System.

A description of an abducted child who meets the criteria for an AMBER alert will be broadcast on local television stations and radio stations. The key element to a successful return of an abducted child is time—how quickly the information is spread through the community or to the nation. A national AMBER alert system became functional on April 30, 2003. A national AMBER alert coordinator oversees the efforts of local law enforcement agencies and local broadcasters.

CODE ADAM ALERT

What is a Code Adam alert?

A Code Adam alert is a notice distributed throughout a building whenever a child is reported as missing. The alert triggers a system of securing the premises and systematically searching for the missing child. A good description of the child is relayed to individuals who monitor doors and parking lots to make sure that no child matching the description wanders out alone or is abducted from the premises. Many local governments have created Code Adam systems for public buildings, and some major retailers have created Code Adam systems.

The Code Adam alert is named after six-year-old Adam Walsh, who was murdered after his abduction from a shopping mall in 1981. Adam's father, John Walsh, became an advocate for better police response in kidnapping cases, and he later hosted the television series *America's Most Wanted.*

MEGAN'S LAW

Seven-year-old Megan Kanka from New Jersey went missing from her home in 1995. When the police found her body, they determined that she had been raped and brutally murdered. At the time of Megan's death, information about convicted sex offenders could not be released to the public. In 1996, a law, known as Megan's Law, was passed that allowed public access to this information.

WHAT TO DO IF YOUR CHILD IS MISSING

1. Take immediate action.
2. Call your local police department.
3. Initiate a Code Adam or an AMBER alert.
4. Give the police a description of your child, including the type

of clothes he was wearing, age, weight, hair color, appearance, etc. A recent photo of your child is invaluable.

5. Ask that your child's informaton to be entered into the National Crime Information Center's missing person files.

6. Call the National Center for Missing and Exploited Children at 1-800-THE-LOST (1-800-843-5678) and report that your child is missing.

7. Call your friends and relatives and ask everyone to sign up for a wireless AMBER alert at www.wirelessamberalert.org or through the Web site www.missingkids.com (the Web site for the National Center for Missing and Exploited Children).

8. Keep several copies of your children's photos with you when you go to crowded public places. If your child is lost, it is very helpful to pass out several pictures of your child to the police and security. Keep a current picture on your cell phone camera or digital camera.

9. Send an e-mail to a trusted friend with digital photos of each of your children. These photos can be retrieved by you or your friend to send to the police via the Internet.

10. It is a good idea to have your children dress in the same colors if you are going to a large recreational attraction. The children can be easily recognized by the colors they are wearing.

11. Certain cell phones and phone companies are equipped with GPS services. If your child has a cell phone with this feature, the police may use this to find her.

 TOTAL PARENT POINTERS
MY CHILD IS LOST

1. Most abductions are carried out by a divorced parent, and the vast majority of children are found or returned home.
2. **Teach your children about stranger danger** and how to never get in a car or go anywhere with someone they don't know or trust.
3. Know where your children are at all times and remind them to stay in touch with you as to their whereabouts.
4. Remind your children about how they should answer the phone and front door, and go over safety tips so that they will know how to respond in an emergency.
5. **Keep pictures of your children handy so** you have a current picture to share with police if you do become separated or they are abducted.
6. **AMBER alert**—A child who has been abducted and meets the criteria for an AMBER alert will have his description broadcast on local television stations and radio stations.
7. **Code Adam alert**—A Code Adam alert is distributed throughout a building when a child is reported as missing.
8. **Megan's Law** allows public access to information about convicted sex offenders.

40

Keeping Your Child Safe in a Hospital

We are fortunate that our country has some of the best medical care in the world. However, medicine is not a perfect science, and healthcare professionals are just human beings like you and me who can make mistakes. As a result, it is important for you to know how to protect your child and prevent any medical errors from occurring.

To do this, you must take an active role in your child's care. The keys to keeping your child safe include:

1. Talking to your physician so you have a good understanding about your child's illness, treatment, possible side effects and complications.
2. Asking one of the nurses to call your doctor if you have a question that cannot be answered by the nursing staff.
3. Communicating with the nursing staff and other staff members who come into the room to assist with your child's care.

4. Asking questions if you have any concerns or doubts about medications, procedures, etc.

The Joint Commission for Accreditation of Healthcare Organizations (JCAHO) and the Healthcare Facilities Accreditation Program (HFAP) are responsible for accrediting hospitals across the country, confirming that they meet very strict standards for patient quality, safety, education, etc. Make sure that your hospital is accredited by JCAHO or HFAP.

JCAHO, for example, has established several national patient safety goals over the past few years.

PROPER PATIENT IDENTIFICATION

Healthcare providers are instructed to confirm that they are dealing with the correct patient by using two separate identifiers. They will ask the patient's name and will confirm the answer by asking the date of birth. For children who are too young to communicate, they will check the wristband to make sure it has the child's name and hospital ID number. Medical staff are instructed to do this before giving any medications and prior to any procedures.

PREVENTIVE MEDICAL ERRORS

Your job is to make sure that nurses double check that the medication is the proper medication for your child. Ask the nurse the name of the medication before it is given and, if you don't know why it's being given, ask what it is for. The nurse should also ask the parents about any allergies the child may have prior to giving the medication.

CORRECT SITE AND LOCATION OF SURGICAL PROCEDURES

Before a child has a surgical procedure, the surgeon is required to confirm the procedure with the child and the parents prior to going to the operating room. Usually the surgeon will meet with the child and the parents in a presurgery holding room. The surgeon should write his initials on the patient's body near the site of the surgical procedure. (There have been instances in the past in which a surgical procedure was done on the wrong side of the body.)

Nurse doing a practice resuscitation in the pediatric unit with the Ambu bag on an infant mannequin

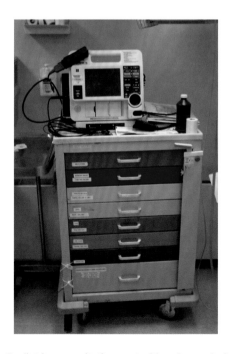

Pediatric resuscitation cart with color-coded drawers and equipment based on weight of infant

APPROPRIATE PAIN CONTROL

Check with both your physician and nurse regarding the name of the pain medication being used and how often it may be given.

COMPLETE STOCK OF ALL SIZES OF PEDIATRIC RESUSCITATION EQUIPMENT

Ask your nurse where the pediatric resuscitation cart is located. Ask how often it is checked. Ask if it contains the appropriate-size equipment for your child based on his weight. You might also ask who responds to a pediatric code blue in the pediatric nursery or the pediatric unit. Is it a doctor from the emergency room? Is it a board certified emergency physician, pediatrician, or pediatric intensive care specialist? This will largely depend on whether your child is in a university or a community hospital. Ask the nurses how often they practice pediatric resuscitations to maintain their skills and to make sure that all equipment is present on the resuscitation cart.

DRUG, FOOD, LATEX OR OTHER ALLERGIES

Make sure the hospital has a list of any medication, food, or latex allergies.

TOTAL PARENT POINTERS
KEEPING YOUR CHILD SAFE IN A HOSPITAL

1. Ask the nurse to tell you the **name of the medication** and the **reason for the medication** before any medications are given to your child.

2. Make sure that the hospital and the nurse has the correct name, age, and birth date for your child. Before any medications are given, nurses must check two separate Identifiers for your child, such as their full name and birth date. In infants and young children, make sure that the information on their hospital wristbands is correct.

3. Ask if the **pediatric resuscitation cart** is nearby and if it has the correct weight-based equipment for your child.

4. Ask how often the pediatric staff practices doing resuscitations on the pediatric unit.

5. **Before any surgery, make sure that the surgeon double checks and marks the location of the surgery on your child's skin before the child goes into surgery.** This is primarily for a surgical procedure that could be done on either side of the body, such as a knee or an eye. Some surgeries have been done on the wrong knee, wrong eye, or wrong arm. Your job is to make sure that the surgeon marks the proper side of your child's body.

6. When you leave the hospital, make sure that you have a written list of instructions regarding any medications to be given to your child.

41

Baby-Sitter Tips

When you are ready to leave your child with a responsible caregiver so you can go out, your first hurdle will be finding a reliable baby-sitter. One way to find a good baby-sitter is to ask your friends and family for recommendations. Often your friends and relatives can recommend a baby-sitter with whom they have had experience. Another way to find a baby-sitter is by contacting a local university. Most universities have a career center where you can contact a student who may baby-sit.

Your church bulletin may also carry classified ads from area high school teens whose families you know. I generally do not recommend putting an ad in the local newspaper. The people who respond may require extensive background checks, which can be costly.

Whether you are placing an ad with a university, church, or describing the job in an interview, you need to be able to explain the responsibilities of the position. You should begin with a brief statement of the number and ages of your children. You can either mention the salary or indicate that it is negotiable. You should also request that the baby-sitter has CPR training.

Your sample job description could read like this: Baby-sitter wanted part/full time for three children age three, four, and seven in our home near University Park. Prefer CPR training. Must be mature and responsible. Salary negotiable. Please contact Mrs. _____ at (XXX) XXX-XXXX.

If you need childcare on a full-time basis, another option is to look for a childcare provider in the classified section of the newspaper under childcare/daycare providers. Ask your friends who have children to recommend the best daycare centers.

INTERVIEWING A BABY-SITTER

Summarized below are important questions you should ask when interviewing a baby-sitter:

1. What kind of experience have you had baby-sitting for children?

2. List the names and contact information for two to four references of other families you have helped with childcare.

3. What is your major in college or what year are you in high school? What kind of educational background do you have?

4. Do you have any special talents or interests, such as singing, dancing, playing the piano, acting, etc. that you can share with our children?

5. Do have your own reliable car for transportation?

6. What kind of hobbies do you have?

7. How far do you live from our house?

8. What is the most difficult situation you've had when providing care to another child?

9. What kind of games do you like to play with children to keep them entertained?

10. What would you do in the event of an emergency, such as a fire?

11. What kind of meals would you prepare for dinner?

12. How many children are in your family?

13. What would you do if the children were badly misbehaving?

HIRING A BABY-SITTER

The key to hiring the right baby-sitter is relying not only on your experience but also your gut instincts. If your maternal instincts tell you things don't feel right about someone, go with your instincts, which are usually right. Calling references is obviously very important. Call at least two or three references to make sure the person is mature, reliable, and conscientious. If there is any doubt, you can always have the person come back for a second interview.

PAYMENT

It is usually a good idea to pay by check to keep track of your expenses for tax purposes.

INSTRUCTING THE BABY-SITTER

It is up to you to set the ground rules and explain your expectations for the childcare provider. For example, besides providing childcare, we also expect the baby-sitters to clean the kitchen and put away the dishes after the children are asleep. We expect the house to be at least as clean as we left it. Leave clear instructions about the following:

1. The maximum time the children should spend watching TV.

2. Whether the sitter should play with the children outside or stay inside watching TV or an approved movie.

3. The educational goals you have for your children for that day, such as reading a book with your three-year-old, reviewing your ten-year-old's social studies homework, reviewing your twelve-year-old's math homework, or making sure your ten-year-old spends thirty minutes practicing the piano.

SPECIFIC INSTRUCTIONS

It is helpful to have written instructions for your baby-sitter. This will save time with each new baby-sitter. Also, it's very easy for a new sitter to forget something you tell them verbally. Having a written list enforces the notion that you take the baby-sitter's job seriously. Be specific about what food the baby-sitter should prepare for the children and keep it simple. The following are examples of our written instructions for baby-sitters:

1. Safety is first.
2. Please make sure that the children finish their homework before playing.
3. Everyone has milk for dinner. No soda is allowed Monday through Thursday.
4. Playing outdoors is encouraged.
5. Children ten and younger should never be out of your sight.
6. Read to the children for twenty to thirty minutes before bed.
7. Older children can review their homework with you or you can practice spelling words with them.
8. Start putting children to bed at around 7:30 p.m. on weekdays. On Friday and Saturday you can start putting the children to bed at 9:00 or 9:30 p.m. Baths or showers should be completed early so the child can be in bed on time.
9. Keep the house doors locked at all times. Do not open a door when people come to the door. This includes package delivery. Speak to the person through the door.
10. Contact us through our pager or cell phone if you have any questions.
11. In case of an emergency or if you cannot reach us, contact our neighbor, Jennifer Smith at 123 Maple Street, Chicago, IL (XXX) XXX-XXXX. Her pager number is (XXX) XXX-XXXX. Her cell phone is (XXX) XXX-XXXX.
12. In case of a medical emergency, call for an ambulance at XXX-XXXX or call 911. Check your area for the proper number to call.
13. In case of a medical emergency requiring hospitalization, we prefer _____ hospital. The phone number is (XXX) XXX-XXXX.
14. See our baby-sitter medical information form for other important details.

IMPORTANT MEDICAL INFORMATION ABOUT OUR CHILDREN

Name _____ Age _____ Birth Date _____

Medical Problems   _____

Allergies   _____

Medications Child Is Taking   _____

Child's Doctor(s)   _____

Doctor's Phone Numbers   _____

Name _____ Age _____ Birth Date _____

Medical Problems   _____

Allergies   _____

Medications Child Is Taking   _____

Child's Doctor(s)   _____

Doctor's Phone Numbers   _____

Consent for medical treatment

The parents of the children above are _____

We can be reached at:

    ❑ Home   _____

    ❑ Cell   _____

    ❑ Work   _____

    ❑ Pager   _____

    ❑ E-mail   _____

Nearest relative to notify:

    Name   _____

    Phone   _____

    E-mail   _____

Neighbor or friend to notify:

    Name   _____

    Phone   _____

    E-mail   _____

TOTAL PARENT POINTERS
BABY-SITTER TIPS

1. **The best way to find a baby-sitter (childcare provider) is:**
   a. Ask you friends and relatives for suggestions of people they know.
   b. Contact your local university and put an ad on their job lists for students.
   c. Ask your local church teen group or childcare director about any mature teens or adults that she knows who are good with kids.
2. Ask your childcare provider to give you a list of parents who used her services, and contact them for references.
3. Ask if they are **CPR certified.**
4. **Go with your instincts.** If the person comes across in a way that makes your feel uncomfortable, go with your instincts. Don't hire her.
5. Give your baby-sitter **alternatives to watching TV.** Remember, you are paying them to care for your children. Give them books to read to the children, games to play, recipes to make, and things to do outside. Show them the local park.

6. Give her ideas for **healthy and fun snacks** for your children such as carrot sticks with low-fat dressing dip, sliced fruit kabobs on a stick, fruit smoothies to make in a blender, and low-fat yogurt fruit dips.
7. Give them suggestions for **healthy meals** while you are gone.
8. **Make sure they know how to contact you by cell phone, pager, etc.**
9. **Tell them where you will be** in case of an emergency and give them the phone numbers.
10. **Give them a note with your permission to treat** your children signed by you.
11. **Tell them which hospital to take them to in the event of an emergency, and give them the name of your family doctor or pediatrician.**
12. **Give them the name of a trusted neighbor or friend** who they can call if they cannot reach you in an emergency.

42

Poisoning and Overdoses

Poisoning is one of the most preventable injuries in young children and the leading cause of accidental death or hospitalization for children between the ages of eighteen and thirty-five months. Poison control centers across the nation received more than 2.4 million calls in 2004. Of that number, approximately 52 percent of the poisonings occurred in children under the age of six. From 2000 to 2004, there were ninety-nine deaths due to poisoning in children under the age of six reported to poison control centers.

This is a marked improvement from 1961, when there were 450 reported deaths in children under the age of six. This dramatic positive change was a result of federal mandates for childproof bottles and child-resistant packaging, as well as increased parental awareness of the danger of poisons and improvements in the availability of twenty-four-hour poison control centers.

What are the most common causes of poisoning deaths?

All homes contain many products, chemicals, and medications that can be fatal when ingested by a child. The leading causes of death due to poisoning in children under six years of age are:

- Prescription pain medications that contain narcotics
- Analgesics, such as acetaminophen or aspirin-containing products
- Oil (petroleum) products, such as lamp oil, kerosene, turpentine, paint thinner, and furniture polish
- Carbon monoxide poisoning (such as a home furnace malfunction)
- Antidepressant medicines
- Blood pressure and heart medicines
- Iron pills, iron-containing vitamins
- Caustic chemicals such as drain cleaners, oven cleaners, toilet bowl cleaners, rust removers
- Antifreeze, methanol ingestion

What should I do if I think my child has been poisoned?

Treatment depends on the situation. First aid steps depend on the child's age, weight, and the type and amount of poison ingested. If the child is not conscious or not breathing:

- Call 911 immediately
- Get the poison substance away from the child's eyes, skin, or mouth, and if applicable, get the child away from any poisonous fumes. (Sometimes it may be too dangerous to rescue someone from an area filled with poisonous gas. The 911 operator will tell you what to do.)

If the child is conscious and breathing:

- Immediately call 1-800-222-1222 (the poison control hotline). Do not wait for the child to feel, look, or get sick.
- Be ready to answer questions about the child's age, sex, weight, and health.
- Have the poison or its container with you when you call the poison center.
- If you are told to go to an emergency room, take the poison or its container with you to show the doctor.

What should I do if my child eats poison?

- Call the poison control center at 1-800-222-1222, even if the poison was not swallowed.
- Do not make the child vomit. Do not give the child anything to eat or drink unless the poison center expert tells you to.

- Know the exact name of the product involved and/or, in some cases, the active ingredient. If possible, bring the product container with you to the phone or, if necessary, the emergency room.

Be aware that some out-of-date first-aid charts may contain incorrect treatment information. DO NOT give raw eggs, salt, vinegar, or citrus fruit juices to induce vomiting or to neutralize the poison. These treatments are not only ineffective but they may be extremely dangerous. Also, do not give syrup of ipecac unless your doctor or the poison control center tell you to do so. Some poisons cause more harm if they are vomited back up.

What should I do if my child takes an overdose of medicine?

- Call the poison center at 1-800-222-1222 even if the medicine was not swallowed. Do not make the child vomit or give him anything to eat or drink unless the poison center expert tells you to.
- Know the exact name of the medicine involved and/or, in some cases, the active ingredient. If possible, bring the product container with you to the phone.
- Try to estimate the number of pills or the amount of liquid the child swallowed.

If the child vomits en route to the emergency room, note any pill fragments and bring the sample, if possible, with you.

What should I do if my child gets poison on his skin?

- Take off any clothes that have poison on them. Wash these clothes separately.
- Rinse the skin thoroughly with water. Then gently wash the skin with soap and water.
- Call the poison center at 1-800-222-1222.

What should I do if my child gets a poison in his eye?

- Remove contact lenses, if worn.
- Rinse the eyes with water for fifteen minutes. Have the child open and close his eyes while rinsing.
- Call the poison center at 1-800-222-1222.

What should I do if my child is exposed to a poison in the air?

- Open windows and doors to ventilate the area.
- Move to a place where your child can breathe fresh air. Help others leave the area, but be careful not to breathe the poison in yourself.
- Call the poison center at 1-800-222-1222.

POISONOUS MUSHROOMS

What should I know about poisonous mushrooms?

Certain wild mushrooms can be very dangerous and even deadly. Frequently, poisonous mushrooms do not cause symptoms until several hours after they are eaten. The most dangerous mushrooms belong to the amanita family of mushrooms. You should teach your children to keep away from any mushrooms, plants, and berries. For photos of poisonous mushrooms, please visit *TheTotalParent.com*.

What should I do if my child eats a wild mushroom?

- Call the poison center at 1-800-222-1222.
- Collect the questionable mushroom and carefully dig up a few additional mushrooms, complete with underground parts, to help in identifying the variety. If there is more than one kind of mushroom in the area, collect all of the different types.
- Note if the mushroom was growing on wood, soil, or other material and if it was growing alone or in clusters.
- If possible, take a digital photo of the mushroom to send to the poison center staff. Using the digital images, the poison center staff can consult with experts to obtain an initial identification of the mushroom. This will help the poison center staff to formulate an appropriate treatment.

POISONOUS CHEMICALS

What should I do if my child's skin gets exposed to chemicals?

Certain chemicals, such as various acids used for cleaning, can cause chemical burns if they touch the skin. If your child comes into contact with a caustic chemical:

- Remove all clothes that have the chemicals on them. Wash these clothes separately.

- Rinse the skin thoroughly with water.
- Wash the skin gently with soap and water.
- Call the poison control center at 1-800-222-1222.

IRON POISONING

What should I know about iron poisoning?

Iron poisoning at one time was the most common cause of poisoning deaths in children. Today, children frequently either take excessive amounts of their own vitamins with iron or they take their parents' iron pills. Many current formulations, however, are less toxic than previous products.

If you suspect that your child has ingested a large amount of vitamins or iron, contact the poison center at 1-800-222-1222. Poison center specialists will determine if the type and number of pills taken require a trip to an emergency room.

LEAD POISONING

What are the dangers of lead poisoning?

Lead poisoning can cause impaired growth in children, permanent brain damage, and behavioral problems. The most common cause of lead poisoning is the ingestion of lead-based paint. Most homes built before 1978 were painted with lead-based paint. Approximately 9 percent of American children (1.7 million) have some amount of lead poisoning. Even a small chip of lead-based paint can produce lead poisoning in a very small child.

What causes lead poisoning?
- Breathing in lead dust
- Eating something with lead in it (paint chips)
- Lead released from plumbing pipes
- Eating from lead-glazed cups and pots
- Inhaling fumes from a nearby lead smelter
- Inhaling fumes from some imported candles from Mexico
- Some imported toy jewelry

What are the symptoms of lead poisoning?

Symptoms of lead poisoning frequently go undetected for a long time. Lead binds with red blood cells and causes anemia. Moderate to severe cases of lead poisoning can result in decreased arm and leg function, a change in behavior, irritability, a decrease in play activity, vomiting, and abdominal pain. In addition, lead poisoning can damage the brain, kidneys, stomach, and other body organs. It also can cause learning disabilities, slowed growth, and behavior and hearing problems.

Severe lead poisoning can lead to:
- Abdominal pain
- Anemia (low blood count)
- Severe unsteadiness when walking
- Sleepiness and fatigue
- Coma
- Seizures

What should I know about lead poisoning?

Lead poisoning is preventable! Make sure that your child is screened for lead exposure between the ages of six months and two years (especially if you live in a house with lead-based paint or lead pipes). Lead poisoning is most common in children who live in a home that has been renovated recently.

Clean up chipped and peeling paint inside and outside your home. Wash floors and windowsills with dish detergent and water. Hire an expert to remove lead-based paint from your home, and have your home checked for lead pipes. If your home has lead pipes, run cold water for a minute before using the water to drink or to cook. Shower and change your clothes after working with lead, and wash these clothes separately. Tell children to play in the grass instead of in the dirt, as soil may have lead in it. Make sure children wash their hands before they eat or sleep. Serve children food high in iron and calcium, which helps the body absorb less lead.

How is lead poisoning treated?

Children with lead poisoning may be treated with an oral drug or an IV drug depending on how severe the lead poisoning is. Children with very high lead levels can have permanent behavioral and intellectual problems.

CARBON MONOXIDE POISONING AND SMOKE INHALATION

Carbon monoxide poisoning frequently occurs at the beginning of the fall and winter seasons when furnaces are being used for the first time in several months. If the furnace is not working or vented properly, everyone in the house can become a victim of carbon monoxide poisoning.

Signs of carbon monoxide poisoning are:

1. Headache—this is extremely significant, especially if everyone in the house has a headache
2. Weakness
3. Confusion
4. Shortness of breath
5. Dizziness
6. Nausea and vomiting
7. Dim or blurred vision

Smoke detectors and carbon monoxide detectors are a must-have for every home. Smoke alarms, which are appropriately placed in the main rooms of the house, decrease the chance of dying in a house fire by 50 percent. Test your smoke detectors and carbon monoxide detectors on a regular basis. The National Fire Protection Association (NFPA) recommends that battery-operated smoke detectors be checked once a month. They also recommend that the batteries be changed at least once a year.

Practice fire drills with your children at least twice a year. Teach your children the best escape routes in the event of a fire.

Make sure your children's pajamas are not flammable.

Keep fire extinguishers in key locations around the house, such as the kitchen, garage, and near an outdoor grill. You should also check your extinguishers to make sure they have adequate pressure and are ready to use. Lock away any matches and lighters.

TOTAL PARENT POINTERS
POISONING AND OVERDOSES

1. Teach your children to always ask first.
2. **Keep all products in their original containers with their original labels.** Never put a dangerous chemical in a different type of bottle for storage, such as a soda bottle or any other type of container.
3. **Store products in a place where children cannot see or reach them.**
4. Every time you use a product, read the label and follow the directions. Put the product away immediately after use.
5. Keep prescription and over-the-counter medicines in their original child-resistant containers. **Keep all medicines locked and away from children.**
6. **Never call medicine "candy"** or make a game out of taking it.
7. Make sure that when visitors, especially grandparents, come to the house that all their medicines and purses are kept out of the reach of small children. (Frequently, **grandparents have their medicines in easy-to-open containers, which are opened easily by curious children.**)
8. **Teach your children never to put mushrooms or plant parts in their mouths.**
9. **Have smoke and carbon monoxide detectors in your house near each bedroom.**
10. Keep the **poison center phone number (1-800-222-1222)** near each phone in your home and in other handy locations. Program it into your cell phone as well.

Frequently Ingested Products That Are **NOT** Poisonous

Abrasives
Adhesives
Antacids
Antibiotics
Ballpoint pen inks
Body conditioners
Bubble bath soaps
Calamine lotion
Candles (beeswax or paraffin)
Caps (toy pistols, potassium chlorate)
Chalk (calcium carbonate)
Colognes
Contraceptives
Cosmetics
Crayons (marked A.P., C.P.)
Dehumidifying packets (silica or charcoal)
Deodorants

Deodorizers
Elmer's glue
Eye makeup
Fabric softeners
Fish bowl additives
Glues and pastes
Hand lotions and creams
Hydrogen peroxide (3%)
Incense
Indelible markers
Ink
Iodophil disinfectant
Laxatives
Lipstick
Magic Markers
Makeup (eye, liquid facial)
Matches
Paint, latex
Pencils

Perfumes
Petroleum jelly (Vaseline)
Play-Doh
Porous-tip ink marking pens
Putty (less than 2 oz.)
Rubber cement
Shampoos (liquid)
Shaving creams and lotions
Steroids
Suntan preparation
Thermometers (mercury)
Toothpaste (with or without fluoride)
Vitamins (with or without fluoride)
Water colors
Zinc oxide
Zirconium oxide

43

Drug and Alcohol Abuse

Alcohol is still the most commonly abused drug by teenagers. Studies have shown that a child who has a first drink of alcohol before the age of fifteen has a four times greater risk of becoming an alcoholic. Approximately 28 percent of seniors in high school have reported that they have had more than five drinks within a two-week period. There is also a strong genetic predisposition to alcohol abuse. If a child has an alcoholic parent, the chances of the child becoming an alcoholic are approximately 86 percent.

There are several ways to prevent alcohol abuse in your children:

1. Provide a supportive and positive parent-child relationship in the house. A weak parent-child relationship or a difficult and unsupportive home environment predisposes children to alcohol abuse.

2. Provide your children with information about the dangerous affects of alcohol.

For example, tell your children about the increased chances of auto accidents with teenagers who drink alcohol.

3. Pay particular attention to your children between the ages of ten and fourteen. These are children who will be exposed to alcohol and may decide to drink alcohol under the age of fifteen, when the risk of developing a lifelong problem is greatest.

What are the risks and dangers of alcohol that I should discuss with my teenager and preteen?

The major risks of alcohol use include:

- Sexual activity and unplanned pregnancies at an earlier age.
- Violent crime, including rape and assault.
- A decreased interest in school and positive self-development. Children who drink alcohol are more likely to have problems with school.

What are some of the techniques that I can use to discourage my children from using alcohol?

Talk to your children about the negative affects of alcohol, such as auto accidents, embarrassing behavior, and poor decision making. Indicate that this poor decision making can result in unwanted sexual activity, pregnancy, and sexually transmitted diseases.

Establish a strong parent-child relationship. Eat dinner together. Help your children with their schoolwork for twenty minutes per night. Dads should set aside one night per week as family night to do something with your children. Your fatherly influence, role modeling, and overall presence are very powerful tools.

Discuss how television commercials portray alcohol in an unrealistic light and how television often portrays people using alcohol as being in a happy mood. In fact, alcohol is a depressant and can cause significant emotional problems as well as dependency. It can also result in depression, poor judgment, auto accidents, etc.

Other than alcohol, what are the most commonly abused drugs by teenagers?

1. Marijuana is the most common illicit drug used by teenagers.
2. Ecstasy and LSD are drugs that can cause hallucinations.
3. Cocaine is a stimulant drug that can result in brain hemorrhage and cardiac arrest.
4. Spray inhalants such as glues, nail polish remover, freon, paint products, lighter fluid, correction fluid, butane or propane gases, and deodorizers. These different types of sprays are known on the street as huffing, bagging, or sniffing.
5. Amphetamines are speed or stimulants. Drugs such as methylphenidate (Ritalin), used to treat ADHD, are considered stimulants.
6. Cigarette smoking

ECSTASY

What do I need to know about the drug called Ecstasy?

Ecstasy is a stimulant. It is also called MDMA (methylenedioxymethamphetamine), Methamphetamine, or meth. The popularity of Ecstasy rose rapidly from 1998 to 2001. However, the use of the drug dropped sharply in 2003 as more teenagers became aware of its terrifying dangers, such as brain hemorrhage.

MARIJUANA

What type of drug is marijuana?

Marijuana (commonly called pot or weed) contains THC (tetrahydrocannabinol). It is usually ingested by smoking (marijuana cigarettes are called joints or reefer). In 2003, approximately 35 percent of twelfth graders indicated they had smoked marijuana in the prior twelve months. In addition, approximately 13 percent of eighth graders indicated they had smoked marijuana in the past twelve months.

Marijuana causes sedation, distorted perception, and psychological dependency. Children can be tested for marijuana and several other drugs with a simple urine test. In some cases, you may decide as a parent to persuade your child to do a urine drug test if you have a reasonable suspicion of illicit drug use. You should discuss this situation with your pediatrician or family doctor. The test can be done in one hour at certain labs. Other drugs that can be checked for with urine tests include:

1. Cocaine
2. Speed (amphetamines) (speed causes dilated pupils)
3. Sedatives called benzodiazepines (Valium, Xanax, and Ativan)
4. Narcotics such as codeine, Vicodin, OxyContin, and Tylenol with codeine
5. PCP (phencyclidine), or angel dust, can cause hallucinations and psychotic behavior
6. Barbiturates (downers)—one example is phenobarbital
7. Marijuana (grass or weed) alters perceptions

NARCOTICS

What are some of the narcotic drugs that teenagers abuse?

Two of the most commonly abused narcotic drugs include Vicodin and OxyContin. Vicodin is a narcotic pain reliever. OxyContin is a very powerful narcotic pain reliever that has the potential to be highly addictive.

INHALANTS

What percentage of eighth graders use inhalants?

A 2003 study found that approximately 8.7 percent of eighth graders used inhalants.

CLUB DRUGS—DATE-RAPE DRUGS

What are club drugs?

Club drugs are also known as date-rape drugs. They include:

• Rohypnol (date-rape drug)
• GHB (gamma hydroxybutyrate)
• Ketamine

What do I need to know about club drugs and date-rape drugs?

A significant number of teenagers have overdosed on drugs used for anxiety, such as alprazolam (Xanax), diazepam (Valium), Rohypnol, and lorazepam (Ativan). These drugs are all used to treat anxiety or insomnia. Rohypnol is sometimes called a date-rape drug because it is a short-acting sedative that men place in a girl's drink to make them pass out and forget what happens for the next several hours. Rohypnol is similar to Valium (diazepam) and Xanax (alprazolam). Rohypnol also is called roofies, R2, or tranks. (For a list of nicknames of various drugs, please refer to the glossary at the end of the chapter.)

DOCTOR TIP: *Narcotics cause very small, "pinpoint" pupils.*

GHB
What is GHB?
GHB is a short-acting tranquilizer that causes a person to get sleepy and high. It also causes amnesia. Girls who are given this drug before a rape usually pass out and don't recall what happened or who was involved.

KETAMINE
What is ketamine?
Ketamine is a form of a drug used as an animal tranquilizer. It causes a person to lose contact with reality. The person frequently gets very sleepy and may pass out.

How can I tell if my teenager has a drug problem?
Some of the telltale signs include:
1. A change in your child's behavior. This may include significant alterations in moods, social withdrawal, etc.
2. A deterioration in your child's schoolwork.
3. A deterioration in your teenager's relationship with friends.
4. A complete change in a group of friends who your child associates with.
5. A change in sleep habits. For example, a child who is up all night and sleeps most of the day.
6. Ask yourself:
   - Has my child lost interest in her favorite hobby, sport, or other activities?
   - Does she act tired or depressed most of the time?
   - Does she have red or irritated eyes and a runny nose in the absence of any other cold symptoms?
   - Have I noticed any type of drug materials in the house, such as marijuana papers, marijuana pipes, empty prescription pill bottles, empty aerosol cans in her room, eye drops, etc?

TOTAL PARENT POINTERS
DRUG AND ALCOHOL ABUSE

1. **Alcohol is still the number-one drug abused by teenagers.**
2. **Marijuana** is the second most commonly abused drug.
3. **The key to preventing drug abuse is a strong, positive, and supportive relationship at home.**
4. **Communicate the dangers of alcohol,** such as auto accidents, to your child.
5. Embarrassing behavior is a frequent result of drug and alcohol use.
6. Unplanned pregnancies and sexually transmitted diseases can result from alcohol use.
7. Also discuss with your child the **dangers of drug abuse** such as:
   a. **Cocaine—brain hemorrhage,** heart attacks, death
   b. **Amphetamines**—rapid heart rate, delusions, brain hemorrhage.

Depression and paranoia can occur as the patient withdraws from the amphetamine abuse
   c. **Marijuana**—poor coordination, psychological dependence, other side effects if the marijuana is laced with chemicals such as PCP.
   d. **Inhalants**—inhalants are especially dangerous because they contain a chemical called toluene, which can make the heart very irritable and cause **cardiac arrest.** Repetitive use of inhalants can also lead to permanent brain damage and behavioral impairment.
   e. **Narcotics**—excessive ingestion can cause the child to stop breathing. (Pinpoint sized pupils are a sign of narcotic use.)

TOTAL PARENT POINTERS
ABUSED DRUGS, STREET (SLANG) TERMS, AND DRUG EFFECTS

Drug	Slang Terms	Effects
Amphetamines	Speed, Uppers, Dexies Methylamphetamine is an amphetamine used for ADHD (attention deficit hyperactivity disorder)	Amphetamines are stimulants that cause an increased sense of energy and a sense of feeling happy. When it wears off, depression and paranoid feelings can occur. It also causes increased heart rate, irritability, and insomnia. Amphetamines cause **dilated pupils**.
Benzodiazepines Includes drugs such as Valium (diazepam), Ativan (lorazepam), and Xanax (alprazolam)	Benzos, Downers, Sleepers	Drowsiness and slurred speech as well as confusion. Teenagers may also have trouble remembering what they did.
Cocaine	Coke, Crack, Toot, Nose Candy	Cocaine produces an initial high associated later with irritability, paranoia, and anxiety. Teenagers who use cocaine can die in minutes due to **brain hemorrhage** or **cardiac arrest**. Cocaine can cause bleeding in the brain and spasm of the arteries to the heart. Paranoia frequently occurs when a person is experiencing cocaine withdrawal.
Cold Medicine Abuse Dextromethorphan (DXM)	Dex, DM, DXM, Tussin, Vitamin D	Dextromethorphan is a cough suppressant used in many over-the-counter cough syrups. Teenagers drink this by the bottle because in high doses it can cause hallucinations and a high.
GHB (gamma hydroxy-butyrate)	GHB, Liquid Ecstasy, Liquid X, Sleepers, The Forget Pill	This is a club drug and a depressant that causes sedative effects as well as giving the person a high. Also used as a date-rape drug.
Heroin	Dope, Horse, Smack, White Horse	Heroin, a rapid-acting **narcotic,** causes drowsiness and slurred speech. A teenager with a heroin overdose can die because the narcotic can stop his breathing. It can also cause his lungs to fill up with fluid. Teenagers on narcotics have very **tiny (pinpoint) pupils**, a key sign to look for.
Inhalants (glues, spray paints, paint thinners, plastic model glues, and other aerosol sprays)	Glue, Laughing Gas, Paint, Poppers	Inhalants cause slurred speech and poor coordination. Solvents contain a chemical called **toluene** that can cause sudden death due to cardiac arrest. Toluene causes the heart to become very irritable. Teenagers can have permanent impairment of their brain function and their behavior from repeated use.

TOTAL PARENT POINTERS
ABUSED DRUGS, STREET (SLANG) TERMS, AND DRUG EFFECTS

Drug	Slang Terms	Effects
Ketamine	Horse Tranquilizer	This is a club drug that can cause hallucinations and a sense of euphoria in high doses. Sometimes used as a date-rape drug.
Marijuana	Cannabis, Evil Weed, Grass, Mary Jane, THC, Weed	Marijuana is usually smoked to experience its effects. The user feels a high and distorted perceptions. Psychological dependence can occur. The active ingredient in marijuana is tetrahydrocannabinol (THC).
Meth MDMA* (methylene-dioxymethamphet-amine)	Clarity, Ecstasy, Meth, White Cross	Meth causes hallucinations and increased sensitivity to stimuli. It is very addictive and can cause the same effects as amphetamines (see above).
Narcotics (Oral) codeine, OxyContin, Vicodin (hydrocodone), fentanyl, propoxyphene	Captain Codies, Codies, Narcs	Drowsiness, slurred speech, and confusion. This can also result in death due to the fact that the narcotic can stop the person's breathing. Narcotics cause **pinpoint-size pupils.**
PCP phencyclidine	Angel Dust	PCP can cause people to become very violent. They also do not have a normal sensation of pain. PCP can also cause hyperactivity and loss of appetite.
Rohypnol	The Forget Pill, R2, Roofenol, Rophies	Rohypnol is a date-rape drug. It is similar to sedatives such as Valium and Xanax, except it is very short acting and causes a person to have significant amnesia or loss of short-term memory. As a result, girls who are given the drug prior to a rape sometimes do not recall what happened or who raped them.

44

Child and Sexual Abuse

Nearly 900,000 children are victims of child abuse every year in the United States. Here are some key facts about child abuse.[1]

- 60 percent of child abuse victims suffer neglect
- 15 percent of child abuse is due to physical abuse
- 10 percent of child abuse is sexual abuse
- 10 percent of child abuse is due to emotional abuse

What is the definition of child abuse?
Child abuse is defined as "any recent act or failure to act on the part of a parent or caretaker, which results in death, serious physical or emotional harm, sexual abuse, or exploitation, or an act or failure to act which presents an imminent risk of serious harm to a child under the age of eighteen."[2]

States have the ability to expand the definition of child abuse to make it more specific or inclusive. The rate of child abuse occurs in approximately 12.4 to 15.1 children per 100,000 children.

How many children die from abuse or neglect?

- 1,460 children died from abuse or neglect in the United States in 2005.
- 1,169 children died in 2003.
- Over 40 percent of the deaths were due to neglect. However, physical abuse was a major contributor in each death.
- About 75 percent of the children who died due to child abuse and neglect were younger than four years of age.

Who are the typical perpetrators in the death of a child?
The typical perpetrators are adults in their twenties who did not finish high school and are usually living at or below the poverty level.

Is there any difference in the child abuse rate between boys and girls?
Slightly more than one-half of the victims are girls (51 percent).

How many reports of abuse are made per year?
There were approximately six million children suspected of being

victims of child abuse in 2005. Approximately two-thirds of those reports were made by teachers, police officers, physicians, and social service workers.

Who is responsible for child abuse and neglect?

In 2005 approximately 80 percent of the perpetrators were parents and approximately 7 percent were relatives.[3]

What is the most common type of child neglect?

Neglect is the most common type of child abuse. It can be subdivided into:

1. Medical neglect
2. Supervisional neglect
3. Physical neglect

Medical neglect means that the parents or caregivers do not bring the child in for treatment for acute illnesses. They include not bringing the child in for broken bones or other serious injuries. Failure to thrive is a special type of medical neglect. This refers to a child who has failed to gain weight or grow and develop normally due to a lack of proper feeding and parental care. These children typically are very thin. When these children are hospitalized and fed an appropriate diet, they gain weight rapidly, which confirms the diagnosis of medical neglect and failure to thrive. Of course, other conditions can be ruled out, such as thyroid problems and problems with absorbing nutrients from the intestines.

Supervisional neglect means that the children sustained injuries due to a lack of supervision. This may include burn injuries, drowning, falling out of open windows, and even motor vehicle accidents in which the children are not in a car seat or restrainded by a seat belt.

Physical neglect occurs when parents or caretakers do not provide adequate food, clothing, or shelter for the children. One example is abandonment, when the parents leave the children unexpectedly under the care of a relative for an unknown period of time.

What should I do if I suspect someone I know may be a victim of child abuse and/or neglect?

Call your local department of children and family services or your local child protection agency. If you cannot find the number for this service, call a local emergency room and ask to whom you should report suspected child abuse. You may also call the hospital to speak to a social worker regarding your concerns. The social worker may be able to confirm your gut instincts about this. However, keep in mind that young children under the age of ten typically do not lie about sexual abuse or child abuse. All suspected cases of child abuse should be referred to a professional, such as an emergency physician, pediatrician, family doctor, etc. No cases of child abuse should be referred to a screening committee within an organization to substantiate the abuse claims. These committees lack access to prior reports of suspected abuse.

The department of children and family services will take your report and observations and file them as an anonymous report if you wish. Your concerns will be followed up by a state social worker for further review and validation. Keep in mind that the state agency has a database that may contain prior reports of suspected abuse. Your report may provide further confirmation of abuse when combined with prior reports.

What are the most common types of physical abuse?

Skin injuries are the most common signs of child abuse. These can include bruises, bites, and burns. Emergency physicians are trained to recognize the pattern of burn injuries to determine if the burn is consistent with the parents' or caregiver's story. In addition, bite wounds can be photographed and reviewed by experts to identify the perpetrator.

Certain types of fractures are also indicative of child abuse. Emergency physicians and pediatricians and others are trained to recognize that certain fractures are characteristic of child abuse. For example, a spiral fracture of the upper arm is suspicious for child abuse in a child who is not walking.

In addition, physicians may detect retinal hemorrhages, which are characteristic of brain injuries due to the shaken baby syndrome.

Total body x-rays are taken in cases of suspected child abuse to determine if the child has had multiple fractures in the past. If the child has had multiple fractures in different areas of the body, this

is a very strong indicator of child abuse.

Head injuries are some of the most serious forms of child abuse and are also the leading cause of death and complications in child abuse.

SHAKEN BABY SYNDROME

Shaken baby syndrome occurs when a parent forcefully shakes a baby forward and backward while holding the child up by his chest. This results in the brain being slammed back and forth inside the skull, which causes bleeding and blood clots on top of the brain. It also causes hemorrhages within the eye.

Shaken baby syndrome

The blood clots on the brain can lead to seizures, brain swelling, permanent mental impairment, and learning difficulties as the child grows older. These children will sometimes have rib fractures due to the forceful shaking by the parent or caregiver.

Complications from shaken baby syndrome

Children who are victims of shaken baby syndrome can have several long-term complications, such as:

- Learning disability
- Cerebral palsy
- Paralysis
- Mental retardation

SEXUAL ABUSE

Sexual abuse occurs in approximately 10 percent of all children who sustain child abuse. (Pedophilia is the unnatural sexual attraction to children.) The physician who performs an examination of a child suspected of being abused will do the following:

1. Take a careful history of the incident or incidents causing the sexual abuse.
2. Examine the child for any bruises or physical signs of physical or sexual abuse.
3. Take photographs of injuries.
4. Some physicians may do a video recording of the female genital area or the male rectal area, which can be later reviewed by forensic professionals for signs of sexual abuse.
5. Obtain lab tests that may show a sexually transmitted disease such as syphilis or gonorrhea.

What are some of the long-term psychological consequences of child abuse?

Unfortunately children who are victims of child abuse have developed significant psychological and social problems as they grow older. For example, one study by the National Institute of Justice showed that an abused or neglected child has a 95 percent increased chance of being arrested, compared to other children. In addition, child abuse and neglect increases the chances of adult criminal behavior by 28 percent. It also increases the chances of violent crime by 30 percent.[4]

Abused children often become abusive parents. About one-third of parents who were abused as children will abuse their own children.[5]

ALCOHOL AND DRUG ABUSE

Approximately two-thirds of people in drug-treatment programs reported that they were abused as children.

SOCIAL INTERACTION

Children who were abused tend to have more difficulty with adult relationships than nonabused children.

NOTES

1. U.S. Department of Health and Human Services, Administration for Children and Families, "Summary: Child Maltreatment 2005," http://www.acf.hhs.gov/programs/cb/pubs/cm05/summary.htm.
2. Child Welfare League of America, "National Fact Sheet 2006: Child Abuse and Neglect," http://www.cwla.org/advocacy/nationalfactsheet06.htm.
3. U.S. Department of Health and Human Services, "Summary: Child Maltreatment."
4. Cathy S. Widom and Michael S. Maxfield, "An Update on the 'Cycle of Violence,'" National Institute of Justice Research in Brief, February 2001, http://www.ncjrs.gov/txtfiles/nij/184894.txt.
5. Child Welfare Information Gateway, "Long-Term Consequences of Child Abuse and Neglect: Factsheet," http://www.childwelfare.gov/pubs/factsheets/long_term_consequences.cfm.

TOTAL PARENT POINTERS
CHILD AND SEXUAL ABUSE

1. There are **four main types of child abuse: neglect, physical abuse, sexual abuse, and emotional abuse.**

2. About **80 percent of abusers are parents.** About 7 percent are relatives.

3. The **shaken baby syndrome** occurs when a parent or caregiver forcefully shakes a baby, which results in the brain being slammed back and forth inside the child's skull. This results in blood clots on the brain, bleeding in the retina of the eye, and other bone fractures, such as the ribs.

4. About one-third of parents who were abused as children will abuse their own children.

5. Any person who suspects that a child is being abused or neglected should contact the local health department and file a report, which may be reported anonymously.

6. **Children usually do not lie about sexual abuse.** If they say it happened, they are almost always telling the truth.

PART 5

Educational Success

45

Secrets to Raising a Succesful Student

The secrets to raising a successful student include understanding certain concepts of learning, motivation, time management, and good study habits. Your child's educational success also requires your time, patience, persistence, creativity, and involvement.

One of the key elements of educational success is inspiring your child to become sincerely interested in enjoying school and doing well in school. A close friend who recently graduated from Harvard with a double major in applied mathematics and economics recently advised my eleven-year-old son, Matthew, "Just enjoy school and enjoy learning."

That pretty much sums up what it takes to develop the inner passion to do well in school. When the desire to do well truly comes from within, and when the child enjoys learning, he will become self-motivated to learn.

Parents can shape this attitude when children are young by:

- Instilling a love of reading.
- Praising your child.
- Modeling the behavior you want in your children.
- Becoming involved with your child's education.
- Instilling in your child a sense of joy and mastery in taking responsibility for doing the work necessary to be a successful student.

INSTILLING A LOVE OF READING

Read to your child

Reading to your child from a very young age stimulates an interest in reading, language development, brain development, and the integration of positive moral values and character. My wife and I read to our young children from twenty to sixty minutes each night. One of my favorite sights is seeing my wife reading to our youngest sons, ages five, six, and eight. The boys all huddle in bed together, peering in to get a closer look at the book she is reading. Usually their response

after the first story is, "Mom, read us another, please!" Part of the fun is just being with a parent, and part of the fun is the joy of reading.

Even after children become good readers themselves, they enjoy listening to mom or dad read with drama and emotion. We also sometimes ask our children to read a book to the rest of us. And of course they are praised generously for their skillful reading.

Listening to your children read also helps you to appreciate their word fluency, that is, their ability to understand and pronounce words correctly. As children are learning to read, your reinforcement of proper pronunciations helps develop their vocabulary as well as their reading and language skills.

Visit the library often

Frequent visits to libraries help to stimulate interest in reading and also provide children with the skills for becoming familiar with the library and knowing how to locate books they want. Plus, it teaches them how to look after and keep track of their loaned books.

Show your children how much you enjoy reading

Your perceived enjoyment of reading is very important for your children. Let them see you read for pleasure in your spare time. Tell them about an interesting book or article that you read. Whenever I come across an article that I think one of my children would find interesting, I make a photocopy and put it on the breakfast table with the child's name on it.

Use books as a reward

A visit to the library can be a reward for good behavior. You also may decide to go to a local bookstore to buy your child a book as a reward for a good deed or accomplishment. You may want to make it a tradition to include a special book as a birthday or holiday gift.

An economical way to shop for books with your child is by taking them to a garage or yard sale where books can usually be bought for twenty-five to fifty cents each. Another idea is to buy books at a garage sale and give them to the children one at a time as a reward for good behavior.

Limit TV exposure

As we all know, on many occasions children can probably find better things to do than watch TV. According to A. C. Nielsen surveys, the average child in America spends 3.5 minutes a week in meaningful conversation with parents and 1,680 minutes a week watching television. The average adult watches four hours of TV per day. Children often resort to watching TV because they have nothing else to stimulate their interest. Parents can change this by reinforcing other activities, such as playing board games, playing an educational game on a computer, going to an educational Internet site, reading, or some other fun educational activity.

This is not always an easy task. All of us as parents are challenged by all kinds of distractions. In many cases, both parents are working, and television affords an easy way to keep the kids occupied while the parents recharge their batteries. It takes persistence and dedication on the part of both parents to model the proper attitude and behavior.

In our house, our children watch very little TV Monday through Thursday. Our free time is spent finishing their homework first. They also have other activities, such as piano classes, dance classes, soccer practice, etc. In addition, each child is responsible for various duties around the house. One child is assigned dinner cleanup, another is breakfast cleanup, another to keeping the hallway clean, and another to basement cleanup. When all of their responsibilities are completed, there may be an opportunity for a half hour of TV before bed (usually between 7:30 and 8:00 p.m.). We then focus on putting all of the children to bed, which usually takes about an hour at minimum.

PRAISING YOUR CHILD

Generous praise

Psychology has consistently shown that positive reinforcement is the best motivator. Generous praise reinforces your child's self-esteem and pride. It feels good to be reminded of the day's accomplishments before bed. You might acknowledge a good job cleaning up the dishes after dinner or getting an A on a social studies test that day. Praise should be generous, sincere, and frequent.

How many of us can say that we were praised too often as children? In a world that is sometimes perceived as a cold place, parental praise is a vital source of self-esteem and comfort. And it's important for adults too. Think about it—how often do you receive praise for anything in your daily life?

I try to make a point of praising each child for something that he or she did well during the day. Examples include doing well in school, sharing something with one of their siblings, helping mom or dad without being asked, doing something kind or helpful for a friend or neighbor, or working really hard on a project.

A friend told me that when she was younger her mom would put a note about the children's individual achievements on her dad's desk so that when he came home from work he could read what the children had accomplished during the day. When the father came home late, which he frequently did, he knew exactly what they had done and praised the children for their accomplishments at home and at school. She was amazed at how her dad knew about everything she did even though he was working a lot.

Superpraise

Another technique for praising your child is what I like to call super-praise. Superpraise occurs when you praise your child in front of your spouse or in front of other people. For example, when you talk to your spouse and say, "Heidi really did something great today. She got an A on both her social studies test and her math test. She studied really hard, and I'm really proud of her." When you do this in front of someone else, it's megapraise. This can be done with your spouse, friends, and relatives. For example, you might say to one of your relatives, "Susan really did a great job during her band performance tonight. She played her flute beautifully. She really practiced a lot, and I'm very proud of her."

Written praise

An additional technique for recognizing your child for doing something good is to leave a written note for the child to see. When I sometimes get home late from work, after my children are already in bed, my wife lets me know about the positive things the children have done, and I'll then leave a note on the breakfast table for each of the children to see. One note might read, "Mitchell, I am really proud of how well you did on your spelling test yesterday. You're a genius!" I might leave another note for another child saying, "I loved the picture you drew of the rainbow. You're really a good artist."

One method of utilizing written praise is by making a copy of you child's report card and putting it on the bathroom mirror or the refrigerator. Add a note saying, "Great job" or "You're really smart" or "Mom and Dad are really proud of you." We all like to get notes telling us we've done a good job, and children are especially happy to receive complimentary notes.

I know some parents who put messages in their child's lunch box for school. I remember visiting one of my children at school during lunch in second grade. One of her friends had a picture drawn by her dad and a note from her mom in her lunch box. She told me she gets a note from her mom every day in her lunch box, usually with a picture from her dad. The note may say something like, "I love you," "You're special," or "You're smart, and we are really proud of you, Love, Mom and Dad."

It's great to have a place to display your child's pictures, papers, and awards. It might be the refrigerator or a bulletin board in your kitchen or over your desk. Children are happy to see that their work is displayed and that you are proud of it. You can put a sticky note on their paper or certificate saying "beautiful picture" or "great job."

Another idea for recognizing good behavior is to repeat a positive comment that someone else made about your child. For example, "Your teacher told us what an excellent student you are and how well you behave." Or you might say, "Bobbie's mom was really impressed when you were over at Bobbie's house today. She said, you have really good manners and that you shared things very well."

With five children in our house, my wife and I are challenged to praise each child equally. Our goal is to find something sincere we can say about each child each day. However, it should not be made up just for the sake of saying something. Sometimes our children will ask, "How come you didn't say something nice about me?" We will usually respond by saying we are always on the lookout for good deeds and behavior. A child may sometimes then be prompted to tell us about an accomplishment we hadn't noticed.

MODELING THE BEHAVIOR YOU WANT IN YOUR CHILDREN

Role modeling

We hear a lot about role models. Some people think celebrities and athletes should be role models for children. But there is no better role model for any child than her parents. As a role model, you need to act and speak in a way that shows your child your interest in school, education, the joy of learning, and

good behaviors. Children learn so much by mimicking their parent's behavior! If we act like school is fun and learning is enjoyable, our children will develop the same type of attitude.

Role modeling positive school behaviors may be a special challenge if you were frustrated with school when you were younger, but if you communicate your frustrations to your children, it will probably be harder for them to be positive about school. It is very important for those parents who did not enjoy school very much to project a positive image of education and the joy of learning.

BECOMING INVOLVED IN YOUR CHILD'S EDUCATION

Study habits

Being a good student requires a lot of support at home. Sticking to a consistent approach to study habits is critically important for children. One of the most important things they develop during their first few years is their attitude and perception of school. When our children get home from school, the first thing we do is to sit down with a snack and talk about what happened during the day. Then we encourage them to do their schoolwork. By consistently reinforcing the habit of doing schoolwork early, the children integrate this into their routine.

My wife deserves most of the credit for teaching good study habits to our children. She is passionate about instilling this work ethic into their lives. It also makes the day run more smoothly because there are no discussions or arguments about when to do their homework or what TV show to finish watching.

When homework is done early, it also eliminates nagging from the parents about getting it done.

In addition, the parents know early in the evening whether the child is missing a book or needs some information from a friend regarding a homework assignment.

Parent-teacher conferences

Make a point to attend every parent-teacher conference. Let your children know how much you value parent-teacher conferences, and share with them the positive and constructive comments from your conference. If an issue comes up that needs more attention, schedule an additional conference.

Enriching a child's education

There are a lot of opportunities for enriching a child's education. If your budget allows, you might offer your child music, dance, or art lessons. You can take your child to visit museums, zoos, or historical places.

Another way to enrich your child's education is to provide educational games, videos, and computer games. Viewing movies that are family oriented or that teach important values or principles of life is a painless way to enrich your child's education. For example, a biographical movie about Thomas Edison and his inventions would be interesting for many children to watch. In addition, a family movie such as *Swiss Family Robinson* teaches important values such as courage and teamwork.

We have a list of educational and family-oriented videos at *TheTotalParent.com*. Our list of family-friendly movies includes a brief description of how each movie exemplifies specific moral values and positive character traits.

Larger cities often have excellent children's museums. Our Web site lists a few. You can also check an Internet search engine such as Google or Yahoo for a children's museum near you.

Keep in mind that you can help facilitate a child's learning experience at a museum or zoo by doing a little preparation prior to your trip. For example, we bring a few books along in our van when we are on our way to a particular place, such as the zoo. A book for our five-year-old might be an alphabet book of animals that he could identify. We would talk about the different animals and what they look like before we get to the zoo. With the older children I might ask them to look up something such as the different types of bears or the different animals that live in Africa on the Internet before we leave home.

Of course, it helps to learn and have fun at the same time, so we usually play the alphabet game based on a particular theme. In the alphabet game, players take turns naming something (such as the animals at the zoo) that begin with the letter a, b, c, and so on. The first child names an animal that begins with the letter a, and the next child has to think of an animal that starts with the letter b, etc. To add a memory development feature to the game, each child repeats all the letters and animals named before hers.

These are a few of the many things you can do to help your children become successful in school. It will take a commitment on your part to help your children love learning and enjoy school. If your child has special needs, be sure to do all the research you can to find the services that are available to you. If your local school district does not have what your child needs, it may very well pay for you to obtain special help in another district or in a private school.

Try to enjoy all of the educational and extracurricular activities along with your children and share your special interests with them. See additional information below.

Learning with mnemonics and acronyms

When I am helping one of my children study for a test, I sometimes teach them how to utilize a mnemonic (memory aid). One example of a memory aid is an acronym. An acronym utilizes the first letter of each word to make another word. A familiar example of an acronym is using the word *homes* to remember the five Great Lakes: Huron, Ontario, Michigan, Erie, and Superior.

Here's an easy mnemonic for remembering all of the planets in the correct order from the sun outward: My very excellent mother just served us nachos. (Keep in mind that Pluto is no longer a planet.) The first letters of each word correspond to Mercury, Venus, Earth, Mars, Jupiter, Saturn, Uranus, and Neptune.

Help save your child's homework and back

Since children sometimes forget to bring home all the books they need for their homework, it is good to know if your local library has copies of your child's schoolbooks. Many libraries keep current textbooks in the reference section, so a child who needs a book for homework can do his work at the library.

We keep a used copy of each of our children's textbooks at home. If a child forgets a social studies book, we have an extra copy at home. A great resource to buy used schoolbooks is Amazon.com or Follett Books (www.follett.com). At the beginning of the school year I ask the assistant principal or the office secretary for the ISBN numbers of each of the textbooks for each child. I then order the most important ones from one of those two sources. Since their books don't change very frequently, children can usually pass the books down to younger siblings.

Having textbooks at home also saves the child from carrying those heavy books back and forth each day. If your child does carry books home, look for book bags that have wheels on them. Wheeled bags relieve the stress on your child's back and shoulders.

TOTAL PARENT POINTERS
SECRETS TO RAISING A SUCCESSFUL STUDENT

1. **Read, read, read. Read to them when they are young for at least fifteen to twenty minutes each night.** Show them how much fun reading is. Let them read to you when they are older.
2. **Teach your children to enjoy school.**
3. **Set high but realistic expectations for them.** Let them know that doing well in school is something that you expect of them.
4. **Be a good role model.** Tell them stories about how much you enjoyed school. Tell them about how good it feels to learn about different things. Tell them how school will prepare them for a good job when they are older.
5. **Limit their TV time.** This is one of the most important issues that you as a parent need to control. If necessary, unplug the TV if they do not obey your rules. Sometimes it takes a no-TV ban for a week to break them of this habit.
6. **Limit their time playing computer games and other electronic games.** Use these on weekends as rewards after they have read something.
7. **Enrich their education** by doing other things that they can learn from. Take them to a zoo and have them read about the zoo animals before they go and in the car.
8. **Look for educational events in your area.** Examples, reading hour for young children at you local library or bookstore.
9. **Visit the library often.** Use this as a reward for good behavior.
10. **Buy used children's books at garage sales.** They can usually be found for as little as twenty-five to fifty cents each.
11. **Go to every parent-teacher conference at school.** If your child is having trouble in a subject, ask to meet with the teacher earlier or simply make a phone call to discuss what you can do to help make your child successful in school.
12. **Let your children see you reading a book or magazine instead of watching TV.**
13. **Teach them tricks to help them remember things that they study at school.** Use mnemonics and acronyms to help them remember a list of things.

For more information about helping underachievers become better students, consult Harvey P. Mandel and Sander I. Marcus, *"Could Do Better": Why Children Underachieve and What to Do About It* (New York: Wiley, 1995) .

TheTotalParent.com also has a summary article on underachieving students by Dr. Sander I. Marcus.

46

Tips for Educating Your Child Every Day

One of the keys to educational success for your children is to look for unique learning opportunities each day. All it takes is a little creativity, some planning, and using some of the ideas in this book. Here are some key concepts and skills that I've found useful for our children. I am confident you will find them beneficial also.

INFANTS AND YOUNG CHILDREN

The keys to stimulating the brains of infants and young children include:
1. Smiling at them.
2. Making them feel comfortable and secure.
3. Stimulating them with images they find interesting.
4. Using physical stimulation such as hugging and caressing their backs.

A smile from mom or dad is one of the most important stimulating influences for a young child's brain. Holding your child close to you and stimulating their brain with hugs, kisses, and caresses is also important for bonding and a feeling of security. Studies of children who were raised in institutions with minimal social interaction in war-torn countries after the Second World War demonstrated that these children had more difficulty with social and intellectual functioning as adults.

PRESCHOOL CHILDREN

One of the most important skills for the intellectual development of a preschool child is reinforcing the child's verbal skills. This can be done simply by rephrasing the child's last sentence using proper grammar. For example, if the child says, "I want crayon," the parent may repeat that correctly to the child as, "I want the crayon, please," or "May I please have the crayon?" This will help your child to understand proper grammar. I cannot emphasize how important this is. If you are a stay-at-home mom, this is obviously one of your key priorities and one of your advantages. If you are a working mom, this is something that you need to communicate to your child's caregivers. Teach your baby-sitter or nanny how to rephrase each child's sentences using proper grammar.

Read to your children every night for at least twenty minutes

Reading to your children every night achieves several goals:

1. It stimulates an interest in reading.
2. Your child learns to read better.
3. It helps your child to learn about grammar.
4. It exposes your child to different concepts of sharing, friendship, honesty, etc.
5. Having the child read to you aloud also enables you to hear how he pronounces different words. You can correct these accordingly.
6. You expose the child to important values by choosing books that exemplify important values. It is a time to finish up the reading session by talking about spiritual ideas such as religion, values, gratitude, pray, etc.
7. The child has time to relax and wind down after a sometimes hectic day.

8. It is an important time to talk and answer questions the child may have about different things that occurred during the day.
9. It gives you a chance to spend uninterrupted personal time with your child, which he correctly interprets as love and caring.

Visiting the library is fun and exciting

Teach your child that visiting a library can be an exciting experience. You can do this by being a role model for your child by making comments about the library as being a fun and interesting place. In fact, you can use library visits as a reward for good behavior. If your child does something good you can allow them to visit the library and pick out two or three new books. Teach them where the age-appropriate sections are in the library. Let them know how much fun it is to read about different subjects.

For example, if you recently saw a movie about outer space, encourage them to read a book about the astronauts or the planets. If you are planning a trip to the museum, suggest that they pick up a book about dinosaurs, zoo animals, or other topics of interest to them in order to learn about them before visiting the museum.

Visit museums often

Visiting local museums can be an excellent learning experience for your children. It can be both a fun and educational experience if you approach it with the proper attitude and preparation. Instead of simply going to the museum, talk about this trip for one or two weeks beforehand. Suggest that your child pick up a few books at the library to study different things about the museum. For example, if you are going to visit the Museum of Science and Industry in Chicago, you should suggest that the your child read up on electricity, airplanes and the wonder of flight, the human body, or computers.

If you really want to get your child totally involved in this experience, ask her to also write an essay about the book she read. You can then review her essay for proper grammar and correct it accordingly. She can then be given rewards when she is at the museum.

After our children do the above, they will receive a small financial reward or a treat of their choice. If they do a second version of the essay to correct grammar and punctuation, they will receive an additional reward.

This also gives you an opportunity to praise your children for their accomplishments. Be sure to praise them for each of the following:
1. Reading the book.
2. Writing the essay.
3. Revising the essay prior to the museum trip.

Try to determine what type of reward they would like. This may be a simple financial reward or a special treat, such as ice cream she may choose at the museum.

Let me also put the preceding paragraphs in perspective. My wife and I have days when this approach works well with some or occasionally all of the children. We also have days when the kids are just not in the mood to do what mom and dad think is educationally important. We might even have a bad day when several (or all) of our children are misbehaving. (We actually had to turn around and drive home just as we arrived at a Great America amusement park. The children were behaving so badly en route that my wife and I decided to turn around and take them home. Boy, were they surprised!—and disappointed.)

The important point is perseverance, enthusiasm, and creativity. If your children don't like your idea of educational fun, then try something else. If all else fails, give them a chance to relax and talk about other things. If you live with them in the moment, you will enjoy just being with them and listening to their stories.

Use drive time as an educational opportunity

Use the car ride to the museum as a valuable opportunity to stimulate your children's interest in an educational goal. Keep in mind that the children are excited about going to the museum. If you inspire them to read or write something while in the car en route to the museum, they will be more likely to complete this if they know that there will be a reward when they arrive at the destination. This is a good time to think about bringing along your library books about the human body, mummies, inventors, or the planets.

Encourage your children to write a short essay about one of the above topics during your ride to the museum or planetarium. This is also a great way to keep kids from fighting during the car ride. It even allows mom and dad time to talk while the children are busy reading books and writing essays.

Keep several notepads and pens in the car for the children to write their essays.

Educational ideas for older children

Older children may be asked to search the Internet for various topics prior to a museum visit. For example, preteens or teenagers may be asked to search the Internet for various topics pertaining to the human body, electricity, various scientists, explorers, and historical events. Ask them to write a brief two-page essay about the topic. This may include any of the following possibilities:

1. The planets in our solar system
2. Being an astronaut
3. Inventors
4. Computers
5. Mummies
6. One of the presidents of our country
7. The human body
8. The U.S. Civil War
9. American Indians
10. Famous scientists

Professional sports games can be educational

We recently took our children to a Chicago Cubs–White Sox baseball game. However, several weeks prior to the game, all of our children were informed that they needed to memorize the players on the teams as well as the positions they played. They were also required to learn all the names of the pitchers and the coaches of the teams.

This was a very interesting experience. Not only did they learn the names of the players but they also began watching the teams on TV and learned about some of the recent games prior to the game we attended. I was amazed at how they talked about various players and some of the great plays during the game. This knowledge made them seem like they were little sports aficionados even before they attended the game. They actually knew several things that I didn't know.

Can world politics be fun for children?

The answer is (and I hesitate to say this) yes. The key is to approach it in a positive manner. Keep in mind that children will perceive different topics based on how their parents present them. For example, if you talk about various political topics in an interesting and exciting manner, the children will pick up that interest, and their curiosity will be stimulated.

Talk to your children about some recent political events and why they are important. For example, talk about how raising the minimum wage in the United States helped so many people or what our country is doing about the homeless situation.

Ask your child to research a recent political topic such as the Iraq War or a recent political election. Ask them to find out who some of the world leaders are. Some other topics that children can review on the Internet might include:

1. What were some of the inventions by Thomas Edison?
2. Who was Mahatma Gandhi?
3. Who were the last five presidents and vice presidents of the United States?
4. Who are the main leaders in our government now, including the president, vice president, secretary of defense, Speaker of the House, etc.
5. Who is the mayor of our city and the governor of our state?

Visit historical sites

Visit various historical sites in your area or make plans to visit a historical site within driving distance. If at all possible try to visit Washington DC at least once so that your children will have a more complete understanding of the history of our country. Washington DC has a plethora of information, museums, and monuments that are important to our country. In addition, monuments such as the Vietnam Memorial are an awesome sight for the children to see.

Find educational Web sites for your children

Make it a point of finding educational Web sites for your children to visit. Instead of allowing your children to spend time in chat rooms talking to their friends, encourage them to visit various Web sites about science, history, mathematics, politics, etc. For a complete list of educational Web sites go to *TheTotalParent.com* and search for kids' Web sites or educational Web sites.

TOTAL PARENT POINTERS
EDUCATING YOUR CHILD EVERY DAY

1. Repeat your child's sentences with proper grammar to improve her verbal skills.
2. Smile, caress, and hold your infant as much as possible.
3. **Read to your child every night for at least twenty minutes.** Let her read to you when she is able to.
4. **Make trips to the library fun and interesting.** Use this as a reward for good behavior.
5. **Visit museums, zoos, and historic places.** Have your children read books about the topics beforehand. Have them write a short essay about the topics before you go. Give a reward to the children who read a book and/or wrote an essay.

6. **Use event-related timing to motivate your child to achieve a specific goal.** If the child really wants to go to a certain place (for example, party, museum, fun park), have her complete an educational task before she goes. Give her a reward and praise for completing the task.
7. **Professional sports games can be educational.** Have your children memorize the names of the players, their positions, etc. before going to the game.
8. **History and current events can be fun.** Have your older children research a political topic on the Internet and write a brief essay about it. Visiting historical sites brings this to life even more.
9. Visit *TheTotalParent.com* for a list of excellent educational Web sites.

PART 6

Parenting

47

Teaching Values and Character

We all want to raise our children to have solid values and character. But how do you most effectively do this, and what are the most important values to teach? My approach is focused on helping parents to acquire the knowledge, to learn how to communicate that knowledge, and to model the appropriate behavior. The more we improve ourselves in terms of character and values, the better parents we become and the more likely our children will become value-oriented individuals as they model our behavior.

Is there really a need for teaching values? You really don't hear it mentioned much in the popular media, but I would answer with an emphatic yes! When you look at the amount of crime and violence in our society, it's pretty clear that children need to learn about and improve their character, ethics, and values. Studies of high schools offer some shocking statistics. A recent study on high school students' behaviors released some shocking statistics:

- 34 percent of high school students said they had intercourse before the end of ninth grade
- 5 percent of students reported carrying guns to school within the past year
- 23 percent smoke cigarettes
- 8 percent attempted suicide over the past year
- 43 percent had a drink of alcohol in the past month
- 20 percent used marijuana in the past month
- 12 percent of high school students tried inhalants at least once[1]

These numbers clearly illustrate a serious problem in our teenage population stemming in part from:
- Lack of adequate parental time with children
- Many influences from violent TV shows and movies
- A socially more tolerant approach to inappropriate behaviors
- Lack of a grandparent in the household who can share

wisdom regarding values and character

So how do you communicate these important values to your children? What are these values?

I think the most important values for children include:

- Honesty
- Kindness
- Tolerance
- Obedience
- Responsibility
- Sacrifice
- Respect
- Acceptance and appreciation
- Love
- Faith

The power of being a positive role model

There are several ways to communicate these values to children. Of course, one of the most important is role modeling: showing your children that you have the values and character that you are trying to instill in them. Children will mimic your actions whether they are good or bad. If they hear you lie to someone, they learn that lying is okay. In addition, if they notice that you're talking in a critical or negative way about someone, they will do the same thing. The basic goal, therefore, is to focus on improving and demonstrating your value-based actions to your children. As you focus on how you can become a better person, those positive, character-building behaviors will be apparent to your children. They will then adopt and mimic the behavior that they see.

Tell them about your positive life stories

The second way to communicate the importance of decision making pertaining to life values is by telling your own life stories. You should make it a point to tell your children about the times in your life when you dealt with difficult moral decisions. Take time to think about examples of inspirational real-life decisions that you can share with your children regarding each of the values mentioned earlier. Don't be afraid to use other methods, like the local newspaper, for example, as a teacher. As your children become teens, it never hurts to point out when a neighborhood child or someone they might know from school is written up in the local paper for theft, underage drinking, or other crimes. It serves as a harsh reminder that criminal acts are prosecuted, made public, and become life-changing events in the most negative way.

Talk about values at the dinner table

Eating together at the dinner table is an important opportunity to discuss values, life principles, and personal issues. Sitting with your child at the dinner table is a great opportunity to ask the following:

1. How are things going at school?
2. How are things going with your friends?
3. Are there any problems on the bus with other children?
4. Are there any students in your class that you could help out?
5. Is there anyone in your class who seems to get left out of things?

6. Are there any bullies at school? Who do they pick on?
7. Are there any kids that get teased a lot at school?
8. How does everyone get along during recess?
9. What did you do to help someone at school today?
10. Is there anyone at school who could use a good friend?

This opens up a variety of topics for discussion. Obviously if your child is being bullied or socially excluded, this is a time to obtain information and discuss the information with your child's teacher.

It is also an opportunity to teach your child how to be a supporter of child who is being bullied by his classmates. For example, if you child knows that Johnny is being picked on at school, you can encourage your child to be friendly with Johnny and to help eliminate some of the socially inappropriate behavior toward him.

You can also use this opportunity to educate your child via role playing and scripting. For example, if one of the other students says, "Johnny, I think you are ugly," you can teach your child to say something like "I think Johnny is a really nice guy, and he is my friend." You can then instruct your child to say to Johnny: "Let's go over there," and get away from the child who is badgering Johnny.

You can also suggest that it would be a good idea to befriend that student and invite him into your group of friends so that he feels a sense of belonging to a social group. Your child will feel good because he has done something good for someone else and because it's the right thing to do.

You can also instruct your child to be an ally to Johnny so that when Johnny approaches his parents about the situation, he has a second person to verify his concerns about the bullying by his classmates.

Another situation you can discuss at the dinner table might involve the baseball coach who must decide how long he should play each of the players for a game. Should he give each player an equal amount of playing time? Or should he focus on keeping his best players in the game so that the team will have a better chance of winning? What should he do? You can pose this question to your children and ask them what they would do if they were the coach. Then discuss with your children the pros and cons of each side.

Be sure to emphasize that winning alone is sometimes not the most important goal. Sometimes participation by children who may have less talent is important because it helps build up their self-esteem and helps them feel like they are part of the group. Plus, you can help your child understand why the coach does not want to make the child feel bad by leaving him out of the game, and how that is more important in some cases than winning the game.

HONESTY

Here's one example of how to communicate the principle of honesty to your children. You might tell your child about a time you were in a grocery store and a clerk accidentally gave you an extra twenty-dollar bill for change. (You can adapt this story, of course, to your true-life experiences.) You then gave the bill back to the clerk. Of course, you did this because it was the right thing to do. Second, you knew that this clerk would also probably have to pay the twenty dollars out of her own pocket, since the cash drawer would be missing the twenty dollars.

You should also explain to your children the emotional component that goes along with this. In other words, tell them how you felt good by doing the right thing. In contrast, you can tell them how bad it would make someone feel if he kept the money and was dishonest. It is important to have children understand the intellectual as well as the emotional component about feeling good when they do the right thing. (Or feeling bad when they do the wrong thing.)

KINDNESS

Another important concept to teach your children is how to do the right thing in spite of peer pressure to do something negative. For example, let's say a group of students are sitting at a lunchroom table and making fun of another student. You should teach your children how to be a positive role model in this situation. The first thing to teach them is to not say anything negative about that person. The second thing is to teach them to have the courage to go against the negative influence of the group. Finally, teach them that a good way to deal with this is to have your children mention something that they like about the person who is being criticized.

For example, they can say, "Well, I know that Susan might be a little shy, but I think she is a really nice person. In fact, one day she helped me with my science project. By the way, is anybody going to the basketball game after school today?" This shows the child the technique of saying something positive about the person in question as well as diverting the focus of the group to another topic. With this example, you have taught your child how to act in a way that is consistent with good values. You've taught them the courage of standing up to peer pressure, and you have also taught them valuable interpersonal skills in dealing with a negative conversation by changing the topic to focus on something else.

TOLERANCE

Tolerance is probably one of the most important virtues. Tolerance allows children to accept and appreciate people who have different beliefs, ideas, and cultures from their own. Make sure that you are a good role model for demonstrating to your children that people should not be discriminated against because of their race, religion, or culture.

OBEDIENCE

Obedience is clearly an area all parents struggle with. The key to teaching obedience lies in a consistent approach to dealing with appropriate and inappropriate behaviors. I learned an important concept from a mother who came to our emergency room many years ago. As I examined one of her children, I couldn't help but notice how well behaved her other three children were. Her children were relatively young. Their ages were approximately five, eight, and ten. They, were sitting together, talking softly, and behaving extremely well.

I asked the mother how she taught her children to behave so well. She responded with a very concise summary of parental wisdom regarding childhood behavior: "I simply figure out what each child wants the most. When I know what that is, I just take it away when they do something wrong."

This simple concept summarizes the psychology of behavioral modification in children. Find out what they want the most and take it away until they change their behavior.

That mother's approach is basically what I use with our children when they misbehave. For example, I know one of the main sources of enjoyment for my oldest son when he is at home is the privilege of using the computer. Therefore, if he misbehaves, he will lose computer access for one to seven or more days, depending on the extent of his negative behavior. My second oldest enjoys watching TV. Therefore, taking her TV privileges away for a number of days is her punishment. The return of TV privileges

is her reward when the behavior is changed. For my eleven-year-old son, his punishment might mean taking away his iPod for a day or two.

We also use a star system for keeping track of good things, such as good grades, acts of kindness, good behavior, etc. We keep a piece of paper posted on a kitchen cabinet with each of the children's names on it. Whenever one of the kids does something exceptionally good, we place a star on their chart. When they have a total of ten stars, they may turn these in for either ten dollars or some other reward equivalent to ten stars. One of the rewards might be a special day with dad or a special day with mom. On the special day, my wife or I will take that child out or we may do something together at home. For example, if my third-oldest child has ten stars, we might go out for dinner at a fast-food restaurant and have a nice talk. Or we might go out to a movie, buy a book, go for a bike ride, or go to the library.

Establishing a good work ethic and pride in one's accomplishments goes a long way in developing self-esteem and self-confidence.

RESPONSIBILITY

Many parents find that teaching responsibility can be challenging. The key point is that once you get started and your children understand that everyone has a job to do, it becomes progressively easier. The starting point is to come up with a list of simple duties for your children to do each day or each week around the house to help them to develop a sense of responsibility. Typical duties might include:

- Breakfast table cleanup
- Dinner table cleanup
- Cleaning up the hallway
- Cleaning up the family room
- Folding the laundry
- Cleaning their room
- Doing the dishes
- Mowing the lawn

We typically assign each of these duties for one week and then rotate them. As you might expect, our children feel that certain duties are harder or easier than others, and rotating the duties gives everybody a chance at each of them. These can also be used as a consequence for unacceptable behaviors. For example, if one of the children made an inappropriate or disrespectful comment, she might clean up the dinner table for a week as punishment.

SACRIFICE

One of the key values that is seldom spoken of is the value of sacrifice. Sacrifice means giving up something you want to achieve a greater goal. It means training your mind and your spirit to focus on what is important in life.

It sometimes means working hard and delaying your gratification in order to accomplish a future goal.

By teaching your children the value of sacrifice, you can teach them about things that are much more important. These include:

1. Doing acts of kindness for others: By sacrificing their time and effort, they will learn how good this feels and they will develop a sense of self-esteem.
2. Learning how to control their impulses and emotions: By sacrificing their desire to stay out late with their friends, they will earn the respect of their parents by coming home at the promised time.
3. Learning how to delay gratification while working on something that is important to them: By sacrificing their free time to spend extra time on their homework, they will learn the joy of achievement and self-discipline.
4. Learn how to strengthen their character: By sacrificing their focus on themselves, they will learn how to think about others.

The advantages of good timing

Another important element in teaching responsibility is the principle of timing. It is amazing how quickly children can accomplish a task when they are eager to do something else that they really enjoy. For example, if my son wants to go to his friend's birthday party on Saturday afternoon, we tell him on Friday night or Saturday morning that he can only go if he cleans his room first. It is amazing how quickly and efficiently he accomplishes this task. This illustrates the art of timing and the concept of finding out what really motivates your child.

RESPECT

There is less respect toward adults among the children of this generation compared to when I was a child. Perhaps our generation is too busy to take the time to teach our children about respect.

Good communication skills are a must

One of the key principles of respect is teaching children how to communicate appropriately with people in different social situations. This means talking to their friends and others with respect and consideration. This includes simple things like reminding your children to say "please" and "thank you." Good communication also involves making eye contact with the person they are speaking to.

Avoid making negative comments

Respect also means teaching your children how to avoid making negative comments. Help them to look for the good qualities in each person. Everyone has different abilities. When they learn to look for the good qualities in people, they also find that they develop good relationships with people who they might not have been friends with otherwise.

Another example about teaching respect might be learning to not say anything negative about food that is offered to them at a friend's house. We tell our children that if they don't like something that is being served at their friend's house, they should only focus on the good things that they like. In situations such as this, we remind them to say thank you to both parents for inviting them for dinner.

Addressing adults as Mr. and Mrs.

I feel that addressing people as Mr. and Mrs. is also very important. We instruct our children to address adults by Mr. or Mrs. Sometimes they can use the adult's first name, such as "Miss Shelly" or "Miss Jennifer" or "Miss Michelle." It's up to you, but we prefer our kids not address adults by their first names.

Teach your children how to introduce themselves to adults

We also teach them how to shake hands to introduce themselves. For example, they might say, "Hi, my name is Mitchell. It's a pleasure to meet you." And when the person leaves the house, the children are all instructed to say "good-bye" and to say "Thank you for coming over to visit."

ACCEPTANCE AND APPRECIATION

In the process of teaching our children the right ways to live and being positive role models for them, we also acknowledge that we are human and that we've made our share of mistakes. It's just as important for our children to learn forgiveness, mercy, the ability to put our mistakes behind us, and the ability to fully accept ourselves and others for the person each of us really is, imperfections and all.

We appreciate the uniqueness of each one in our family—strengths as well as weaknesses—and we appreciate each one as a wonderful human being who is worthy of love and support. Having one talent or another has absolutely nothing to do with our unconditional love. The only thing we ask is that all of our family memebers try to do their best and try to be the best people they can be.

LOVE

Teaching your children about love is done by showing the love you and your spouse have for each other as well as the love you have for your children. When children see parents behaving in a loving way toward each other, they learn how to act in a loving relationship. When they see the husband doing things for his wife and vice versa, they learn the give and take of a normal loving relationship. In addition, although I think it is important to keep certain disagreements out of earshot of the children, minor disagreements can be educational for the children. Children need to see how their parents resolve minor disagreements.

They also learn by seeing how their parents can disagree without resorting to inappropriate language or behavior. They see that two people can have different ideas and disagree about a subject but come up with a workable solution that they are both happy with. This is an important lesson for children. It teaches them not only about love but also about compromise, as well as appropriate interpersonal skills.

FAITH

One of the best ways to teach your children about faith is by doing the things that a faithful person does. That includes going to your place of worship, taking religious education classes, reading the Bible, talking about your religion at the dinner table, and doing volunteer work at your place of worship. Encouraging your teenagers to participate in your church youth group is also very beneficial. Sometimes they will listen to another adult role model more than their own parents.

However, the most important thing to do is to live your faith. Let your children know how important faith is in your life.

NOTES

1. Centers for Disease Control, "National Youth Risk Behavior Surveillance System," *Morbidity & Mortality Weekly Report*, June 9, 2006, 1–108.

TOTAL PARENT POINTERS
TEACHING VALUES AND CHARACTER

1. **Look for opportunities to talk about values** at the dinner table, in the car, etc.
2. Let your children know why values and good character are important.
3. **Be a good role model** for each of the values of:
   - Honesty
   - Kindness
   - Tolerance
   - Obedience
   - Responsibility
   - Sacrifice
   - Respect
   - Acceptance and appreciation
   - Love
   - Faith
4. **Focus on one of the core values each month.** Ask your children to focus on doing something pertaining to the specific value each day and tell you what they did relative to this value during the day, week, or month.
5. **Use rewards to reinforce good behaviors.**
6. **Teach them how to introduce themselves to adults,** communicate effectively, be polite, use good manners, and avoid making any negative comments.
7. Look for the good qualities in everyone.
8. Learn how to deal with difficult social situations.
9. Teach them why obedience is important.
10. **Teach them to help other, less-fortunate people.**
11. **Teach them about their faith.** Show them how to practice their faith.
12. **Encourage them to get involved with a local youth group at your church or place of worship.**
13. Talk about values at the dinner table. Instead of asking, "What did you learn in school today?" ask, "Did anyone do anything at school to help someone?" or "Is there anyone at school who needs you to be their friend?"

48

Parenting Techniques and Skills

No one teaches you how to be a parent, so I think it's good to get insight from other experienced parents who are friends and family. The most important concepts that you need to focus on with your child include:

1. Be a positive role model.
2. Let the child know who is in charge.
3. Be consistent, honest, and fair.
4. Have a written set of house rules and another version for older children.
5. Use your words and punishments creatively.
6. Use timing to your advantage.
7. Maintain your composure and avoid anger.
8. Provide frequent praise and support to your children and show that you trust them.
9. Provide frequent signs of love, affection, acceptance, and appreciation.

Children want us to be in charge and to give them direction and to set boundaries for them, even if they don't always act that way. Kids will always push the envelope and test you. But ambiguity confuses them, which is why children feel safe and secure when they understand the rules and what's expected of them. And we adults are just the same.

None of us wants to work in an environment where the rules are ambiguous or inconsistently applied. Many times parents are afraid to follow through with certain punishments or loss of privileges because of the child's persistent whining and crying. But caving into that trap is a mistake. Instead of feeling sorry for your children if they cry or act upset, you should feel satisfied that the punishment that you provided has had an impact on the children and has created consequences. If you think about it, the issue isn't punishing bad behavior, but rather teaching self-control and proper behavior and the fact that there are consequences to unacceptable behavior.

DON'T LOSE YOUR TEMPER

The toughest but most important part of parenting is not losing your temper. When you lose your temper you usually lose your ability to think logically, and you may not behave rationally. You then run the risk of role modeling a negative behavior for your children. These are the key tips to avoiding anger:

1. Take a deep breath before responding to the incident.
2. Remind yourself that whatever happened, it is probably not the end of the world.
3. Think to yourself about how you are going to handle and respond to the situation so that you don't say anything that you will regret or that you cannot follow through with.
4. Try to turn this into a positive encounter instead of an anger-ridden argument, which frequently results in an escalation, an exchange of sometimes hurtful words, and no resolution to the problem.
5. Understand that we are human and that we all make mistakes. This is much more easily said than done.
6. Understand what kind of emotional state your body and your mind are in. If you are sleep-deprived, hungry, upset from some other event, or otherwise in a generally bad mood, understand that this underlying emotional state will create a dark cloud over your perspective. By contrast, if you are feeling rested, positive, and in a good mood, then you will be in a much better emotional state to sit back and think about how you are going to handle the situation. Looking at things with a good sense of humor goes a long way to not getting yourself frustrated and bent out of shape.

KNOW WHAT EMOTIONAL STATE YOUR BODY AND MIND WAS IN

Mothers and fathers need to be particularly aware of their emotional state when they are dealing with a misbehaving child. All of us can get into a negative emotional state when we are fatigued, stressed out from our job, overworked or upset about some other financial or personal issue.

If you are in a bad mood or just having a bad day, and your child does something upsetting, it's usually best to remove your child from the room for five or ten minutes. If necessary, remove yourself from the situation for five or ten minutes in order to sit back, think, and decide how to deal with the situation effectively.

The key trap to avoid is the endless cycle of arguing and yelling, which becomes a pointless escalation of the situation. Many times small problems or accidents, such as a spilled bowl of cereal, can turn into much more angst than is necessary. Keep in mind that it is best not to sweat the small stuff because most of it really is small stuff. Easier said than done, I know.

THE MOST IMPORTANT PRINCIPLE OF CHILD BEHAVIOR AND PSYCHOLOGY

One of the most important lessons I learned about childhood

behavioral modification was from a mother of three young children that I met in the emergency room many years ago. (I wrote about this in the previous chapter, but it is so important that I want to reiterate it here.)

She summed up an entire childhood psychology textbook in a simple phrase: "I find out what they like the most, and when they don't behave, I take that away from them." She is absolutely right. I can tell you that I've used that simple principle several times a week (and sometimes several times a day) with our five children.

HOME RULES OF BEHAVIOR

Pick an evening to sit down and have a family meeting to talk about certain house rules of behavior. Then write them down. This is very important so that everybody understands what the rules are, and there is no question as to what your expectations are. After they are written down, they should be posted in the kitchen or some other visible place. Then no one can deny not knowing or remembering the various rules of the house. Examples of some rules and issues to discuss at your family meeting are:

1. Time to go to bed.
2. Family chores.
3. Time to wake up in the morning.
4. Time to do homework.
5. Hours of TV, electronic games, and Internet use per week.
6. Responsibilities for keeping bedrooms clean. Consider a reward at the end of the week if your children achieve the goal of keeping their rooms clean every day. The reward may be extra hours of time at their friends' house, additional time with their computer games, or extra TV viewing time.
7. Treating each other with dignity and respect.
8. Respecting each other's personal property and privacy.
9. Showing respect to parents through appropriate communication. This includes talking to parents in an appropriate tone of voice. It also means teaching them that they should not raise their voice to you and that they should maintain eye contact when they speak to you.
10. Curfew hours for teenagers.

To give you some ideas, here is a list of our house rules that have been modified over time, depending on the age of our children.

1. Children in fifth grade or younger are in bed by 8 p.m. on school nights. Children in sixth, seventh, or eighth grade may stay up until 8:30 p.m. or 9 p.m. on school nights. If there is additional homework requirements, the children may stay up to 10 p.m.
2. Everyone takes turns with the following chores that are rotated each week:
   a. Breakfast table cleanup
   b. Dinner table cleanup
   c. Family room cleanup
   d. Hallway cleanup
   e. Basement cleanup

3. Children must have their rooms clean prior to going out to any birthday parties, day trips with friends, movies, etc.

4. Everyone is responsible for separating and folding their clothes and placing their clothes in their drawers. This is for children age seven and older.

5. Before going to a friend's house they are coached on proper etiquette, which includes:

   a. Remind them how to introduce themselves. We might tell them to say, "Hi, Mrs. Smith. My name is Mitchell. Thanks for letting me come over to play with Billy."

   b. They are also instructed to say please and thank you.

   c. We encourage them to focus on being good at sharing toys and other things. We tell them to be a good play pal and to not be bossy.

   d. If they are served food, we tell them to show their appreciation. We ask them not to complain about any food they may not like. Older children may be coached on how to tactfully ask for a different food in a considerate way. When finished with a snack or meal, we remind them to say thank you. They should be instructed to clean up their mess after eating.

   e. Remind them not to run around at their friend's house and to be careful not to break anything.

   f. Set a clear time for when your child will return home, usually within two to four hours.

6. Children should be encouraged to be friendly and respectful toward other children at school.

7. Encourage your children to read at least twenty minutes each night before bed. Better yet, sit and read with your children.

8. Remind them to brush their teeth after each meal and before bed.

9. Expect your children to do their best every day in school and with their homework. Set high but realistic expectations for them. Children do well in school when they know that their parents have clearly expressed their high expectations for them. (When I was younger, I never would have thought that I had the potential to become a doctor. Both of my parents came from a blue-collar background. My father only had a sixth-grade education and grew up on a farm in Wisconsin. My parents never told me that I should be an A student. I had to figure this out for myself. Fortunately, I was exposed to premed students in my freshman biology classes. I soon realized that I could do just as well as they did—and look where I am now!)

10. Make your faith part of your life. Going to your place of worship each week is a positive experience for you and your children. Get your children involved in a church youth

group where they can meet other good kids with parents like you who share your values.

THE IMPORTANCE OF DOING HOUSEHOLD DUTIES

Children who have responsibilities around the house learn that they are an important part of the family team. It helps them to develop a sense of responsibility as well as a sense of self-esteem. It also teaches them valuable lessons and habits for life. For example, it teaches them how to be organized and neat by maintaining their room in some semblance of order. It also helps them to appreciate the work that mom and dad do when they have to do it themselves. When children take turns cleaning up the mess after breakfast, lunch, or dinner, they learn to be more careful about not making such a big mess in the first place.

ROLE MODELING AND COMMUNICATION

Role modeling is discussed in chapter 47, however, it is worthwhile to repeat here that role modeling is an extremely powerful way to teach positive behaviors. To our children, we parents are the blueprint for what all adults are like. In essence, children learn much of their behavior by watching how their parents react in different situations. If their parents communicate with each other with respect, consideration, and dignity, children learn that this is the appropriate way to communicate.

However, if their parents' communication involves a lot of negative, destructive talk, the child learns to communicate in this manner. We have to maintain our best behavior and our best face in front of our children. This is not to say that parents should never argue. Quite the contrary, children need to see that their parents have disagreements, talk about them, and come to a reasonable compromise. However, this should be done with appropriate communication, consideration, and respect for each other. If the children see the parents engaging in negative behavior, such as using inappropriate or demeaning language, the children will learn to use that language and that type of response in the future. The key is that all of us are human, but we need to strive to be on our best behavior, both for the sake of our spouses and for our children. Our good behavior is the template for our children's behavior in the future.

However, keep in mind that you are not going to be the only role models in your child's life. Whenever possible, it is important to allow your child to establish relationships with other adults who are good role models. This may involve the adult leaders of a youth group, a religious group, or teachers at school. When you find those people who you think set a good example for your children, try to encourage your children to establish an ongoing, positive relationship with that person.

TOTAL PARENT POINTERS
PARENTING TECHNIQUES AND SKILLS

1. **Role Modeling**—Be a good role model for your children. If you show them that you enjoy reading, they will enjoy reading also. If you have problems with temper outbursts, then your children will model your behavior and do the same. What you do teaches them one thousand times more than what you say.

2. **Everyone has a job**—Give everyone a job around the house. Make it simple at first so that they can get it done and build on their success.

3. **Teach them good manners.**

4. Teach them to call adults by Mr. or Mrs. to show their respect.

5. **Show them how to introduce themselves** and shake hands with an adult.

6. **House rules**—Write down the rules for bedtime, TV limits, curfew, chores, and rewards.

7. **Reward Poster**—Keep a reward poster somewhere prominent where they can see the rewards they earned. For example, staying up an hour later on a weekend or going to a friend's house.

8. **Teach your children to do things for others.** This helps them take the focus away from what they want all the time. Teach them to think about other people.

9. Get them involved in a local church group This will help them to make more friends, give them a deeper understanding of their religion, put them in contact with other good kids, provide them with positive role models, and usually help them do some local charity or volunteer work.

10. **Teach them how to work for a goal,** delay their gratification, and then later enjoy what they have accomplished. This gives them an understanding of the work ethic as well as the value of sacrifice.

49

Teaching Your Kids Skills for Social Success

I don't have to tell you that educating your children about appropriate verbal and interpersonal skills is critically important. I mentioned previously about how you can reinforce or teach your children about proper grammar by rephrasing their sentences using correct grammar. This is something that can be done from an early age and should be done every day. Children with poor language skills will be perceived as less intelligent by their peers with good verbal skills. They will also perform less successfully in various interviews and social situations as a result of their poor language skills.

TEACH YOUR CHILDREN HOW TO SPEAK TO ADULTS

Teach your children the key skills of social etiquette, such as saying please and thank you. A child with good manners will be welcome and appreciated in all social situations. It seems as though good manners have not been emphasized enough by the parents of the most recent generations. Fred Astaire once said, "The hardest thing children face today is learning good manners without seeing any."

Although it may be perceived as old-fashioned, we encourage our children to call adults by Mr. and Mrs. instead of by their first name. Although some might consider this to be stuffy and unnecessary, I think this is an important way to convey respect from a child to an adult. In some cases they can address them by their first name as long as they use Mr. or Mrs. For example, our baby-sitter might be called Ms. Susan or Ms. Patty.

TEACH THEM HOW TO SHAKE HANDS WITH ADULTS

Teaching your child how to shake hands with an adult shows their maturity, respect, and good communication skills. The child should also be taught to look the person in the eyes and smile while shaking their hand. This conveys confidence and helps build a relationship with the other person.

TEACH YOUR CHILDREN THE VALUE OF FRIENDSHIP

It is very important that parents articulate to their children the importance of friendship. This includes what it means to be a good friend and how to be a good friend. It means supporting your friends, but it also means doing the right thing. It does not mean doing what your friend wants to do if it is something that is wrong. It also means not laughing or talking in class while the teacher is trying to teach. It also means not teasing or alienating other children.

Teach your child that being a good friend means:

1. Talking nicely to each other. This means not criticizing the other person.
2. Using appropriate language. This means not using any foul or vulgar language or mean words.
3. Having good manners with your friend. This means being a good houseguest and not being bossy, demanding, or angry.
4. Learning how to share things appropriately with your friend.

5. Instructing your children on how to introduce themselves to another child's parents. Parents are impressed when a child shakes their hand and looks them in the eye and says, "Hi, my name is Bobby Smith. Thanks for letting me come to your house today."
6. Instructing your child not to yell while in the friend's house or run around the friend's house.
7. Instructing your child to say thank you whenever food or beverages are offered. They should also not complain about any of the food but should eat whatever is offered, even if they don't like it.
8. Your child should say thank you to their friend's parents when they leave the house and, "Thank you for letting me come to your house. I really had a nice time."

These simple manners repeated and reinforced will teach your children the behavior that is expected while at a friend's house and enable them to develop good social skills. It will also promote a positive image of your children with their friends' parents.

I cannot emphasize enough the importance of simple, common courtesy as a core value not only for our children but for all of us.

HOW TO BEHAVE AT A FRIEND'S HOUSE

When our children visit at their friends' houses, they also get instructions on how to behave. For example, we review all of the items noted above, such as saying please and thank you and being pleasant. We also remind them to make sure they play fairly and not to argue or make a fuss about things. We tell them we expect them to be on their best behavior.

HOW TO DEAL WITH AN ANNOYING SIBLING

Teach your children how to deal with annoying situations in a positive and productive manner. For example, if one of the children is annoyed because his brother keeps tapping his fork on his plate, we tell our son to simply ask his brother to stop doing that or to move away from him.

Don't forget that using humor or distraction are also excellent techniques for helping another person to focus on something else.

Organized sports teaches your child valuable lessons about life

Organized sports for children has been criticized by some in recent years for fostering a "win at all costs" attitude and a false sense of what is important in life.

However, being on a team can teach your children several important lessons about life. They can learn that they are not the only person in the universe. They can learn that they need to share the spotlight and the activity with the other members of the team. They can also learn about good work ethics, team cooperation, and sportsmanship. They may also learn that their participation is sometimes based on their ability instead of the concept

Good friends

of equal time for all players. In some cases, this may result in a negative experience, because they may find out that they are less talented in that sport then they expected.

We experienced this with one of our sons who was involved in baseball. We initially expected the coaches to play all of the players equally. However, as the season progressed, we realized our son was sitting on the bench most of the time and only played one and a half innings each game. We understood that he was not the best player on the team, but we were somewhat surprised that the coaches focused so much on winning the game with players that were only ten or eleven years old. Some coaches do not base participation on ability, but many coaches do. It was somewhat difficult for our son to come out of this experience with a positive attitude toward the sport. Fortunately, our son found other sports he was more skilled at (soccer, tennis, and cross-country).

It is also important that parents not take sports too seriously. Many parents get overly involved with their children's sports activities and sometimes get into overly zealous yelling and screaming on the sidelines, sometimes deterring from the positive attitude of the sports event. Keep in mind that the key is to let your children develop a sense of cooperation and team spirit. If you have any concerns about your son's lack of participation on a team, I encourage you to talk to the coach and discuss these concerns. If concerns continue after talking with the coach, you may need to make other decisions for the next year regarding your child's participation in that sport or other sports.

Church-based social groups for children
Participate in organized religious activities to get your children involved in church-based social groups. These social groups offer a positive experience to children in a spiritual environment. Many times group leaders are positive role models for your children and can be a secondary source of teaching your children about values, character, and important principles of life. Your children will also be exposed to other children in these groups from families who have similar values.

Our two oldest children have participated in a local church group that has made a significant impact on their lives. My oldest son recently went on a one-week trip to Mexico with a group of fifty children and adults and built houses for two needy families in Mexico. This trip taught our son valuable lessons about sacrifice, the realities of the world, teamwork, work ethics, spiritual values, good character, goal setting, and accomplishment. All parents should seek out adult leaders in your religious community who can be mentors to your children for further reinforcement of the values and principles that you feel are important.

TALKING DURING CAR RIDES
A valuable opportunity for communication
A friend of mine told me that one of the most valuable times that he shared with his daughters was when they drove to various places. I found this surprising, but as he explained it, I understood his wisdom. Time in a car is very special because it presents a unique opportunity for communication without outside interruptions. The radio was turned off, there were no phone calls, and there were no other distractions. This was a time he could talk to his daughters about was going on in their lives, their concerns, their anxieties, and their goals in life.

I realized how true this was when my daughter and I traveled to various events together. It gave us time to also share different experiences, stories her life, her friends, school, and her goals in life. It also enabled me to share with her my values, goals, and some of my expectations for her. I discussed how important school is for success in life, the importance of family and friends, the importance of social skills, and the importance of religion in life.

In this world of TV, cell phones, iPods, MP3 players, and other electronic gadgets, it is very important for us to find time for one-on-one communication without distractions. These simple car rides provide that opportunity if we are conscious of it and use that time wisely. In the past I had regretted long car rides, but now I look forward to them. I recently took a two-hour car ride to one of the universities in Chicago, and it was a great opportunity for me to share some funny stories with four of our five children. (Our oldest son was at an educational summer camp.) My wife was kind enough to drive for us. In fact, I am looking forward to my two-hour car ride with my oldest son in a few days. I will pick him up from a camp and have two hours to discuss everything that has been going on in his life on the way back home. This is a great opportunity for bonding, relating, and discussing some of the important issues of life and whatever else comes up.

TEACH YOUR CHILDREN ABOUT HUMOR

One of the most important traits that anyone can have is a sense of humor. I have made a conscious effort to share funny stories with my children. I have also made it a point of showing the children movies that I think are funny. We have watched movies by many great comedians, such as Tom Hanks, Jim Carrey, Steve Martin, Will Ferrell, and Jerry Lewis.

You can help your children look up jokes on the Internet. Teach them some of the techniques for being a good joke teller.

But beware. Some humor has a hostile, put-down quality. Simply making fun of someone may seem like a funny joke, but it steps over the line of healthy humor and can become only hateful sarcasm. Sometimes a discussion with your children about the difference between sarcasm and healthy humor can go a long way toward helping them not only appreciate the great humorists but also to see the genuine humor in life.

Try to model this humorous attitude by being funny yourself. Sometimes all it takes is having a humorous attitude about things. Show your children how to crack a joke at times when you might get upset about a situation, especially if the joke pokes fun at yourself. This simple skill will enable your children to have a more relaxed and calm view about the world and about themselves. A good sense of humor is a very positive personality trait and a great asset to making friends.

TOTAL PARENT POINTERS
TEACHING YOUR KIDS SKILLS FOR SOCIAL SUCCESS

The keys to teaching your children skills for social success include the following:

1. **Talk to them about the values that you think are important.**
2. **Teach your children how to talk to adults with respect.** Teach them how to give someone a handshake while making eye contact and smiling.
3. Talk about the importance of friendship and what it means to be a good friend.
4. **Discuss the importance of being on a team** and the importance of team building.
5. Have dinner discussions with your children regarding important topics in their life, values, goals, and spirituality.
6. Utilize car rides as key opportunities to spend uninterrupted time with your children to discuss the important topics noted above.
7. Teach your children good dental hygiene. **Let them know that a good smile is a great asset.**
8. **Teach your children about good manners,** social skills, and the importance of common courtesy.
9. **Teach your children how to develop a good sense of humor.** Help them to see the humor in their daily lives
10. **Teach your children to appreciate and enjoy each day of their lives.**

INDEX